# ANTIQUE TRADER'S

# GUIDE TO GAMES & PUZZLES

## HARRY L. RINKER

Antique Trader Books
A division of Landmark Specialty Publications

Copyright © 1997 by Rinker Enterprises, Inc. All rights reserved. No part of this publication may be reproduced, stored in a retrieval system, or transmitted in any form or by any means, electronic, mechanical, photocopying, recording or otherwise, without prior permission in writing from the publisher.

ISBN: 0-930625-62-5
Library of Congress Catalog Card Number: 97-75160

To order additional copies of this book
or a catalog, please contact:

**Antique Trader Books**
**P. O. Box 1050**
**Dubuque, IA 52004**
**Phone: 1–800–334–7165**

Front cover illustrations clockwise from top left:

McLoughlin Bros., New York, NY, children's jigsaw puzzle, Fire Engine Picture Puzzle, pressed board, 68 hand cut pcs, ©1887, 18 x 25", cardboard and wood frame box, $350.00.

Unknown Manufacturer, adult jigsaw puzzle, Palm Beach, hand cut, diecut thick pressed board, 44 pcs, c1940, 6¼ x 11½", green and white striped cardboard box from Henri Bendel with paper label, $30.00.

Tic–Tac Dough TV Quiz Game, Transogram, TV/game show, quiz game, cover with show host Jack Barry, game board with "X" and "O" squares, man and woman contestants behind panel, TV camera at right, includes "Exclusive Automatic Category Selector," 1956, $25.00.

Dr. Busby, J. Ottmann Lith. Co., medical, board game, 6⅜ x 8⅝", lid shows doctor in long coat and vest with glasses on forehead, man in bathrobe seated in chair with feet in tub, St. Nicholas Series, unknown date, $30.00.

Back cover:

Mystic Skull, Ideal, mystical/ voodoo, board game, cover shows cauldron and skull hanging from branch, "The Game of Voodoo...with the mysterious moving skull," mfg logo bottom right corner, 1964, $40.00.

# TABLE OF CONTENTS

# INTRODUCTION

Some of my earliest childhood memories involve games and puzzles. I came from a large nucleated family, dozens of aunts, uncles, and cousins lived within a five mile radius of my home. Each home's door was a revolving one. One never knew who was coming to dinner and to play.

I loved visiting the Victorian home of Uncle Charles and Aunt Marie, my mother's sister, in Lancaster, Pennsylvania. The children's playroom was located atop a tower that formed the northern front corner of the house. I distinctly remember playing Go to the Head of the Class and Monopoly. Cousin Charles, older than me by a few years, always won. Now that I am older, I understand why. I should have recognized the advantage he had at the time, but I was blinded by my competitive instincts.

I have always owned a wooden toy chest filled with boxed board games and puzzles. Although the vast majority of my collection now rests on metal shelves at my office, my toy box at home houses over a dozen games and puzzles. Alas, they see little use. Today's visitors and grandchildren are more interested in watching rented videos than playing games or working puzzles.

While far better known within the antiques and collectibles community for my jigsaw puzzle collection, I have a fairly substantial boxed board game collection. I own a few pre–1945 games, but my love remains decidedly post war. My collection focuses primarily on board games licensed by television shows from the early 1950s through today. I have always been a TV junkie. As a result, it is impossible to look at a game without it evoking a strong nostalgic memory.

All my boxed board game playing memories involve my cousins and childhood neighbors and friends. My card game memories involve my aunts and great aunts. Aunts Annie and Naomi, my grandmother's sisters, loved to play Finch. Most visits included a game or two. Canasta was the hot card game of the early 1950s. Everyone in my extended family played. Bridge and poker were adult games. After seeing the violent reaction of some of my Uncles when they lost, I remain thankful to this day that I never learned either.

My jigsaw puzzle memories are basic and simple. Grandpop Prosser, my mother's father, always had a card table set up in his living room with a jigsaw puzzle in progress. I remember dozens of conversations held while searching for one or more elusive pieces.

I do not know when I became a game collector. I cannot remember a period when I did not own a substantial number of games. I still have several games I received as a child, including an extremely well cared for example of an early Tudor Electric Football in its period cardboard box.

I do know when I became a jigsaw puzzle collector. The year was 1989. I was photographing the puzzles for Anne Williams' *Jigsaw Puzzles: An Illustrated History and Price Guide.* Annie called Don Friedman in Chicago to ask permission for me to come to Chicago and photograph his advertising jigsaw puzzles. He refused.

"How difficult and expensive is it to collect advertising jigsaw puzzles?," I inquired.

"Not hard at all," Anne replied.

Before I knew what was happening, I had assembled a collection of over 50 examples, many of which are pictured in Anne's book. Don Friedman and I are now fierce rivals and very good friends. In the not too distant future we plan to combine our knowledge of advertising jigsaw puzzles and write the magnum opus on the topic. All we have to do is find the time. Maybe "not too distant future" is a bit optimistic.

Given my jigsaw puzzle memories with Grandpop Prosser, it really was only a matter of time before I was bit by the jigsaw puzzle collecting bug. Thank goodness I was. I now own two groups of jigsaw puzzles that represent major links to my families' past. First, I discovered that Grandpop Prosser cut wooden jigsaw puzzles. I own a 1,000–plus piece puzzle that he cut. He was an average cutter at best. But, who cares? How many collectors own a puzzle cut by a member of their family?

Second, shortly after I began my jigsaw puzzle collecting odyssey, my Aunt Doris, the family saver, gave me a box of puzzles she had in storage for over 50 years. The box contained approximately a dozen Depression–era weekly, diecut cardboard puzzles. Several boxes contained the notation "Paul Rinker" in pencil. Paul Rinker was my father, and the handwriting was his. I wish I could tell you that I remembered doing these puzzles with my father, but I do not. We did not have this type of relationship. However, I have done the puzzles that belonged to my father several times. They are among the few puzzles in my collection that I have taken apart once I or someone has done them. I plan to work each puzzle several more times in the years ahead.

## NOSTALGIA AND ITS ROLE IN COLLECTING GAMES AND PUZZLES

Nostalgia plays a major role in the games and puzzles most individuals collect. Human nature dictates that all games and puzzles are not created equal. Every individual has one or more favorites, the memories of which become more romanticized as the number of years separating the individual from the initial play period lengthens. It is impossible to look at a surviving example without being immediately drawn back into one's childhood.

Games and puzzles are not inanimate objects; users personalized them. They became extensions of their inner souls. They are part of the family. This is why they are remembered so fondly and why playing with them again and again is so satisfying.

Childhood memories are often as much about what one did not own as what one did. Few adult memories are free from the recall of a game or puzzle owned by a relative or friend that they wished they possessed. Fortunately, collecting tempers, if not erases, such memories.

Collectors do not buy back their childhood. If they did, their collections would be relatively small. Few children owned more than 50 games and/or puzzles. What collectors really do is buy back the childhood they wish they had if their parents had an unlimited supply of money and bought them everything their hearts desired. They want everything that was denied to them as a child. While most collectors absolutely deny this is the case, considered reflection on what and how they collect reveals how true it is.

## COLLECTING GAMES AND PUZZLE AS AN OLD AGE TONIC

Collectors of games and puzzles never grow up. They understand that childhood and adulthood coexist. There is a small child in every adult. The roses they smell are the hours they spend relaxing and enjoying the play involved. Type A personalities aside, games and puzzles are an excellent escape from the stress and pressures of the modern adult world.

Games and puzzles are a ticket to eternal youth. Few games and puzzles play the same each time. Each time one is removed from its box, an adventure begins. In some cases, especially puzzles, a respite is possible. The anticipation of returning and completing the adventure provides pleasure of its own.

For a tonic to be effective, it needs to be taken. The same is true for games and puzzles. They need to be used. It was never the intention of their inventors and manufacturers that they reside on a display shelf. Games and puzzles are designed for repeat play. There is no planned obsolescence in games and puzzles. A game or puzzle will serve multiple generations if cared for and used properly.

## SHARE THE MEMORIES

The mandate is simple: Go forth and play with your games and puzzles.

While it is possible to do a jigsaw puzzle alone, games are entirely different. They require multiple players and often act as a magnet to draw generations together. Further, there is no reason why multiple individuals cannot work on a jigsaw puzzle. The only thing to remember is that hanging is not good enough for the individual who hides a piece so he has the honor of inserting the last piece into the puzzle.

Many adults wonder why their heirs do not want the family heirlooms they treasure so dearly. The answer is simple. The heirs were never allowed to touch or use the objects. People treasure memories, not things. This is why it is critical to encourage younger generations to play with those games and puzzles that are being passed down through the family. Creating memories ensures preservation.

## RETURN TO THOSE THRILLING DAYS OF YESTERYEAR

Many individuals will buy and use this book only as a reference. Too bad for them. They will miss much of its value.

Sit back, prop up your feet, and allow yourself to become a kid again. Skim through the pages and see how many games and puzzles you remember. The number may surprise you. A word of warning—the minute you feel a major attack of nostalgia beginning, close this book and set it aside. If you do not, you run the risk of becoming hooked as a game and/or puzzle collector. Collecting is addictive. Once you begin, it is almost impossible to stop. But, then again, why would you want to?

Those thrilling days of yesteryear are every bit as memorable today as they were decades ago.

# ACKNOWLEDGMENTS

I begin these acknowledgments by thanking three authors—Lee Dennis, Bruce Whitehill, and Anne Williams—for the pioneering work they did in the field of games and puzzles research. I had the privilege of recruiting and assisting in the editing and production of each of their books. It was a wonderful learning experience.

As with all books prepared at Rinker Enterprises, this book was a team effort. Although my name appears on the cover as author, many individuals contributed their talents. I express my deepest appreciation to them for turning my initial vision into reality.

Thanks to modern computer technology, this book was researched and prepared in camera–ready pages by the staff of Rinker Enterprises, Inc. Mrs. Barbara Davidson, a person who found herself learning more than she ever wished about boxed board games and puzzles, was responsible for most of the data input and for the extensive games subject index.

Dana Morykan designed the book's layout. Kathy Williamson, project coordinator, scanned the images and prepared the final camera–ready pages. She was assisted by Dena George. Additional support came from Nancy Butt, librarian, and Virginia Reinbold and Richard Schmeltzle.

I did the vast majority of the photography for this book. Additional images resulted from the photographic efforts of Harry L. Rinker, Jr., or through the direct scanning of items from The Puzzle Pit, home to my personal jigsaw puzzle collection.

Deborah Monroe of Landmark Communications believed enough in this project to put it under contract. Jaro ˇebek provided technical support and was responsible for final production. Rick Spears and Allan Miller also contributed.

I also thank those auctioneers, collectors, and dealers who shared their knowledge and expertise with me. Any attempt to list them would result in the exclusion of several names. As a result, my thanks to this group must be a general one.

## COMMENTS INVITED

Every effort has been made to make this price guide useful and accurate. Your comments and suggestions, both positive and negative, are needed to make the next edition even better.

You are especially encouraged to send information and a photograph of any games and puzzles that do not appear in this book. Send comments and information to: Rinker Enterprises, 5093 Vera Cruz Road, Emmaus, PA 18049.

| Rinker Enterprises, Inc. | Harry L. Rinker |
|---|---|
| 5093 Vera Cruz Road | Author |
| Emmaus, PA 18049 | August 1997 |

# — Chapter One —

# COLLECTING GAMES

When most collectors hear the word *game,* they immediately think of the boxed board game: a game that comes in a box containing a game board, an assortment of playing pieces, and instructions. Actually, the game category is much broader. Also included are adventure games (adult strategy games of the 1960s through the 1990s), card games, and skill games.

Games played an integral part in everyone's childhood. Therefore, it is only logical that when the collecting urge strikes, games are one of the first places many collectors turn. What gives vitality and viability to the game market is that most collectors collect the games of their youth. As each new generation of collectors enters the market, a new generation of collectibles is born. Game collecting will continue forever.

## A BRIEF HISTORY

Games utilizing game boards date back to antiquity. A gaming board, playing figures and dice were found in the tomb of Egyptian Pharaoh Tutankhamen. Checkers is a game with roots in antiquity.

It is common to find the same games in many cultures. "Chaturanga," a form of chess, was played in India as early as 600 A.D. It worked its way west via trade routes, assuming slightly different forms and names as it passed from country to country. View games as evolving, rather than being invented.

There are only a limited number of game types; there are thousands of variations of each.

By the end of the seventeenth century, a host of generic games were in place. In addition to backgammon, checkers, and chess were cribbage (based on an early game called "niddy–noddy"), dominoes, fox and geese (a marble–jumping game), lotto, mah–jongg, nine men's morris (a version of tic–tac–toe), and parcheesi.

Games played a part in the lives of American colonists. In New England, tenpins evolved from the banned game of ninepins; the Dutch in New York played skittle; Southerners found time for gambling and card playing. However, it was not until the industrialization of America in the first decade of the nineteenth century that games began to be mass produced and widely distributed.

The first mass–produced American games date from the 1840s. W. & S.B. Ives Company, stationers in Salem, MA, published several card games to supplement a line of stationery products. In 1843 the first American board game, Mansion of Happiness, was introduced, followed in 1850 by Reward of Virtue. Both games had strongly moralistic overtones. By the mid–1840s, game manufacturing had spread across the country.

By the middle of the nineteenth century, McLoughlin Brothers (1828),

Milton Bradley (1860/61), and Selchow and Righter (1867 as Albert J. Swift, 1870 as Elisha G. Selchow) had entered the manufacturing picture. Parker Brothers followed in 1883. These four companies dominated the game market in the 19th and early 20th centuries. Following in their footsteps were hundreds of other manufacturers. Some, like J.H. Singer, had a national presence; others, like George A. Childs, were regional in scope.

Nineteenth–century games are distinguished by the extremely high quality of the chromolithography on their box covers and game boards. As for playability, the amount of mental skill required was minimal. The playing pieces also were rather plain.

Competition between game companies was fierce. To update a game, cover art was changed. Historical events quickly found their way into game form, such as Parker Brothers' The Siege of Havana. Many small companies only lasted a game or two. The sit-

uation continued until the end of World War I.

In 1920 Milton Bradley bought McLoughlin Brothers, and the big four became the big three. Actually,

Selchow and Righter was always a weak sister in the market. It is more correct to write about the "big two." Each company strived to introduce games that would enjoy large popular success. Parker Brothers had a winner in its 1915 hit Pollyanna; Milton Bradley kept pace with Uncle Wiggily in 1918.

In 1935 Parker Brothers introduced their version of Monopoly. Recent scholarship has traced the origin of the concept for the game to Lizzie J. Magie's 1904 The Landlord's Game and a host of similar generic games played in different section of the country in the 1920s. Charles Darrow, who is credited as the inventor of Monopoly, actually patented a version of the generic game developed by Ruth Thorp Harvey and a group of players in Atlantic City. Parker Brothers further strengthened its position by entering into a licensing agreement with Walt Disney.

In the 1920s the game industry discovered that comics, movies, and radio programs were adaptable as board and card games. Games such as The Game of Nebbs and Eddie Cantor and Tell It to the Judge are among the many that were developed. Popular books, such as The Wizard of Oz, also inspired board games. In the area of generic games, Milton Bradley had hits with Go to the Head of the Class and Sorry.

New companies emerged. Among the more important are E.S. Lowe, J. Pressman & Co., Rosebud Art Co., Transogram, and Whitman (Western Publishing). But gone were the great chromolithography covers of the past. Although 1920s and 1930s box covers were flatter and often less detailed, they more than adequately represent the variety of illustration styles of the period. Die–cast gaming pieces appeared. During World War II game companies stressed military theme games and old generic standbys.

In the 1950s the board game enjoyed a renaissance, due in part to the numerous games licensed by leading television programs. A host of new manufacturers such as Hasbro, Ideal, Lowell, Mattel, Remco, Standard Toycraft, and Whiting entered the picture. Milton Bradley, Parker Brothers, and Transogram continued as major players. Few television shows of the 1950s and early 1960s escaped having games created from them.

The most recent development in the game industry was the arrival of the adventure game, led by manufacturers such as Avalon Hill. These strategy games, designed primarily for adults, often last for days or weeks. The popular game of Dungeons and Dragons and its copycats is a juvenile market spinoff.

Game companies did not escape the corporate acquisitions and mergers of the 1970s and 1980s. Milton Bradley and Parker Brothers became part of Hasbro. The recent emphasis on family values has resulted in a game renaissance. Annual sales are increasing.

### BOXED BOARD GAMES

Collector interest in boxed board games can be divided by era into four distinct groups: mid–nineteenth century through 1915; 1915–1940; 1940–1965; and post–1965. Games made before 1940 hold the strongest interest among game collectors; games made after 1940 are only of mild interest. There is no question that this attitude is extremely short–sighted, but it is the prevailing attitude among the traditionalists.

In the period from 1915 to 1940, games were far more responsive to larger events, making this an excellent period in which to develop theme collections, for example, automotive, electrical, or movie. Many playing pieces were die cast in shapes ranging from automobiles to radios.

One characteristic of the post–World War II game is the large number of playing pieces, ranging from play money to credit or penalty cards. Before purchasing any game, check its contents against the list found in the instructions. Subtract up to twenty–five percent of the price if up to ten percent of the contents are missing; do not buy the game if the number exceeds ten percent.

Board games from 1940 to 1960 are subject to collector crazes. Since game collectors collect on a broad bases, they buy at the low point of cycles.

1970s games are in transition from a speculator–driven market to a more stable market subject to an occasional price run. Boxed board games from the late 1970s through the 1990s are being bought and hoarded by collectors and dealers in hopes of doubling and tripling their money in three to five years—this is pure speculation.

### ADVENTURE GAMES

Because of the fairly recent arrival of the adventure game on the game scene, the bulk of its collectors are within the player community. For this reason, the adventure game remains far outside the mainstream of game collecting.

Although the adventure game has American roots, the greatest player/collectors are Japanese. They are willing to pay premium American market prices for an unopened game.

The two principal ways of collecting adventure games are by manufacturer and theme. Prices for the most commonly found games range from $25 to $40. There are many games priced in the low hundreds.

## CARD GAMES

Card games are often confused with playing cards. Collectors of playing cards, card decks with four suits of numbered and lettered cards, are not part of the traditional game collecting community. They have their own literature, collectors' clubs, and show circuit.

Card games that attract the interest of game collectors have an organizational basis other than the four standard playing card suits (clubs, diamonds, hearts, and spades). Old Maid is an excellent example.

This is one of the most overlooked segments of the game area. Many fine examples can be found in the $10 to $25 range. Prices above $50 are rare, except for very early card games. When purchasing a card game, check to make certain that you have the instructions (it is not always clear from the cards how the game is to be played) and all the cards required.

## SKILL GAMES

Games using eye–hand coordination and played on a tabletop or on the floor, such as table croquet or tenpins, are skill games. Skill games went through several crazes, notably in the 1880s to 1890s, the late 1920s and early 1930s, and the 1970s.

This area of game collecting is largely ignored by most game collectors. The boxes that house most of the skill games are not appealing. The games are difficult to display and not especially showy when displayed. Many nineteenth–century examples sell for less than $75. Examples from the 1920s and 1930s can be purchased in the $20 to $40 range, while 1970s skill games generally sell for a few dollars, at most.

## GENERIC GAMES

For the collector fascinated with variation and its meaning over time, the generic game offers an ideal opportunity. It is the most affordable of all the game categories. Most examples cost between $5 and $15 because the number of examples is large and collectors minimal.

**References:** Mark Cooper, *Baseball Games: Home Versions of the National Pastime 1860s–1960s*, Schiffer Publishing, 1995; *Board Games of the 50's, 60's, and 70's with Prices*, L–W Book Sales, 1994; Rick Polizzi, *Baby Boomer Games*, Collector Books, 1995; Desi Scarpone, *Board Games*, Schiffer Publishing, 1995; Bruce Whitehill, *Games: American Boxed Games and Their Makers, 1822–1922, With Values*, Wallace–Homestead, Krause Publications, 1992.

**Periodicals:** *Toy Shop*, 700 E State St, Iola, WI 54990; *Toy Trader*, PO Box 1050, Dubuque, IA 52004.

**Collectors' Clubs:** American Game Collectors Assoc, 49 Brooks Ave, Lewiston, ME 04240; Gamers Alliance, PO Box 197, E Meadow, NY 11554.

# — Chapter Two —

# COLLECTING PUZZLES

## WHAT IS A JIGSAW PUZZLE?

When someone normally uses the word *puzzle,* they mean jigsaw puzzle. Although technically the word refers to puzzles cut on a jig saw, it has been broadened to include dissected, diecut, sliced, and water jet–cut puzzles. It is not necessary for pieces to interlock for a puzzle to be classified as a jigsaw puzzle. The key is that when assembled, jigsaw puzzles make a picture.

Jigsaw puzzles are only one type of puzzle. There are many others, e.g., put–together puzzles, interlocking solid puzzles, disentanglement puzzles, sequential movement puzzles, dexterity puzzles, and folding puzzles.

## A BRIEF HISTORY

The origins of the jigsaw puzzle is open to debate. John Silsbury, a London map maker, is credited with producing the first dissected map jigsaw puzzles sometime in the early 1760s. Recent scholarship has revealed possible Continental antecedents prior to that date. Whatever the facts regarding the jigsaw puzzle's origin, it is safe to state that jigsaw puzzles were an accepted part of the toy market by the early nineteenth century.

The first jigsaw puzzles in America were English and European imports and aimed primarily at children. Prior to the Civil War, several game manufacturers, e.g., Samuel L. Hill, W. & S.B. Ives, and McLoughlin Brothers included puzzle offerings as part of their product line. However, it was the post–Civil War period, especially the 1880s and 1890s, that saw the jigsaw puzzle gain a strong foothold among the children of America. In the late 1890s and first decade of the twentieth century, puzzles designed specifically for adults appeared. Both forms have existed side by side ever since.

While jigsaw puzzles are usually associated with children rather than adults, it was the adults who were responsible for the two major, twentieth century puzzle crazes: 1908–1909 and 1932–33. Since the first craze focused on the wooden puzzle, its societal impact was limited. Not true for the 1932–33 craze. The principal driving force was the diecut, cardboard puzzle, and its appeal was universal. The diecut, cardboard puzzle evolved in the

1920s. By the mid–1930s it was the principal jigsaw puzzle manufacturing technique. It made the jigsaw puzzle part of everyone's life.

Interest in jigsaw puzzles has peaked and declined several times since the mid–1930s. Mini–revivals occurred in 1938–39, during World War II, and in the mid–1960s when Springbok puzzles entered the American scene. At the moment, jigsaw puzzle sales are steady.

The arrival of the diecut, cardboard puzzle did not end the manufacture of wooden puzzles. Among the large manufacturers, Parker Brothers continued making Pastime Picture Puzzles until the late 1950s, and Joseph K. Straus Products Corporation stopped cutting wooden puzzles in 1974. Skilled amateur cutters, semi–professional cutters, and small commercial firms, important suppliers of wooden jigsaw puzzles since 1900, never ceased cutting jigsaw puzzles. Modern hand–cut examples tend to be expensive. However, a number of firms are experimenting with laser and water jets which may once again result in inexpensive wooden puzzles appearing on the market.

## ADULT PUZZLES

When discussing adult puzzles, it is necessary to differentiate between those individuals driven by a collecting mentality and those individuals driven by a puzzle making compulsion. Within the antiques and collectibles collecting community, most collectors focus on wooden puzzles made before the 1940s, although a few collectors now include some of the post–World War II Parker Brothers and Straus puzzles. a small number of collectors have discovered the diecut, cardboard puzzle. However, even their collecting emphasis is concentrated almost exclusively on pre–1945 examples.

Within the puzzling community, those individuals who derive pleasure solely from the act of doing the puzzle, there is a strong emphasis on the diecut, cardboard puzzles from the mid–1960s to the present. The reason is simple. They can be acquired cheaply at auctions, flea markerts, and garage sales. Once they have been assembled, they are frequently given away, traded, or sold to get new stock for assembling. Within the contemporary puzzling community is a small nucleus of individuals who have begun to collect large blocks of puzzles from a single manufacturer. Provided they keep their collections intact, they will be viewed as pioneers in the twenty–first century.

Collectors and a small group of the traditionalist puzzlers are attracted to wooden puzzles for a large variety of reasons. First, many wooden puzzles, especially earlier examples, lack a picture key. They are viewed as more challenging. Second, wood puzzles are found in a large number of cutting variations. There are three basic types: (1) interlocking; (2) partially interlocking; and (3) non–interlocking. Variation is added by the use of figural pieces, cutting on color lines, inclusion of false corners, open space in the center, non–rectangular borders, etc. Third, the artwork on wooden puzzles reflects the social tastes of the period when the puzzles were cut.

Collectors divide evenly between those fascinated with the puzzles cut in the period surrounding the 1908–09 craze, those who focus on the 1920s cutters, and those interested in the puzzles made just before, during, and immediately after the 1932–33 puzzle craze. It is for this reason that age often factors heavily into pricing considerations. Interest in post–1940 wooden puzzles is virtually non–existent. This is a good entry level for the new collector wanting wooden puzzles.

By far the most important wooden jigsaw puzzle collecting criteria is cutting skill. There are basically six major classifications: (1) large scale commercial cutter, e.g., Milton Bradley and Parker Brothers; (2) medium size and small commercial cutters, often surviving only for a few years; (3) semi–commercial or part–time cutters; (4) skilled amateurs; (5) rank amateurs; and (6) skilled cutters working at a high quality, low volume level who sell almost exclusively to wealthy customers, e.g., Par and Stave. Within the first four categories, the level of cutting skill varies over a wide range. While the definition of what constitutes quality cutting differs from collector to collector, two criteria seem to be degree of difficulty in putting the puzzle together and amount of space between pieces.

A key cut–off point for the adult diecut, cardboard jigsaw puzzle collectors is the mid–1950s, the time when Tuco ended production of its thick, non–interlocking pieces in favor of the thin, interlocking pieces used by most of its competitors. Collectors are making a serious mistake in ignoring the adult puzzles of the mid–1950s through the early 1980s. As has been noted earlier, a few members of the puzzling community are pointing the way. These puzzles are inexpensive and plentiful. Where else can you build a collection for dimes and quarters?

## CHILDREN'S PUZZLES

Collectors make a clear distinction between puzzles designed for children and those designed for adults. Although there are collectors of children's puzzles, the vast majority of children's puzzles are sold to theme collectors with interest in other categories. For example, an individual collecting television cowboy heroes is likely to pay more for a Gunsmoke frame tray puzzle than would a child's puzzle collector. Even children's puzzles from the late nineteenth century fit this mold. A McLoughlin Santa Claus puzzle set will attract more attention from a Santa Claus collector than a children's puzzle collector.

Traditional collectors clearly prefer children's puzzles of the pre–1915 period because of their strong chromolithography pictures. Since the number of pieces is low and the cutting not very challenging, all the value rests in the surface image. Since the image was often duplicated on the box lid, the box is critical to value. Early children's puzzles focused on the four to twelve year age group, frequently combining education with entertainment.

After 1920 it is necessary to divide children's puzzles into two groups: (1) those designed for children between the ages of two and seven and (2) those designed for children ages eight and up. Children's puzzles designed specifically for the two to seven age group have limited appeal unless they are early, as indicated previously, or contain artwork by a famous illustrator.

Until the mid–1920s teenagers and young adults were expected to content themselves with simpler adult puzzles. In the mid–1920s a number of major manufacturers, e.g., Milton Bradley, began offering diecut, cardboard puzzles numbering between 50 and 100 pieces. The complexity of the pictures and size of the pieces clearly identify them as focusing on the eight and over age group. Since an adult could solve these puzzles in a very short time, they clearly were not designed for adults.

These juvenile puzzles tested the market for the diecut, cardboard jigsaw puzzle. Their success set the stage for the jigsaw puzzle craze of the 1930s. Many of the early puzzles are movie–related, meaning that the puzzle collector is in direct competition with the movie collector. When the jigsaw puzzle craze hit in the early 1930s, the juvenile puzzle was entrenched in second place. Adult puzzles were king. Juvenile puzzles do exist, although once again largely ignored by collectors. Disney–theme puzzles and the Saalfield cartoon sets are the two major exceptions.

It was not until the early 1950s, with the advent of the television–era puzzles, that children's puzzles received the attention they deserved. It was the juvenile, not small child's puzzle, that dominated. Although present before World War II as a form, the frame tray puzzle finally achieved a status equal to the box puzzle. Most of these puzzles are character– and personality–related, meaning that the puzzle collector must compete against a theme collector for almost every example.

## COLLECTING OTHER TYPES OF JIGSAW PUZZLES

There are several dozen jigsaw puzzle collectors who specialize in collecting point and proof–of–purchase advertising jigsaw puzzles. These collectors must compete against advertising, product, and theme crossover collectors.

Thanks to the pioneering work of Chris McCann of Ballston Lake, New York, more and more jigsaw puzzle collectors are focusing their attention on puzzles with artwork from a single illustrator, e.g., Hintermeister or Thompson.

Occasionally a jigsaw puzzle is part of a larger unit, e.g., a mystery jigsaw puzzle where the puzzle provides additional clues to solve the crime or to indicate how it was done. These are multipurpose puzzles.

Finally, no jigsaw puzzle collection is complete without some jigsaw puzzle ephemera. A jigsaw puzzle theme is surprisingly adaptable.

**References – Dexterity and Skill:** *Dexterity Games and Other Hand–Held Puzzles,* L–W Book Sales, 1995; Jerry Slocum and Jack Botermans, *The Book of Ingenious & Diabolical Puzzles,* Times Books, 1994; Jerry Slocum and Jack Botermans, *New Book of Puzzles: 101 to Make & Solve,* W. H. Freedman & Co., 1992; Jerry Slocum and Jack Botermans, *Puzzles Old & New: How To Make and Solve Them,* University of Washington Press, 1986.

**References – Jigsaw:** Evan J. Kern, *Making Wooden Jigsaw Puzzles,* Stackpole Books, 1996; Norman E. Martinus and Harry L. Rinker, *Warman's Paper,* Wallace–Homestead; 1994; Anne D. Williams, *Jigsaw Puzzles: An Illustrated History and Price Guide,* Wallace–Homestead, 1990.

**Collectors' Club:** National Puzzler's League, PO Box 82289, Portland, OR 97282.

Mr. I. Magination · JAYMAR · Television Stars · JIG SAW PUZZLE · OVER **400** INTERLOCKING PIECES

# — Chapter Three —

# CARING FOR GAMES AND PUZZLES

The best way to care for your games and puzzles is to use them. This allows you to check their condition from time to time, taking proper preventative measures and making necessary repairs. Never forget that games and puzzles are foremost toys. They were designed to be played with; you do not have to handle them with kid gloves. On the other hand, exercising a little extra care in handling makes sense. They have survived this long; do not be the one to ruin them.

Humidity, temperature, and sunlight are the great enemies of games and puzzles. Consider all three when using, displaying, or storing them.

## STORAGE TIPS

Store games and puzzles in an area that is relatively dust free, semi–dark or dark, has a humidity level between forty and sixty percent, and is not subject to quick changes in temperature. An unheated or non–air–conditioned attic or basement is definitely off limits.

If possible avoid stacking game and puzzle boxes on top of each other. The weight of the upper boxes can crush the lids of the boxes on the bottom. If you must store boxes vertically, cut a piece of poster board approximately 1/4 inch wider than the box lid dimensions and put it on top of the box to help distribute the weight. Never store more than six boxes on top of each other under any circumstances.

Ideally, store boxes vertically with a piece of poster board between them. This prevents the printing ink from bleeding from one box to the next. Vertical storage for puzzles presents problems because the boxes do not want to stay closed. When this happens, you must use a stacking method.

Never use rubber bands to hold any game or puzzle box closed. Rubber bands rot and often stick to the box. If you must secure boxes, use soft yarn.

Make a practice of checking inside each box once every few months. Mildew has a bad habit of cropping up on boxed board game playing boards. The outside of the box looks fine, the inside is not. When this happens, wipe off the mildew and place the playing board outside in direct sunlight for a few hours. This should kill the mildew.

Consider placing a sheet over the games or puzzles to prevent the boxes from becoming dusty. Keep it loose so air can circulate. Never store games or puzzles in plastic bags.

## DISPLAY TIPS

If possible, do not locate the display area for your games or puzzles on an outside wall. The temperature of outside walls is often quite different from room temperature. Outside walls also are often damp to the touch. Use inside walls whenever possible.

Consider constructing a series of stepped flat shelves that set out from the wall between five and ten degrees and have a lip on the bottom. Although this displays the game or puzzle on a slight angle, it allows for an attractive presentation.

Consider shrink wrapping assembled puzzles with an acid free paper surfaced mat board for backing. Some collectors prefer having a cover mat cut that allows the puzzle to set into the recess.

Never put glue on the back of a puzzle or tape its piece to a backing board in order to display it. This process destroys the collectible value of the puzzle.

Sunlight is not the only light that can damage games and puzzles. Spot and flood lighting also fades colors. Such lighting also can cause heat build–up, thus creating rapid temperature shifts that are best avoided.

No matter what display method you use, rotate your games and puzzles every four to six months. This reduces their exposure to light and other potential damage from display. Further, it allows maximum enjoyment of the collection.

## PURCHASING TIPS

Always check any game or puzzle for signs of insect or mildew damage. Unless the game or puzzle is extremely scarce, avoid purchasing damaged puzzles. Never assume all the silverfish or other insects have died and gone to heaven or hell. Whenever possible, avoid subjecting yourself to the time, effort, and uncertainty involved in getting rid of mildew.

When you find a game or puzzle with a price sticker on its lid or with its sides taped, insist that the seller remove the offending items prior to agreeing to buy. Place the burden on the seller, not yourself. The sad truth is that most collectors are absolutely, positively certain they can safely remove any stickers or tape. Everyone has dozens of horror stories related to their failures.

Instructions to the contrary, you probably will try to remove stickers and tape yourself. First try heating the sticker or tape with a portable hair dryer. Avoid getting it too close to the box and scorching it. If luck holds, once heated, the sticker or tape can be removed easily. However, this process does not remove the glue residue.

Using a Q–tip, rub the area with some acetone or rubber cement thinner. Consider wearing rubber gloves and a face mask when doing this. In order not to use too much, place the cement thinner in a small squirt can. All these supplies are available at art supply stores.

Some collectors avoid the first step and apply thinner directly to the label surface. This increases the mess and is misdirected effort. Apply the thinner to the edge of the label or tape. Lift with a twizzers, continue to apply more thinner as the label or tape lifts off.

If a game or puzzle box is dirty, do not necessarily walk away. Many box surfaces are easily cleaned. Test a small section by wetting your finger. If the dirt comes off but the ink does not, chances are the surface can be cleaned.

Avoid any temptation to use an eraser, even an art gum eraser, to remove dirt from a box surface. The old household remedy of crumpled bread also should be avoid. Any residue left behind will attract bugs.

Water–stained boxes and playing parts are another matter entirely. Repairs must be done professionally; and, cost money. Do not purchase any game or puzzle with a water–stained surface.

# — Chapter Four —

# STATE OF THE MARKET REPORT

There has not been much change in the games and puzzles market in the last five years. This is both good news and bad news.

The good news is that prices for games and puzzles are steady. Everyone can buy with confidence. The decline in prices and collector and dealer interest, a result of the recession of the late 1980s and early 1990s, has ended. Confidence has returned to the marketplace.

The bad news is that excitement and market growth is minimal. A "same old, same old" attitude prevails. Established collectors and dealers dominate the market. They have seen the same merchandise for so long, it has become stale. These collectors have assembled their core collections. The games and puzzles they need to make their collections grow are scarce and priced high. Enough new collectors enter the market each year to replace those older collectors who drop out. There is no decline, but there also is no growth.

Games and puzzles are two collecting categories where crossover collectors have a stronger influence on value than those collecting within the category. The current market value for pre–1945 sports–theme boxed board games relies exclusively on baseball, football, basketball, etc., collectors. Game collectors are continually appalled by the prices paid for these games at auctions and shows.

A person collecting the artwork of R. Atkinson Fox perceives the value of a jigsaw puzzle featuring an illustration by Fox to be three to four times greater than the value assigned by a puzzle collector. Several examples of the mid–1930s Keen Kutter advertising jigsaw puzzle have sold at auction in excess of $1,500, one selling for close to $3,000. These were bought by Keen Kutter collectors. Advanced advertising jigsaw puzzle collectors would balk at paying more than $500, if that much.

Most games and puzzles are sold for their artwork, not their playability. Adventure games and skill puzzles are the exceptions. As a result, the image on the box lid, playing board, or card surface of board and card games or the surface illustration on a jigsaw puzzle plays a major factor in determining value. This emphasis on artwork lessens the importance on completeness as a value factor. As long as the artwork components are present, the absence of playing pieces in a game or a non–descript box for a jigsaw puzzle can be overlooked.

Games and puzzles are very much caught up in the trendiness of the 1990s antiques and collectibles market. In the 1970s and early 1980s, game collectors concentrated on pre–1920 games, primarily because of their colorful lithograph covers. Within a short period of time, prices in the $250 to $500 range were common. By the mid–1980s pre–1920 games became very pricey. A few younger game collectors assembled collections of 1950s and 1960s television–related games, primarily because of their affordability. However, the minute interest was shown, dealers began raising prices, stopping the collecting surge in its tracks.

The number of individuals who specifically collect games and puzzles is small—roughly 1,000 game collectors and 200 puzzle collectors. The top end of each market is dominated by fewer than twenty–five individuals. Do these numbers mean that interest in games and puzzles is marginal? Absolutely not! Remember, most games and puzzles are bought by crossover collectors. This introduces thousands of buyers into the games and puzzles marketplace. This is why the games and puzzles market is strong and viable.

It may no longer be possible to talk of a general game and puzzle market, even within the games and puzzles collecting community. Collectors specialize. There are few generalists. Game collectors focus chronologically, by subject matter, or by game type. Adult wood jigsaw puzzles, Depression–era weekly, advertising, and war theme are among the major subdivisions within the jigsaw puzzle community. The number of key collectors in each of these subcategories in often fewer than five.

The 1980s introduced the concept of generation collecting into the toy marketplace. "What will happen to the value of toys when the generation who grew up and played with them dies" became a critical issue. As the 1990s ends, an answer has emerged: In the vast majority of cases, values decline. At a recent paper show, I saw a 1933, Pepsodent "Goldberg's" advertising jigsaw puzzle priced at $18 and remaining unsold. When I asked the dealer why the price was so low, she replied: "No one remembers the Goldberg radio show. I'll be lucky to even sell the puzzle." Boxed board games from the 1920s and 30s currently are tough sells, as are commonly found pre–1920 examples.

As part of the toy market, games and puzzles are harbingers of new collecting trends. Toys are the first indication that a generation's objects are becoming collectible. Boxed board games from the 1970s are increasing in value more than any other group of games. Adults who grew up during this period are beginning to buy back their childhood. Currently it is easier to sell a Charlie's Angels boxed board game than it is a Hopalong Cassidy boxed board game. It does not require a genius to recognize the generation difference between Farrah and Hoppy.

Games and puzzles survive in large quantities. How likely is it that supply will exceed demand? The probabilities are high for any post–1945 game or puzzle and a certainty for any post–1980 game or puzzle. In the 1980s the value of Flip Your Wig, the Beatles boxed board game, rose steady from $50 to over $200. The market collapsed in the mid–1990s. Every game and Beatles collector who wanted an example had acquired one. Dealers who bought at $100 and hoped to sell at $200 or more found themselves stuck with unsalable merchandise.

The level of scarcity is frequently overstated by dealers who do not sell games and puzzles on a regular basis. Most examples are far more common than their sellers wish to admit.

Further, game and puzzle collectors are aware of the vast quantity of material, especially from the post–1945 period, that is still available in the garage sale and flea market circuits. If one is willing to invest the time, it is relatively easy to find a common 1960s, '70s, or '80s boxed board game for less than a dollar as opposed to the $15 to $25 dollars asked at a toy or paper show.

Unlike some toy markets, e.g., Hot Wheels or Matchbox die–cast cars, where virtually every example holds some collector interest, large numbers of games and puzzles have no collector value. Generic games such as Monopoly and Go to the Head of the Class are an example. Current jigsaw puzzle collectors have little interest in the 500–plus piece, post–1945 puzzles. Pre–1945 generic scenic jigsaw puzzles, e.g., Ann Hathaway's Cottage or the mountain and lake scene, are also viewed as worthless.

Dealers unfamiliar with the collecting mentality of game and puzzle collectors assume that age alone is enough to make something valuable. Nothing is further from the truth. Age is a minor value factor. Condition, scarcity, desirability, theme, and completeness are the dominant value factors. There are many pre–1920 games that are tough sells at $25.

In today's collecting market, the mathematical principal that the whole is equal to the sum of the parts no longer applies. Many dealers break apart games and puzzles to increase their potential sales return. For example, a 1930s Saalfied Popeye jigsaw puzzle set consisting of a box and four puzzles has a value in the $100 to $125 range. Each puzzle sold separately retails between $45 and $50. The box alone sells for $30 to $40. Added together, a dealer can realize over $200 if the set is split apart. The sum of the parts can easily be greater than the whole.

Splitting a unit apart to sell its components individually is despicable. The practice will not stop until collectors unite and refuse to buy divided units. Refuse to do business with sellers who do this. Fortunately, some of the collecting trends, e.g., collecting only the game boards from boxed game board sets, that encouraged splitting have lost favor among collectors.

At the moment, the games and puzzles collecting categories are relatively free of reproductions (exact copies), copycats (stylistic copies), and fakes (copies deliberately meant to deceive). Milton Bradley did reissue several of its early games and puzzles, e.g., its American Fire Department Puzzle, for one of its anniversaries. The box is clearly marked; the games and puzzles are not. Serious collectors will not be fooled, beginning collectors may be.

The major area of concern involves those dealers who are using modern computers and copying machines to duplicate the artwork of boxed board game lids and playing pieces. With some empty board game boxes selling in the high hundreds of dollars, the temptation to duplicate is enormous. The same holds true for instructions and other supplemental paper material, such as paper play money. No problem exists when the seller indicates what is period and what is duplicated. A boxed board game without instructions has a much lower value in a collector's eye than one with its instructions. Problems arise when the seller represents the copy as period or simply fails to indicate during the course of the sale what is and is not period.

At the moment, the international collector plays only a minor role in the games and puzzles marketplace. In fact, it is the American collector who has the greater international perspective. American games and puzzles collectors are beginning to add foreign games and puzzles to their collections. Look for the Internet to significantly increase this trend in the future.

In summary, while struggling in some areas, the games and puzzles market is a healthy one—the crossover collectors ensure that. Collector emphasis continues to focus on pre–1945 examples, especially in the area of jigsaw puzzles. As a result, there are tremendous collecting opportunities in the post–1945 period.

Sales of contemporary games and puzzles increase each year, a result of a growing emphasis on spending quality family time together. This should translate into a renewed interest in collecting older games and puzzles, initially for their playability but ultimately as the social documents that they are.

# — Chapter Five —

# KEYS TO USING THIS BOOK

This book is a price guide. Its approach is selective, not encyclopedic. Ideally, you will find exact information relating to the specific game or puzzle you are seeking. The vast majority of games and puzzles included in the listings are commonly found in the antiques and collectibles marketplace.

Many games and puzzles are found in more than one edition and/or variation. The game or puzzle being researched needs to be an exact match in order for the value in this book to apply. Most editions and variations can be identified by the artwork on the game box lid or puzzle surface. This is why these are described in detail.

If you do not find the exact game or puzzle, you will find plenty of comparables. Use this checklist when deciding if a listed game is a valid comparable: (1) date, (2) maker, (3) quality of box lid or image art, and (4) type of play. Seek out three or four comparables. Average the values. Take a realistic approach to pricing.

## PRICE NOTES

The values in this book are based upon complete games or puzzles in fine condition. Fine condition means there are no visible signs of aging or wear when the item is held at arm's length. When such signs are visible, deduct forty to fifty percent from the value.

Complete means complete. In the case of a game, it means that the play-

ing board, playing pieces, and all supplemental materials are present. Although most collectors are willing to forgive some incompleteness in respect to playing parts for pre–1920 boxed board games, the complete game always will be viewed more highly and as having greater value than one missing pieces.

Shrewd 1990s buyers are comparison shoppers. They do not buy unless a game or puzzle meets their high standards. Go out and do likewise!

A jigsaw puzzle missing a piece is incomplete. Switching pieces in a diecut cardboard puzzle between seemingly identical puzzles is nearly impossible. Use of different cutting dies, poor diecutting registration, and different printing shades of surface colors are only some of the reasons. It costs approximately $25 per piece to have a missing piece cut and the surface colored to match for a missing piece from a wooden puzzle.

Value relative to missing pieces is not a question of percentages. One missing piece of a jigsaw puzzle does reduce its value by twenty percent. It destroys the value of the puzzle. If the puzzle is scarce and the piece is along the border, maybe, just maybe, some modest level of value is maintained.

The prices found in this book are retail prices—what a buyer would expect to pay at an antiques mall or collectibles show, not what someone should expect to get if they were selling the same object. This book is a buyer's guide, not a seller's guide.

If you have an object listed in this book and wish to sell it, expect to receive thirty to forty percent of the price listed if the object is commonly found and fifty to sixty percent if the object is harder to find. Do not assume that a collector will pay more. In the 1990s antiques and collectibles market, collectors expect to pay what a dealer would pay for merchandise when buying privately.

The simple truth is that there are no fixed prices in the antiques and collectibles market. Value is fluid, not absolute. Price is very much of the time and moment. Change the circumstances, change the price.

This book is a price guide. That is all it is—a guide. It should be used to confirm, not to set prices.

## USING THIS BOOK

Take a few minutes and familiarize yourself with the table of contents. The book is divided into three units: front matter consisting of five chapters designed to provide historical background and introduce you to the intricacies of collecting games and puzzles, and sections on games and puzzles.

Games are listed alphabetically by title. This approach was chosen because it is the easiest and quickest way to locate a game. "A" and "The" are not generally considered part of the title for alphabetical purposes. Many games have titles that begin "Game of..." These are not listed as a "G" title, but alphabetically by the balance of the title.

Some games are cross–referenced in the listings. This was done when key identification words were found in the middle, rather than at the beginning of the title.

The puzzle section is a bit more compicated, largely because puzzles divide into three major groups—jigsaw, dexterity, and skill. Further, jigsaw puzzles divide first into adult and juvenile puzzles and second into wood versus diecut cardboard. It is important that you glance through these various sections so that you have an understanding of where information about a puzzle you are researching is most likely to be found.

## INDEXES

This book has two major indexes. The first is a list of games by crossover collecting categories. More games are purchased by crossover collectors than by game collectors. If all possible crossover collecting categories were included, this index would easily double or triple in size. This index provides the crossover collector only with an initial starting list. It will expand quickly once the hunt begins.

The second index is an alphabetical listing of jigsaw puzzles by title. This is necessary because of the many subdivisions within the jigsaw puzzle listings. The index does not include the titles of dexterity or skill puzzles. Listings in these chapters are alphabetical.

You will not find a manufacturer's index. With few exceptions, e.g., jigsaw puzzles by PAR, games and puzzles are not collected by manufacturer. The key is thematic subject matter.

## ABBREVIATIONS

| | | |
|---|---|---|
| approx | = | approximately |
| illus | = | illustration |
| info | = | information |
| orig | = | original |
| mfg | = | manufacturer/manufacturing |
| pcs | = | pieces |

# GAMES

*The Owl And The Pussy Cat, E.O. Clark, No. 351, Tokalon Series, contains 4 wooden counters and cardboard spinner, 19$^{1}/_{4}$ x 10$^{1}/_{2}$", c1890s, $300.00*

*Wagon Train Game, Milton Bradley, board game, 1960, $30.00*

## –A–

**A.A. Milne's Winnie–The–Pooh Game,** Kerk Guild, classic book, track game, 10$^{1}/_{2}$ x 16 x $^{3}/_{4}$", lid shows map of Pooh–land with picture of Christopher Robin, Pooh, and other characters, includes cloth playing surface, 19$^{3}/_{4}$ x 19", 4 metal Pooh bears, spinner, ©1931 by Stephen Slesinger, Inc. . . . . . . . . . . . .    **50.00**

**A-Team, The,** Parker Brothers, TV/crime, board game, shows cast members on lid, 5 dots around "A," 1984 . . . . . . . . . .    **12.00**

**ABC Monday Night Football,** Aurora, TV/sports, board game, lid shows board playing field, quarterback in throwing position, plastic game, endorsed by Roger Staubach, 1972 . . . . . . .    **40.00**

**ACME Checkout Game,** Milton Bradley, supermarket shopping, board game, lid shows ACME store sign, contains spinner and cards featuring actual products of the day, 1959 . . . . . . . . . . .    **35.00**

**Account of Peter Coddles Visit to New York, An,** Milton Bradley, book series, card game, 5 x 6", lid pictures gentleman in top hat, formal attire, and carnation in lapel, contains printed cards and reading booklet, c1890 . . .    **30.00**

**Acquire,** 3M, business/real estate, board game, man on cover seated at desk holding pair of glasses, 1968 . . . . . . . . . . . . . . . .    **15.00**

**Across the Board Horse Racing Game,** MPH, sports, board game, lid shows horses racing on turf, 1975 . . . . . . . . . . . . .    **15.00**

**Across the Continent,** Parker Brothers, "The United States Game," travel, board game (3-fold board), lid shows train travelling through mountain scene, metal pcs, 1952. . . . . . .    **40.00**

**Across the Continent,** Parker Brothers, travel, board game, map of USA with designation symbols on lid, 8-pointed star in upper right corner, 1960. . . . . .    **20.00**

*Across The Yalu*

**Across the USA,** Hasbro, travel, skill game, lid shows circle type gameboard, 1966 . . . . . . . . . .    **15.00**

**Across the Yalu,** Milton Bradley, military, board (track) game, 15 x 9", cover shows armed Russians on one side and Japanese on the other side of the Yalu River, contains 12 colored wooden counters and spinner, c1905 *see illus*. . . . . . . . . . . .    **165.00**

**Addams Family Card Game, The,** Milton Bradley, TV/monster, card game, 5 members of family pictured in shield over sword, multi-colored game name, floral background, 1965 . . . . . . . . .    **32.00**

**Addams Family Game, The,** Ideal, TV/monster, board game, lid shows family, skeleton, and haunted house, 1965 . . . . . . . .    **60.00**

**Addams Family Game, The,** Milton Bradley, TV/monster, board game, lid shows 5 members of family and other show members, haunted house, 1974    **30.00**

**Addams Family Reunion Game, The,** Pressman, TV/monster, board game, lid shows Gomez, Morticia, and the rest of the family, box contains board, movers, "Thing" spinner, cards, coins, tokens, and instructions, 1991 . . . . . . . . . . . . . . . . . . .    **10.00**

**Addiction,** Createk, educational word game, game title appears as dictionary entry on lid, 1968    **5.00**

**Admiral Byrd's South Pole Game: "Little America,"** Parker Brothers, travel, board game, 17 x 13", lid shows Admiral

*Adventures of the Nebbs*

*Aero–Chute Target Game*

Byrd in flying gear saying "Hello America," ship, penguins, and city skyline, pcs include 4 counters with attached microphones, 4 playing pcs, and instruction sheet, c1934 . . . . . . . . . . . . .     **350.00**

**Advance to Boardwalk,** Parker Brothers, business, board game, lid shows man wheeling baby carriage on boardwalk, high–rise buildings and beach scene, "Parker Brothers Game of High Rises and Fast Falls," 1985     **10.00**

**Adventureland Game, Walt Disney's,** Parker Brothers, Disney, board game, lid shows Disneyland Park waterways, a boat, and animals, contains cards and boat playing pcs, 1956 . . . . . . . . . . . . . . . . . .     **35.00**

**Adventures of Robin Hood,** Bettye-B., TV/book board game, cover photo shows Richard Greene as Robin Hood, contains 3–dimensional vacuum form board with built–in gravity spinner, 8 magic windows, 8 wooden window covers, 4 plastic playing men, 10 chests of gold, 10 horses, 10 shields and armor, 10 bows and arrows, 2 steel balls, 1956 . . . . . . . . . .     **60.00**

**Adventures of Sir Lancelot,** Lisbeth Whiting, TV, 3–dimensional board game, lid shows players at round table, film strip down right, contains 4 wooden pawns, board has attached spinners, dials, paths, 1975 . . . . . . . . . . . . . . . . . .     **45.00**

**Adventures of the Nebbs,** Milton Bradley, comic strip, board (track) game, 19 x 10", lid

shows family in living room with dog, view of staircase behind curtains, contains 20 colored numbered wooden counters, 2 dice cups, 2 dice,   4 wooden blocks, c1925–27 *see illus* . . . .     **85.00**

**Adventures of Tom Sawyer and Huck Finn,** Stoll & Edwards Co., Inc.,book, lid shows 2 barefoot boys with fishing poles walking in field, 9¼ x 18 x 1½", ©1925     **75.00**

**Aero–Chute Target Game,** American Toy Works, aviation, board game, 19³/₁₆ x 13³/₁₆ x 2¹/₈", lid shows airplane, 2 parachutists in the clouds, flight wings symbol, contains 3 airplanes, 2 parachutists, dowel, dart, c1930s *see illus* . . . . . . . .     **65.00**

**Aeroplane Race, No. 60 "Mac" Whirling,** McDowell Mfg. Co., aviation, 10¼ x 10¼ x 1³/₄", lid shows 2 planes flying over fields, mountains, and trees with cloud background, "MAC" in circle at lid top advertises manufacturer's toys and games, c1930s. . . . . . . . . . . . . . . . .     **85.00**

**Aggravation,** CO-5 Company, generic, board game, reissued as Deluxe Party Edition, 3–pronged crown-like symbol upper left corner, 1960s . . . . . . . . . . . . .     **8.00**

**Aggravation,** Lakeside, generic, board game, Standard Edition lid shows family of 4 playing game in circle inset, 1970. . . . .     **5.00**

**Aggravation Game, The Original**, CO–5 Company, generic, board

*The Air Ship Game*

game, lid shows marble and
dice game pcs, 1962 . . . . . . .    **7.00**

**Aggravation, Split-Level,** Lakeside, generic, board game,
3–dimensional version of game,
oval on lid shows game pcs,
1971 . . . . . . . . . . . . . . . . . .    **5.00**

**Air Mail, Game of,** Milton
Bradley, postal, board game,
15 x 15", lid shows bi-level
plane with 1 propeller over
lit–up airport, round wooden
counters and spinner, c1926-28    **225.00**

**Air Mail, The Game of,** Milton
Bradley, postal, board game,
12½ x 6¼", lid shows bi–level
plane flying over houses and
trees, contains marbles, c1927    **75.00**

**Air Ship Game, The,** McLoughlin
Brothers, The Yankee Doodle
Series, aviation, board (track)
game, 12½ x 12½ x ¾", lid
shows dirigible–type aircraft
with passengers riding in suspended basket–type seats flying
over mountain scenery, contains
spinner, 4 colored pcs, ©1904
*see illus*. . . . . . . . . . . . . . . .    **350.00**

**Air Traffic Controller Game,**
Schaper, aviation, (Be the First
to Land Your Planes Safely),
board game, lid shows air traffic
controllers in look-out tower,
1974 . . . . . . . . . . . . . . . . . .    **25.00**

**Airline,** Mulgara Products, aviation, board game, lid shows

plane's flight control board,
1985 . . . . . . . . . . . . . . . . . .    **10.00**

**Airplane Game, The,** Hasbro, aviation, action game, cover shows
pilot with goggles in plane, helicopter and airport in background, "AIRPLANE" in large
letters, 1966. . . . . . . . . . . . .    **15.00**

**Alee–Oop,** Royal Toy, comic strip,
skill game, canister has game
name in circle, subtitle is "Oscar
and his Oops, The Life of the
Party," includes angular wooden
pcs that can be flipped a distance when hit, 1937 . . . . . . .    **20.00**

**Alfred Hitchcock Presents Why,**
Milton Bradley, mystery, board
game, picture of Hitchcock with
jacket and tie on cover with
"WHY" letters in spook–type
print, border strip of Milton
Bradley "Key to Fun" logo, 1958
*see also Why?*. . . . . . . . . . . .    **35.00**

**Alfred Hitchcock Why Mystery
Game,** Milton Bradley, mystery,
board game, lid shows
Hitchcock holding sign "...Real
Thinking, Planning and
Memory," "WHY" in fringed circle drawing, 1967 . . . . . . . . .    **25.00**

**Alien Game,** Kenner,
movie/space, board game, lid
shows Kenner Alien toy as outer
space creature, 1979 . . . . . . . .    **20.00**

**Aliens,** Leading Edge Games,
movies/space, role-playing
game, "This Time It's War," contains pewter pcs, 1986 . . . . . . .    **15.00**

**All-American Football Game,**
Cadaco, sports, board game, lid
shows football player running
with ball, 1960. . . . . . . . . . . .    **30.00**

**All American Football Game,**
Cadaco, sports, board game, lid
shows player with ball in tackle
scene, player #84 and #28 visible, fans in background, 1969. .    **15.00**

**All in the Family,** Milton Bradley,
TV/situation comedy, board
game, lid shows seated Archie
Bunker, his wife, son, and
daughter, 1972. . . . . . . . . . . .    **15.00**

**All My Children,** TSR, TV soap
opera, board game, lid shows
color photos of cast members,

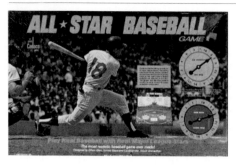

*All–Star Baseball*

*All–Star Basketball*

box contains board, 2 decks of cards, 2 dice, 12 playing pieces, and character profile cards, ©American Broadcasting Companies, Inc., 1985 . . . . . . .    **8.00**

**All–Pro Baseball,** Ideal, sports, board game, 2 players on lid with game name in boxed area titled "Official American National Baseball League Game" with American League emblem, 1967 . . . . . . . . . . . .    **40.00**

**All–Pro Football,** Ideal, sports, board game, lid shows play dia-gram, 2 teams in play with quarterback throwing ball, game name in separate boxed area titled "Offical National Football League Game" with N.F.L. emblem, 1967 . . . . . . . . . . . .    **25.00**

**All–Pro Hockey,** Ideal, sports, board game, lid shows 3 players in action, game name in sepa-rate boxed area titled "Official National Hockey League Game" with N.H.L. emblem, 1969. . . .    **20.00**

**All–Star Baseball, Ethan Allen's Manager's Supplement to,** Cadaco–Ellis, sports, board game, lid shows runner with #18 shirt releasing bat, running, supplement supplies additional stats for the game, 1957 *see illus*    **50.00**

**All–Star Basketball,** Whitman, N0. 2005, box contains card-board fold–out basketball court, rubber balls, metal shooter, no date *see illus* . . . . . . . . . . . .    **20.00**

**All–Star Bowling,** Gotham, sports, action game, lid shows bowling

alley and 2 bowlers, metal game, 1960s . . . . . . . . . . . . .    **20.00**

**All The King's Men,** Parker Brothers, military, board game, lid shows 2 groups of playing pcs resembling knights,1979. . .    **20.00**

**Allan Sherman's Camp Granada Game,** Milton Bradley, generic, board game based on his come-dy song, lid shows cartoon–like camper in green shirt holding a pencil and dreaming of home, tent and bus–type vehicle, 1965    **32.00**

**Alumni Fun,** Milton Bradley, TV/quiz show, board game, lid shows graduate's hat above game name, 4 cheering alumni, contains quiz booklet, playing cards, and 4 playing pcs, 1964    **20.00**

**Amateur Golf,** Parker Brothers, sports, board game, 16 x 10", lid shows 4 golfers on course, 1 golfer putting, "A Practical & Interesting Game for Young Golfers and Their Dads," con-tains 52 cards, 4 pins, advertis-ing and, instruction sheets, ©1928. . . . . . . . . . . . . . . . . .    **65.00**

**Amazing Dunninger, The,** Hasbro, TV/mind reading, board game, lid shows face of mentalist Joseph Dunninger, 3 lines of numbers, signs and letters cross-ing his head as brain thoughts

"...You, too, can read thoughts...," 1967 . . . . . . . . .    **20.00**

**American Boy Game,** Milton Bradley, adventure, board game, 19 x 9¹/₂", lid shows 6 boy scouts on camping trip, rowboat in lake scene, contains 4 round wooden counters, spinner, c1924–26 . . . . . . . . . . . . . . .    **150.00**

**American Derby, The,** Cadaco-Ellis, sports, board game, "Authorized by the Washington Park Jockey Club," lid shows 3 racing horses ridden by jock-eys, 1945 . . . . . . . . . . . . . . .    **40.00**

• Reissued by Cadaco, 1951 . . . .    **35.00**

**American History, The Game of,** Parker Brothers, educational, card game, 8¹/₄ x 5¹/₂", lid shows large eagle, river, and forest scenes in 4 circle insets, con-tains cards, c1890 . . . . . . . . .    **45.00**

**American History in Pictures,** Interstate School Service, set of 4, set C1, No. 61–75, educa-tional, card game, 4³/₄ x 3³/₄", lid shows gathering of men dressed in early colonial cloth-ing, each set has 15 black and white cards, c1920s . . . . . . . .    **25.00**

**American Pachinko,** Pressman, generic, skill game, lid shows group of people, game shown slanted on round table, 1970s    **20.00**

**Amoco Mileage Game, The,** Cadaco, travel, board game, lid shows Amoco Motor Club Emblem and membership card in highway maze, 1976 . . . . . .    **25.00**

**Amusing Game of Innocence Abroad, The,** Parker Brothers, travel, board game, 19¹/₄ x 10¹/₄", cover shows figures walk-ing near water and ships, con-tains block spinner, 8 colored wooden counters, 1888 . . . . . .    **300.00**

**Anagrams,** Peter G. Thomson, educational, card game, 6 x ³/₅", game name in upper half of lid, "or WORDS ALIVE" slants from bottom left to top right corner, many small designs, triangular trim across lid top, c1885 . . . . .    **20.00**

*Angel Spiel*

**Angel Spiel,** German, lid shows 2 children on bridge fishing, box contains fold–out square shaped board with fish illustration, wooden dowel type fishing rods with metal hooks, cardboard fish pieces with metal rings in mouth for catching, c1910–20 *see illus* . . . . . . . . . . . . . . . . .    **75.00**

**Animal Game,** Saalfield Publishing Co., generic, board game, folded board shows rabbit running from wolf, open board shows animal trails, tree stumps, small hut, and Peter Rabbit in bottom left corner, c1920s . . . .    **50.00**

**Animal Talk Game,** Mattel, educa-tional, board game, lid shows 3 children with board and game pcs, animal sounds come from "Chatty Cathy" ring included in set, 1963 . . . . . . . . . . . . . . .    **25.00**

**Animal Trap Game,** Multiple Products Corp., generic, board game, lid shows buffalo, ele-phant, and other animals and warrior–type figure in headdress holding shield and spear, con-tains plastic animals, 1950s . . .    **20.00**

**Animal Twister,** Milton Bradley, generic, action game, lid shows children in twisted positions, game sheet has animal draw-ings, child's variation of adult Twister game, 1967 . . . . . . . . .    **15.00**

**Annie,** Parker Brothers, movie/comic strip, board game, "Path

*Annie Oakley Game*

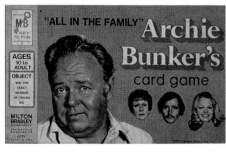

*Archie Bunker's Card Game*

to Happiness Game," picture of Little Orphan Annie and dog on lid, 1981 . . . . . . . . . . . . . . . .    **10.00**

**Annie Oakley Game,** Milton Bradley, western, board game, lid shows Annie on horse in ranch scene with mountain background, 1955; reissued 1958 *see illus* . . . . . . . . . . . .    **35.00**

**Annie Oakley Game,** Game Gems/T. Cohn, TV/western, board game, lid shows cowboys and Indians on horses, cactus, and Annie in western gear hold-ing gun, 1965 . . . . . . . . . . . .    **40.00**

**Ant Farm Game,** Uncle Milton's Industries, educational, board game, lid shows figure in top hat and white glove pointing to picture of gameboard with underground maze of ant hills,1969 . . . . . . . . . . . . . . .    **20.00**

**Anti,** National Games, business, board game, "The Trust Busters Game," lid shows man holding packages, flying card, and "SHHH," same as Anti–Monopoly without the word "Monopoly" (after court ruling), 1977 . . . . . . . . . . . . . . . . . .    **20.00**

**Anti–Monopoly,** Ralph Anspach, business, board game, lid shows man holding packages, flying card, "The 'Bust–the–Trust!' Game," 1973 . . . . . . . . . . . . .    **40.00**

**Antiquity,** Terri Heit, trivia, quiz game, box contains cards and scoring sheet, made in Canada, 1984 . . . . . . . . . . . . . . . . . .    **15.00**

**Ants in the Pants,** Schaper, gener-ic, skill game, lid has boy and girl playing game, game name at top of lid, contains plastic

"ants" playing pcs and container formed as overalls, 1970. . . . . .    **10.00**

**Apollo A Voyage to the Moon,** Tracianne, space, board game, lid shows space ship traveling from earth to moon, 1969. . . . .    **25.00**

**Apple's Way,** Milton Bradley, TV/ family, board game, lid shows family of 7 and part of farm, 1974 . . . . . . . . . . . . . . . . . .    **18.00**

**Aquaman, Justice League of America,** Hasbro, comic book, board game, lid shows Aquaman fighting off underwa-ter creatures, 7 faces at lid top, 1967 . . . . . . . . . . . . . . . . . .    **150.00**

**Aquanauts,** Transogram, TV/water sports, board game, lid shows underwater diver and ocean scene, game has spinner and "salvage report" card, 1961 . . .    **35.00**

**Arbitrage,** H.C. Jocoby, Inc., busi-ness/Wall Street, board game, lid has partial U.S. seal with US flag colors and eagle head, "100 shares," strip of New York Stock Exchange symbols across bottom, 1986 . . . . . . . . . . . . .    **10.00**

**Archie Bunker's Card Game,** Milton Bradley, TV/comedy, card game, lid shows large face of Archie, smaller faces of rest of family, includes spinner, 1972 *see illus* . . . . . . . . . . . . . . . .    **15.00**

**Archie Game, The,** Whitman, TV/ comic book, Archie strumming guitar wearing striped pants, friends looking on, 1969. . . . . .    **25.00**

**Are You Being Served?,** Toltoys, board game, English, TV/come-dy, 6 people shown on lid,

woman holding napkin, man
with carnation in lapel and
handkerchief in jacket pocket,
1977 . . . . . . . . . . . . . . . . . .    **20.00**

**Arm Chair Quarterback,** Novelty
Mfg. Co., sports, board game,
lid has aerial view of football
stadium, game name on playing
field, 4 corners of lid show
action shots of players, 1955 . .    **25.00**

**Arnold Palmer's Indoor Golf,**
Marx, sports, action game, lid
shows Palmer holding club,
smaller inset picture of golfer
with club at bottom left corner,
large game, players manipulate
miniature golfer via a club–like
handle, 1968 . . . . . . . . . . . . .    **80.00**

**Arnold Palmer's Inside Golf,** The
David Bremson Co., sports,
action game, lid shows Palmer
in golf swing, "Fascinating As
The Sport Itself," 1961 . . . . . . .    **50.00**

**Around The World in 80 Days,**
Transogram, movie/travel, board
game, lid shows balloon–type
travel, half of a globe, 4 faces,
travel scenes, and film strips,
1957 . . . . . . . . . . . . . . . . . .    **35.00**

**Around the World Travel Game,**
Golden Rock Co., travel, board
game, lid shows oval with
scenes of famous travel destina-
tions, airplane, cartoon drawing
of auto–vehicle labeled "Golden
Rock Tours," and 4 block adver-
tising cards, 1975 . . . . . . . . . .    **15.00**

**Arrest and Trial,** Transogram, TV/
crime, board game, lid shows
detective and police arresting
third man, pictures of show
stars, and trial scene, 1963 . . . .    **35.00**

**Art Linkletter's House Party
Game,** Whitman, TV/action,
board game, picture of
Linkletter and playing board on
cover, contains play money and
prizes, 1968 . . . . . . . . . . . . .    **25.00**

**Art Linkletter's Game of "People
Are Funny,"** Whitman, TV/radio,
card game, picture of Linkletter
and 4 laughing cartoon faces on
lid, 1954 . . . . . . . . . . . . . . . .    **35.00**

**As The World Turns,** Parker
Brothers, TV/travel, board

*Auctioneer*

game, lid shows 3 globe–like
spheres, red plane in middle
sphere headed for Paris, 1966 . .    **20.00**

**Assembly Line, The Game of,**
Selchow & Righter, "Assemble
Cars Like the Motor Czars," edu-
cational/automobiles, action
game, lid shows assembly line
with finished car at end, con-
tains plastic pcs, 1950s . . . . . . .    **60.00**

**Assembly Line, The Game of,**
Selchow & Righter, educational/
automobiles, action game, lid
shows car in 4 stages of assem-
bly, people playing game, 1960s    **30.00**

**Astro Launch,** Ohio Art, space,
game board with space patterns,
has plastic sphere in middle,
1963 . . . . . . . . . . . . . . . . . .    **50.00**

**Astron,** (name changed to
Skylanes in 1956), Parker
Brothers, travel, board game,
"The game that moves as you
play," 1955 . . . . . . . . . . . . . .    **40.00**

**Atom Ant,** Transogram, cartoon,
board game, cover shows cartoon ant with space hat and letter "A" on body and 2 cartoon
drawings of adult faces, 1966 . .    **50.00**

**Auctioneer,** Ideal, generic, timed
bidding game, lid shows auc
tioneer wearing bowtie holding-
gavel and bidding item, hands of
bidders holding money, timer

and plastic gavel included, 1972 *see illus* . . . . . . . . . . . .    **25.00**

**Aurora Derby,** Aurora, sports, combines pinball and racing, skill game, cover shows jockey playing game and horse racing scene, contains plastic horses, steel balls, and racing tray, 1970 . . . . . . . . . . . . . . . . . .    **35.00**

**Authentic Major League Baseball Game,** Sports Games, Inc., sports, board game, cover shows batter in swing position, 1962 . . . . . . . . . . . . . . . . . .    **20.00**

**Authors,** E.E. Fairchild, #623–3, literature, card game, 5 x 4", lid shows 2 people as bookends with "A Card Game" printed on bookshelf front, wraparound cover litho was sealed to box bottom, c1945 . . . . . . . . . . . .    **15.00**

**Authors, Game of,** J.H. Singer, educational, card game, 4 x 3", lid shows hand holding card with picture of man and printed game instructions, contains multicolored cards, c1890 . . . .    **25.00**

**Authors, Game of,** J. Ottmann Lith. Co., educational, card game, 5¼ x 7¼", lid shows 2 cats looking at tilted books, bookcases in background, contains cards, c1900 . . . . . . .    **35.00**

**Authors, The Game of,** De Luxe Edition, Parker Brothers, educational, card game, lid has name in large script, 1942 . . . . . . . .    **8.00**

**Authors, The Game of,** Parker Brothers, educational, card game, 5½ x 3⅞", lid shows bearded man, mfg info along lid bottom, circle with 7 spokes at upper right corner, c1890 . . . . .    **15.00**

**Authors, The Game of,** G.M. Whipple & A.A. Smith, educational, card game 4½ x 3¼", lid shows 2 men, open book, and inkwell, publishing info on lid bottom, contains cards, 1861 . .    **65.00**

**Authors Illustrated,** Clark & Sowdon, Tokalon Series, educational, card game, 6⅜ x 4½", lid shows series and copyright data, person on beach, game name upper left corner, contains

*Avalanche*

72 cards and advertising card, ©1893 . . . . . . . . . . . . . . . . .    **35.00**

**Auto Bridge,** The Auto Bridge Co., generic, board game, plain red box lid with white figure in top left hand corner, 1948 . . . . . . .    **10.00**

**Auto Game, The,** Milton Bradley, travel/automobile, board game, 11⅛" square, lid shows open–air style automobile on country road, 2 passengers, woman's scarf blowing in the wind, contains 4 round colored wooden counters and spinner, c1906 . . .    **300.00**

**Auto Race Game,** Milton Bradley, auto racing, board game, 16⅞ x 7¼", lid shows racing car raising dust with speed, contains 4 individual box spinners, and 4 colored metal racing cars, possible earlier title "Auto Racing Game," c1925 . . . . . . .    **250.00**

• Second cover shows 2 cars (one a #12) racing on beach, sailboat in background, c1930 . . .    **150.00**

**Autogiro: Pocket Game,** unknown manufacturer, generic, mechanical skill game, 2½ x 4½ x 1", lid pictures mechanical pc held by thumb and forefinger, "the new fascinating" between fingers in middle of lid, 1928 . . . . . . . . .    **25.00**

**Avalanche,** Parker Brothers, generic, skill game, lid shows playing tray, "Parker Brothers Swinging Gate Game," plastic tray has swinging pcs that block marbles from falling through space area, 1966 *see illus.* . . . .    **10.00**

**Avante,** Franes, generic, strategy game, lid pictures 5 running figures, bright sun, checker-like border strip, 1967 . . . . . . . . . .    **10.00**

**Avilude, or Game of Birds,** West & Lee Game Company, educational, card game, $2^7/_8$ x 4", top half of lid is game names(s), middle has pictures of birds around a tree stump, bottom third has manufacturer location and original price (60¢) info, contains 64 cards, 1873 . . . . . .    **35.00**

**Axis and Allies,** Milton Bradley, Gamemaster Series, military, board game, lid shows military scenes, tank, faces of uniformed men, planes, foreign flags, German Insignia, group of 6 men in suits and ties, contains many plastic pcs, 1984. . . . . . .    **25.00**

–B–

**B.T.O.,** "Big Time Operator," Bettye–B., business/real estate, board game, cover has game initials in large letters, mfg name in bottom right corner, advertises 3–dimensional playing board (Vacuform Design), contains built–in spinner, 200 pcs of play money, 28 property ownership certificates, 280 property value cards, 6 automobiles, 2 steel balls, and 20 property price holders, 1956. . . . . . . . . . . . . . . . . .    **45.00**

**Babar and His Friends, See–Saw Game,** Milton Bradley, book, board game, cover shows elephant Babar with crown sitting on seesaw, monkey at the other end and monkey in middle, seesaw atop rock, flowers, pond, palm trees, giraffe, and other animals in background, 1961 . . . . . . . . . . . . . . . . . .    **20.00**

**'Babe' Ruth's Baseball Game,** Milton Bradley, sports, board game, 19 x 10", lid shows 'Babe' holding bat in right cor-

*'Babe' Ruth's Baseball Game*

ner inset, batter and catcher, contains 12 round wooden counters, 85 cards, autographed authorized Babe Ruth edition, published in conjunction with Christy Walsh Syndicate, c1926–28 *see illus* . . . . . . . . . .    **750.00**

**Babes in Toyland, Walt Disney's,** Parker Brothers, Disney, movie, board game, cover shows marching soldiers in white plumed hats, 2 soldiers on horseback with high hats, soldier playing drum following toy train, striped ballon in left–hand top corner, 1961. . . . . . . . . . .    **30.00**

**Babes In Toyland, Walt Disney's,** Whitman, Disney, movie, board game, lid shows toy soldiers, man in top hat blowing horn, and cluster of buildings, 1961. .    **30.00**

**Balance the Budget,** Elten Game Corp., business/politics, card game, $5^1/_2$ x $3^3/_4$", lid shows elephant and donkey balancing seesaw with dollar sign in middle, advertises "Democrats, Republicans, even Congressmen are playing it!," contains 52 multicolored cards with black backs with red dollar sign, 4 score sheets, and instruction sheet, ©1938 . . . . . . . . . . . . .    **20.00**

**Bamboozle,** Milton Bradley, TV/military comedy (based on show "McKeever & the Colonel"), board game (hide and seek), lid shows military uniformed man holding hat, 2 youngsters peering from hiding place, game name in various colors, 1962. . . . . . . . . . . . . .    **35.00**

*Game of Bang*

**Bamm Bamm Color Me Happy Game,** Transogram, TV/cartoon (based on Flintstones), board game, lid shows 2 Flintsone children, one with blond hair sitting holding color easel and wearing beanie–type cap, second on hands and knees with pony tail tied with bone, plant in bottom left corner, 1963. . . . .    **60.00**

**Bandersnatch,** Mattel, generic, skill and action game, lid shows monster head with large teeth and mouth, a hand in mouth, other on ear, children playing game in top right corner, name across top and down both sides of lid, contains cards, spinner, and building pcs, 1968 . . . . . .    **15.00**

**Bandit Trail Game, featuring Gene Autry,** Kenton Hardware Co., western, board game, lid shows picture of Gene Autry and cowboy on horse, 1950s . .    **75.00**

**Bang, Game of,** McLoughlin Brothers, No. 5160, generic, board game, Pearl Series, 7³/₄ x 15¹/₂", lid shows youngster carrying rifle and bag wearing plumed hat, contains round wooden counters and spinner, ©1903 *see illus* . . . . . . . . . . .    **175.00**

**Bang Box Game,** Ideal, generic, skill and action game, cover shows hammer coming down on box labeled "danger," man and woman looking on, 1969 . . . . .    **18.00**

**Bango! Bango!,** Schaper, generic, skill and action game, lid shows plastic "H" playing pc and 2 colored Bango sticks, 3 cartoon faces down left side, contains playing pc, sticks, and 12 marbles, 1960s . . . . . . . . .    **15.00**

**Bantu,** Parker Brothers, generic, board game, lid has shield, arrow and Indian–type designs, and name in banner, 1955 . . . .    **20.00**

**Barbie Game, The "Queen of the Prom,"** Mattel, toy/doll, board game, picture of Barbie wearing crown, contains playing cards printed with faces of young people in prom outfits . . . . . . .    **50.00**
• Second version contains sorority pins instead of card, 1964 . . .    **55.00**

**Barbie World of Fashion,** Mattel, toy/doll, board game, lid has picture of blond Barbie in striped suit super–imposed over pictures of Barbie's modeling world including 2 people talking on phones, contains playing cards and 4 player pcs, 1967 . .    **45.00**

**Barbie's Keys to Fame Game,** Mattel, toy/doll, board game, cover shows 4 girls playing game, 1963 . . . . . . . . . . . . . .    **40.00**

**Barbie's Little Sister Skipper Game,** Mattel, toy/doll, board game, cover has picture of Barbie's face and horse, white fencing and trees background, 1964 . . . . . . . . . . . . . . . . . . .    **50.00**

**Baretta The Street Detective Game,** Milton Bradley, TV/mystery, board game, cover has picture of show star Robert Blake in open jacket and background pictures of him in action with other characters, game name at top, 1976. . . . . . . . . . . . . . . .    **25.00**

**Bargain Hunter,** Milton Bradley, shopping, board game, cover

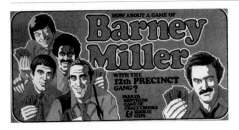

*Barney Miller*

*Game of Base–Ball*

shows gameboard and "Plastic Credit Card Machine" included with game, 1981 . . . . . . . . . . **15.00**

**Barnabas Collins Dark Shadows Game,** Milton Bradley, TV/monster, action game, lid shows man holding snake, flying bat, haunted house, and 2 people playing game building a skeleton, contains box (coffin) holding skeleton bone pcs and fangs, all pcs glow–in–the–dark, 1969 . . . . . . . . . . . . . . . . . . **75.00**

**Barney Miller,** Parker Brothers, TV/comedy, board game, cover shows 5 men holding playing cards, 1977 *see illus* . . . . . . . **15.00**

**Baron Munchausen Game, The,** Parker Brothers, radio ("The Jack Pearl Show")/comedy/literary character, dice game, 5 x 3½ x 2", lid shows Baron spilling dice from cup, contains 5 wooden lettered dice cubes that spell B–A–R–O–N, dice cup, and several round green cardboard counters, ©1933 . . . **25.00**

**Barrel of Monkeys, Giant,** Lakeside, generic, skill game, game container is large plastic simulated wood barrel, name of game and pictures of monkeys band center of container, 1969 . . . . . . . . . . . . . . . . . . **15.00**

**Bas–Ket,** Cadaco, sports, action board game, lid shows 2 players in jump ball position and back of third player with #14 on shirt, name hyphenated in right center of lid, "Real Basketball in Miniature" under name, contains six mechanically con-

trolled levers to sink baskets, 1960 . . . . . . . . . . . . . . . . . . **25.00**

**Base–Ball, Game of,** McLoughlin Brothers, sports, board game, 17⅛ x 9½", lid shows baseball diamond, players in action, several players sitting in bottom right corner, inset of player in left corner, ©1886 *see illus* . . . . **3,000.00**

**Baseball,** Parker Brothers, sports, board game, lid shows batter in full swing, of players with mitts catching ball and sliding into base, earlier version of game exists, 1959 . . . . . . . . . . . . . . **30.00**

**Baseball,** Transogram, sports, computerized action game, lid has pictures of players in various action positions inset onto name letters across top, bottom right corner shows boy and man playing game, strip across lid top shows team emblems, contains plastic stadium, 1969 . . . . **30.00**

**Baseball Game, Mel Allen's,** Radio Corp. of America, sports, board game, lid shows umpire calling play with pitcher in background, contains 33⅓ rpm record "Mell Calls the Plays, You Play the Game," 1959 . . . . **200.00**

**Bash!,** Milton Bradley, generic, action game, lid shows hands holding head of plastic figure being knocked apart, contains plastic pcs, hammer, and Oh Fooey! card, 1965 . . . . . . . . . **15.00**

**Basket Ball,** Russell Mfg. Co., No. 217, sports, action game, 10½" sq lid has illus of walking black man carrying ball, scenery shows house and 2 figures

*Bat Masterson*

*Batman Forever, Battle at the Big Top*

throwing ball, includes balls
and diecut box bottom game
board which hangs over door-
knob, 1 of series of 4 "door-
knob" games, 1929 . . . . . . . .    **85.00**
**Basketball,** Transogram, sports,
computerized action game,
large letters of game name on
lid show inset pictures of players and fans, team logos across
top, man and boy playing game
in bottom right corner, NBA
logo,1969 . . . . . . . . . . . . . .    **30.00**
**Bat Masterson,** Lowell, TV/west-
ern, board game, lid pictures
cowboys in shoot–out scene in
front of western style hotel, inset
of show star Gene Barry, 1958
*see illus*. . . . . . . . . . . . . . . .    **65.00**
**Batman & Robin,** Hasbro, comic
book/superhero character, board
game, "Help Batman and Robin
Capture The Joker," Batman on
left side of cover, Robin hovering over red automobile driven
by The Joker, city skyline in
background, 1966 . . . . . . . . . .    **75.00**
**Batman Card Game,** Ideal, comic
book/superhero character, card
game, cover shows Batman and
Robin flying into action scene,
jewlery store robbery in right
bottom corner, "CARD GAME"
with Ideal logo in top right cor-
ner, 1966. . . . . . . . . . . . . . . .    **50.00**
**Batman Forever, Battle at the Big
Top,** Parker Brothers, comic
book/super hero, action game,
box contains cardboard sheets,
3–dimensional pcs, plastic
tightrope, launcher, batarang

ball, die, bases, and label sheet,
1995 *see illus*. . . . . . . . . . . . .    **15.00**
**Batman Game,** Milton Bradley,
comic book/superhero character,
board game, center of lid shows
batman in full dress with blue
cape super–imposed over smaller action scenes of him and
Robin, city skyline, helicopter,
and Batmobile, 1966 . . . . . . . .    **75.00**
**Batman Pin Ball Game,** Marx,
comic book/superhero character,
board game, lid shows Batman
in top left corner, Robin in bottom right corner, flying bat in
center, 5 small circles across top
with MARX printed in largest
circle, contains bonus score
spinner, 1966. . . . . . . . . . . . .    **100.00**
**Battle–Cry, American Heritage,**
Command Decision Series,
Milton Bradley, "A Civil War
Game," military/educational,
board game, cover shows soldiers on horseback, 5 white stars
in bottom right corner, moun-
tains in background, 1961 . . . .    **40.00**
**Battle Line Game,** Ideal, TV/mili-
tary, board game, lid shows
game name amid artillary fire,
battle scene with soldiers, tank,
and cannon, 1964 . . . . . . . . . .    **40.00**
**Battle of the Planets Game,**
Milton Bradley, TV/space, board
game, game name in center of
lid with background of spaceship and space figures, based on
the Japanese animated series,
1979 . . . . . . . . . . . . . . . . . . .    **20.00**
**Battle Stations!,** John E. Burleson,
military, grid game, lid shows

*Battlestar Galactica*

*Beat The Clock Game*

game offers "excitement and fun for 'Admirals' 9 to 90," column of 4 stars down left and right, comes with sealed secret orders, 1952 . . . . . . . . . . . . . . . . . .  **30.00**

**Battles, Game of, or Fun for Boys,** McLoughlin Brothers, military, skill and action game, 24³/₄ x 21³/₄", lid shows soldiers in different uniforms including high hats, nurse with long dress, soldier with cannon, soldier in letter "B," contains 60 cardboard soldiers nailed to wooden stands, wood and metal parts to make 2 cannons, ammo shells, 2 heavy cardboard tents, and 2 flags, 1889 . . . . . . . . . . . .  **500.00**

**Battleship,** Milton Bradley, military, board game, lid shows son playing game with father holding game pc saying "it's a hit," mother and daughter looking on, contains 2 plastic boxes with plastic battleship pcs, 1967  **40.00**

**Battleship Game, The,** Whitman, military, board game, lid shows naval war scene with airplane overhead, 1940 . . . . . . . . . . .  **15.00**

**Battlestar Galactica,** Parker Brothers, TV/space, board game, lid shows partial view of earth with spaceship headed toward outer space, 1978 *see illus* . . . .  **15.00**

**Battling Tops Game,** Ideal, generic, action game, lid shows players watching spinning tops, game name along bottom,1968  **12.00**

**Bazaar, The Trading Game,** 3M, business, board game, lid shows arch, canopies, and outdoor street bazaar with woman ven-

dor and wares in foreground, 1967 . . . . . . . . . . . . . . . . . .  **10.00**

**Beat Detroit,** Dynamic Games, business/automobiles, board game, cover shows crashing cars with game name in upper left corner, "The game that will crack you up" below name, 1972 . . . . . . . . . . . . . . . . . .  **15.00**

**Beat the Buzz,** Kenner Products Co, generic, skill game, players move metal loop along wire running across plastic base without setting off buzzer, 1958. . . .  **15.00**

**Beat the Clock Game,** Lowell, TV/game show, action game, lid with show host Bud Collyer in front of timer clock promoting show producer Sylvania, lid advertises 40 hilarious laugh provoking stunts, contains timer clock, stunt pcs including rings, balloons, and balls, and an instruction booklet, 1954 *see illus* . . . . . . . . . . . . . . . .  **60.00**

• Second cover shows half of time clock on left, person's hand moving timer on right, pictures of people doing stunts, and host's photograph in top right corner . . . . . . . . . . . . . . . .  **50.00**

**Beat the Clock Game,** Milton Bradley, TV series, action game, cover shows man and woman doing stunts with timer clock, 1969 . . . . . . . . . . . . . . . . . .  **15.00**

**Beatles Flip Your Wig Game, The,** Milton Bradley, rock and roll,

*Ben Casey M.D.*

*The Beverly Hillbillies*

board game, lid shows picture
of 4 Beatles on right, spinning
wig in center, 1964 . . . . . . . .    **125.00**
**Beauty and the Beast, Game of,**
Milton Bradley, book, board
game, 9" sq, lid shows young
girl sleeping next to large beast
resembling lion, mfg info
bottom right corner above small
print border trim that runs
around lid, contains round
colored wooden counters and
spinner, ©1905 . . . . . . . . . . .    **50.00**
**Bee Bopper Game,** Ideal, generic,
action game, lid shows 4 people
playing game, using hand nets
to catch flying "Bees," 1968 . . .    **15.00**
**Beetle Bailey—The Old Army
Game,** Milton Bradley, comic
book character, board game,
cover shows 3 military characters and dog in military coat,
night sky with quarter moon
and stars, contains multicolored
pcs and play money, 1963 . . . .    **50.00**
**Beginner's Bridge, Goren's,**
Milton Bradley, strategy, board
game, cover shows Mr. Goren
and game board, "Learn how—
all by yourself," 1967 . . . . . . . .    **10.00**
**Ben Casey, M.D. Game,**
Transogram, TV/medical, board
game, cover shows hospital
room operation and picture of
show star Vincent Edwards,
contains cardboard Casey
figures, plastic stands, 66 cards,
dice, and instruction sheet,
1961 *see illus* . . . . . . . . . . . .    **30.00**
**Benny Goodman Swings Into A
Game of Musical Information,**
Toy Creations, music/education-

al, quiz game, picture of Benny
Goodman on lid, contains xylo-
phone and questions, 1940s  . .    **75.00**
**Bermuda Triangle Game,** Milton
Bradley, mystery, board game,
cover shows gameboard, and
ship at sea under black cloud,
1976 . . . . . . . . . . . . . . . . . . .    **15.00**
**Betsy Ross and The Flag Game,**
Transogram, educational/histori-
cal, board game, lid shows
seated Betsy Ross and 2 men
dressed in colonial clothing
looking at finished flag, based
on title from Random House's
Landmark Book series, 1961 . . .    **28.00**
**Beverly Hillbillies Game, The,**
Standard Toykraft, TV/comedy,
board game, cover shows 3 family members standing behind
chair, seated woman holding
rifle, surrounded by white pitcher, butter churn, barrel, and urn
with three "x's," left–hand strip
shows  CBS "eye" logo and "As
seen on CBS," 1963 . . . . . . . . .    **50.00**
**Beverly Hillbillies Set Back Card
Game,** Milton Bradley, TV/com-
edy, card game, lid shows
Hillbillies riding in old style car,
tree and building with verandas
in background, 1963 *see illus* . .    **30.00**
**Beverly Hills,** Tonguenchic Corp,
shopping, board game, plain
board has game name in script
lettering, "A Game of Wealth &
Status" printed at lower right
side of lid, 1979 . . . . . . . . . . .    **20.00**
**Bewitch,** Selchow & Righter,
generic, board game, lid shows
mask–type face next to game

*The Game of Bible Lotto*

name in spooky print, 8 cards
with pictures of different animals such as camel, lion, peli-
can, and snake line bottom of
lid, 1964 . . . . . . . . . . . . . .    **18.00**

**Bewitched,** Game Gems,
TV/ comedy, board game, cover
shows Elizabeth Montgomery
on broom and Agnes
Moorehead holding wand,
game name in various colors,
contains 4 cardboard Darrin
figures and stands, 2 spinners,
and cards, 1965 . . . . . . . . . . .    **75.00**

**Bewitched Stymie Card Game,**
Milton Bradley, TV/comedy,
card game, cover shows
Samantha, Endora, and Darrin,
"Stymie Card Game" in top
right, "Bewitched TV Series" in
bottom right, 1964–65 . . . . . . .    **30.00**

**Bible Characters, Game of,**
Zondervan Publishing House,
religious, card game, $7^5/_{16}$ x
$5^3/_8$", lid shows sketches of boy
holding shepherd's staff, head
silhouttes of bearded men in
armor, and rooster, contains
64 cards, ©1939 . . . . . . . . . .    **20.00**

**Bible Lotto, The Game of,**
Goodenough & Woglum Co.,
religious/educational, card
game, $7^3/_8$ x $5^3/_8$ x 1", lid shows
square inset of 3 figures holding
cards, "Bible Incidents,
Characters, Facts & Places,"
c1930s *see illus* . . . . . . . . . . .    **15.00**

**Bicycle Race,** McLoughlin
Brothers, sports, cover shows

2 racers on bicycles with large
front and small back wheels
and waving fans, "A Game for
the Wheelmen" across bottom
of lid, 1891 . . . . . . . . . . . . . .    **1,000.00**

**Bicycle Race, Game of,**
McLoughlin Brothers, sports,
board game, $21^1/_4$ x $12^1/_2$", lid
shows animals riding bikes,
contains lead bicycles and
2 spinners, ©1895 . . . . . . . . . .    **750.00**

**Bid It Right,** Milton Bradley,
TV/ quiz show, card game, lid
shows black price tag with game
name, blue tag with "The Price
is Right," and beige tag with
"A Card Game based on the
Popular TV Show," 1964 . . . . . .    **25.00**

**Big Apple,** Rosebud Art Co., #85,
generic, party game, $11^5/_8$ x $11^5/_8$
x $1^3/_8$," game name across lid
top, apple in center with "for
home" on left and "for party" on
right, "The Game of the Day"
below apple, ©1938. . . . . . . . .    **50.00**

**Big Blast,** Transogram, generic,
skill game, lid shows maze of
gears, dials, and gadgets, "The
Blockbuster Game," contains
plastic ticking bomb, 1967 . . . .    **25.00**

**Big Board,** Eskay Co., business/
stock market, board game, cover
shows stock certificates, "The
Stock Exchange Game," 1975 . .    **15.00**

**Big Business,** Transogram,
No. 1211, business, board
game, separate board and pcs
box, 18" sq gameboard, $4^5/_8$ x 6
x $1^1/_4$" pcs box, US map in center of board with game name
superimposed, closed board has
same picture  with outlined US
map, 1937 . . . . . . . . . . . . . . .    **25.00**

**Big Business,** Transogram, Popular
Edition, business/stock market,
board game, cover shows game
name in large letters superimposed over US map, skyscrapers
and smokestacks at lid bottom,
"How Smart Are You? Here's
$100,000.00—prove it," 1954. .    **15.00**

**Big Business,** Transogram, busi-
ness/stock market, board game,
one cover shows plane flying
across oil derricks, pipelines,

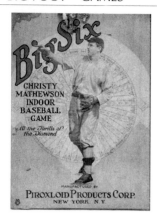

*Big Six*

*Bild–A–Word*

and mfg buildings and man with cigar sitting at desk; second cover has pile of coins and currency at left bottom corner with "How Smart Are You At Business? Here's $200,000.00 —prove it!," 1959 and 1964 . . .    **15.00**

**Big Foot,** Milton Bradley, generic, board game, lid shows youngsters playing game with "Giant Snow Monster" looking on, 1977 . . . . . . . . . . . . . . . . . .    **12.00**

**Big League Baseball,** 3M, sports, board game, cover has player swinging bat, #5 on uniform, catcher and umpire in background, 1966 . . . . . . . . . . . . .    **25.00**

**Big Six: Christy Mathewson Indoor Baseball Game,** Piroxloid Products Corp., sports, board game, 16³/₄ x 22³/₄ x ³/₄", game name diagonally across left corner of lid, Mathewson in uniform, throwing ball, mfg name and location across bottom, 1922 *see illus* . . . . . . .    **600.00**

**Big Sneeze Game, The,** Ideal, generic, action game, cover shows 2 boys and girl watching cards flying, contains cards and mechanical man, 1968 . . . . . . .    **18.00**

**Big Town,** Milton Bradley, generic, board game, cover shows gameboard with town layout, hand operating "dual control," includes magnetic cars and driving test, 1962 . . . . . . . . . . .    **35.00**

**Big Town News Reporting & Printing Game,** Lowell, careers, action game, lid has name of game as newspaper masthead, *Illustrated Press* and "Starring Mark Stevens as Steve Wilson, Managing Editor," contains rubber stamp letters, 1955 . . . .    **75.00**

**Bild–A–Word,** Educational Card & Game Corporation, educational, card game, 6¹/₄ x 6¹/₄ x 1", lid has triangle inset with family playing game, "Game For Children, For Grown–ups; The One Game You Can Play with Children...and Enjoy it Too!," 1929 *see illus* . . . . . . . . . . . . .    **15.00**

**Billionaire,** Happy Hour, Inc., business/uranium hunting, board game, "3–D Vacuformed Plastic," lid shows man in black cowboy hat riding in open donkey–drawn cart, 1956 . . . . .    **25.00**

**Billionaire,** Parker Brothers, business, board game, cover shows man at desk filled with symbols of commerce such as airplane, skyscraper, truck, and ship, global map, "Game of Global Enterprise," 1973 . . . . . . . . . . .    **15.00**

**Billy Blastoff Space Game,** Danlee, space, board game, cover shows spaceship, young astronaut in spacesuit, and 2 planets, sincludes 10 plastic rockets, dice, 25 fuel coupons, and 12 radiograms, 1969 . . . . .    **30.00**

*The Bionic Woman*

*The Black Cat*

**Billy Bumps Visit To Boston,**
George S. Parker & Co.,
travel/educational, card game,
4⁵/₈ x 6¹/₄", cover shows man
holding umbrella under arm,
"Boston" along right side, "A
Reading Game" along bottom,
contains printed cards and
reading booklet, c1887 . . . . . .    **35.00**

**Billy Whiskers,** Saalfield
Publishing Co., No. 280, generic, separate board and pcs box,
board opens to 18¹/₄" sq, 6¹/₂ x
5¹/₄" pcs, box shows ram jumping fence with another goat
looking on, 8 brass–bound
counters, spinner, c1923–26. . .    **50.00**

**Bing Crosby's Game, Call Me
Lucky,** Parker Brothers, suspense, board game, lid shows
5 red stars below Crosby's picture, 4 players at game table,
bottom right corner has music
bar with notes spelling out
"Bing's" (part of "Another one
of Bing's Things, Inc.,") includes
number cards and "Lucky
Seven" card, 1954 . . . . . . . . .    **55.00**

**Bing It,** Matchbox, generic,
action game, similar to badmit-
ton, cover shows game name
"with Ball or Bird for Beach—
Lawn—Playroom," includes
2 tambourine shaped pcs with
game name in hitting area and
hand strap and 1 "bird," 1960s    **15.00**

**Bingo, Deluxe,** Whitman, generic,
card game, cover shows game
name surrounded by game pcs
and the "Magic Dispenser"
included in game, 1957 . . . . . .    **8.00**

**Bingo–Matic,** Transogram, generic, bingo game, lid says "The

Original," instructions on lid for
using "Bingo–Matic Qwik–load
Funnel," shows funnel popping
numbers, 1960. . . . . . . . . . .    **12.00**

**Bingo or Beano A Game,** Parker
Brothers, generic, bingo game,
cover shows group of people
running to Bingo–Beano party,
contains patented scoring fea-
tures, 1930s . . . . . . . . . . . . .    **15.00**

**Bionic Crisis,** Parker Brothers,
TV/ space (The Six Million
Dollar Man), board game, cover
pictures series star Lee Majors,
and space laboratory inset,
1975 . . . . . . . . . . . . . . . . . .    **20.00**

**Bionic Woman, The,** Parker
Brothers, TV/space, board game,
lid has Jaime Sommers autograph next to picture of woman
with long blond hair, background with blue–suited Bionic
Woman and cougar on moun-
tainside, 1976 *see illus* . . . . . . .    **18.00**

**Black Beauty, The Game of,**
Transogram, classic book, board
game, cover shows boy and girl
with black horse in field scene,
another girl sitting under tree,
barn, village, and mountains in
background, 1958 . . . . . . . . .    **35.00**

**Black Cat, The,** Parker Brothers,
fortune telling, card game,
6¹/₂ x 5", lid shows black cat
with curved tail, bow tie around
neck, copyright data below cat,
contains multicolored litho
cards showing cats in varied
situations, ©1897 *see illus* . . . .    **80.00**

*Blockhead!*

**Black Experience, The,** Theme
Productions, educational/histori-
cal, board game, cover traces
history of blacks and shows
faces of famous people, 1971 . .    **15.00**

**Black Hole Space Alert,**
Whitman, movie/space, board
game, lid shows people in
space lab, 4 inset pictures,
"Escape the Doomed Cygnus,"
1979 . . . . . . . . . . . . . . . . . .    **20.00**

**Black Sambo, Game of,** Samuel
Gabriel Sons & Co., No. T264,
book, board game, 17¼ x 13",
cover shows Sambo under
umbrella surounded by tigers,
pcs include several round
cardboard pancakes, cardboard
tigers, 1 Sambo, wooden brack-
ets, and spinner, c1939 . . . . . .    **250.00**

**Blackout,** Milton Bradley, strategy,
board game, cover shows bridge
with many vehicles, city skyline,
and ships, promoted as "Today's
Game of Thrills," second lid has
spotlight beams on bridge and
city skyline, 1939. . . . . . . . . .    **45.00**

**Blacks and Whites,** Psychology
Today, educational, board game,
cover shows round picture of
Afro–American in turtleneck
shirt on top half, game name in
middle, and male caucasian
with hand over mouth on
bottom half, includes game
cards marked "Blacks, Whites,"
and "Deed," 1970–71 . . . . . . .    **20.00**

**Blarney,** Mattel, generic, skil
game, lid shows 2 women and
2 men with broad smiles, game
table, and game pcs, 1970 . . . .    **12.00**

**Blast Off!,** Selchow & Righter,
space, board game, cover shows
traveling rocket, planet encircled
by game name, and "The
Moving Planet Space Game,"
1953 . . . . . . . . . . . . . . . . . . .    **80.00**

**Blast–Off!,** Waddington, space,
board game, cover shows
astronaut and space ship on
moon, different rocket stages,
and planet earth, promoted as
"The Game of Modern Space
Exploration," contains small
space capsule, 1969. . . . . . . . .    **65.00**

**Blizzard of '77,** C.P. Marino, travel, board game, lid shows bus
and walking man in blizzard
scene, 1977 . . . . . . . . . . . . . .    **12.00**

**Block the Clock,** Ideal, generic,
action game, cover shows alarm
clock, person's hand in bottom
left corner, inset of 3 pictures
down strip on right, 1981 . . . . .    **10.00**

**Blockade,** Corey Games, military,
board game, lid shows ship on
fire and sinking, plane flying
overhead, "A Game for
Armchair Admirals," contains
metal ships or cardboard
cutouts, 1941 . . . . . . . . . . . . .    **50.00**

**Blockade,** Milton Bradley, mili-
tary/strategy (Spanish–American
War), board game, 7¼" sq, lid
shows ship at sea, mfg name
and location across lid bottom,
contains 2 wooden counters and
cardboard grid, c1898 . . . . . . .    **30.00**

**Blockhead!,** Parker Brothers,
generic, skill action game, lid
shows 3 people piling up multicolored blocks, game name
across top, contains wooden
blocks, 1976–77 *see illus* . . . . .    **20.00**

**Blondie and Dagwood's Race for
the Office Game,** Jaymar, comic
strip characters, board game,
cover shows Blondie and children in front of house and postman watching Dagwood and
4 dogs running followed by the
word "swish," 1950 . . . . . . . . .    **45.00**

*Bobby Shantz's Baseball Game*

*Bonanza*

**Blow Football,** Hayter, sports, action game, lid shows 5 children playing game, includes 4 straws, 1 ball, 2 stand–up player pcs, and stand–up playing field backgrounds, 1966 . . .    **15.00**

**Blowout Game,** Ideal, generic, skill game, cover shows oil derrick with blue ball, word "Wheeee," oil derricks background, 2 children playing game in bottom left corner, 1978 . . . . . . . . . . . . . . . . . .    **10.00**

**Blox–O,** Lubbers & Bell Mfg. Co., strategy, board game, 6³/₄ x 6⁵/₈ x 1³/₁₆", lid has picture of owl, "o" rings randomly spread across cover, contains 22 pegs, ©1923. . . . . . . . . . . . . . . . . .    **20.00**

**Blue Line Hockey,** 3M, sports, board game, hockey scene with 3 players including goalie on cover, 1970 . . . . . . . . . . . . . .    **35.00**

**Boake Carter's Star Reporter Game,** Parker Brothers, newspaper, board game, 20 x 10³/₈ x 1⁵/₈", lid shows man in hat and bowtie smoking pipe, globe, ship, and newspapers partially covered by strip with game name, 1937 . . . . . . . . . . . . . .    **125.00**

**Bobbin Noggin,** Milton Bradley, TV/stunt show (Shenanigans), action game, lid shows shower pouring water on smiling round face, game name in varied colors at lid top, 1964 . . . . . . . .    **15.00**

**Bobbsey Twins On the Farm Game, The,** Milton Bradley, classic book, board game, cover shows girl holding pitchfork and boy holding dog, background farm scene with barn, cow, and pig, 1957 . . . . . . . . . . . . . . . .    **30.00**

**Bobby Shantz's Baseball Game,** Realistic Games Manufacturing Co., sports, board game, contains gameboard, plastic playing pcs and holders, cards, and instructions, 1954 *see illus* . . . .    **150.00**

**Bonanza,** Parker Brothers, western, Michigan rummy card game, lid shows Cartwrights playing cards, box contains poker tray, red and blue plastic chips, and deck of cards, 1964 *see illus* . . . . . . . . . . . . . . . . .    **40.00**

**Bonkers!, This Game is,** Parker Brothers, generic, skill game, cover shows game name in yellow letters, star and dice among items pictured at bottom, "It's Never the Same Game Twice," 1978 . . . . . . . . . . . .    **10.00**

**Boom Or Bust Game,** Parker Brothers, business, board game, cover shows small pictures of buildings and game name, mfg name above and below game name, includes removable panel in center of gameboard, 1951 . .    **125.00**

**Boss, The,** Ideal, business, board game, lid has picture of business boardroom with standing boss pointing finger at departing man, 1972 . . . . . . . . . . . . . . .    **20.00**

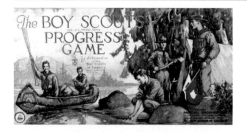

*The Boy Scouts Progress Game*

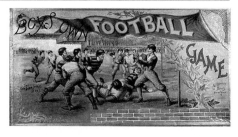

*Boys Own Football Game*

**Bottoms Up,** The Embossing Company, generic, checker game, 6³/₄ x 3 x ⁵/₈", lid shows row of pigs and 2 dice, contains checkers with embossed pigs on bottom, ©1934 . . . . . . . . . . .    **25.00**

**Boundary,** Mattel, strategy, board game, cover shows man and woman with gameboard and pcs, game name across middle of lid, 1970 . . . . . . . . . . . . .    **10.00**

**Bowl–A–Matic,** Eldon, sport, skill game, lid pictures 3 faces looking at plastic bowling toy which automatically resets the pins, 1962 . . . . . . . . . . . . . . . . . .    **75.00**

**Bowl–A–Strike,** E.S. Lowe, sport, dice game, cover shows action picture of bowler and ball hitting pins, 1962 . . . . . . . . . .    **10.00**

**Bowl Em,** Parker Brothers, sport, dice game, cover shows barrel with dice spilling out, scoring sheet, bowling ball and pins in upper right corner, "The Parlor Bowling Game" across top, 1950s . . . . . . . . . . . . . . . . .    **12.00**

**Bowling: A Board Game,** Parker Brothers, sports, board game, 15¹/₂ x 11¹/₂", cover shows men and women bowling with balls lined up on shelves, copyright and publishing data in lower right corner, contains spinner and 4 counters, 1896 . . . . . . . .    **600.00**

**Bowlo,** Feature Games, No. 10, sport, card game, lid shows game name across large bowling ball, hand holding playing cards in bottom left corner, No. 10 in upper right corner, contains numbered playing cards with pictures of bowling

pins, scoring sheets, and official instructions, 1957 . . . . . . . . . .    **15.00**

**Boy Hunter, The,** Parker Brothers, generic, skill game, 15³/₄ x 7", cover shows boy lying on ridge, aiming rifle at lion, contains 4 cardboard targets of wild animals on wooden supports, metal and wood rifle, and 8 wooden pellets, c1925 . . . . .    **90.00**

**Boy Scouts,** McLoughlin Brothers, scouting, board game, separate board and pcs box, 18¹¹/₁₆ x 18³/₄" board, 6¹/₄ x 4¹/₈ x ⁷/₈" pcs box, round track gameboard with scenes of scouting in 4 corners, contains spinner and colored checkers, c1910s . . . . .    **250.00**

**Boy Scouts, The Game of,** Parker Brothers, scouting, card game, 15¹/₂ x 4", lid has game name, copyright, and mfg info "Salem, Mass., New York, London, For any number of Players," and lists other games made by Parker Brothers, contains 50 cards and 2 advertising cards, ©1912 . . . .    **150.00**

**Boy Scouts Progress Game, The,** Parker Brothers, scouting, board game, 19 x 10", cover shows 2 boy scouts in canoe, 3 others setting up camp under tree, 1 holding ax, 1 holding flags and 1 with hands in water, contains 80 counters or honors, 4 different colored wooden playing pcs, dice cup, and 2 dice, authorized by Boy Scouts of America, ©1924–26 *see illus* . . . . . . . . . . . . . . . .    **250.00**

**Boys Own Football Game,** McLoughlin Brothers, sports, lid shows word "Football" in

*Branded Game*

*Break the Bank*

waving flag, boys playing game, brick wall at bottom of lid, The Outdoor Sports Series, unknown date *see illus* . . . . . . . . . . . . . .    **750.00**

**Bozo In Circus–Land,** Lowell, cartoon, board game, lid has large picture of Bozo with red nose and red hair in left corner, bottom right corner shows circus scenes including tents, lion cage, and ticket booth, 1965 . .    **30.00**

**Bozo The Clown Circus Game,** Transogram, cartoon, board game, lid has red and white striped background, Bozo juggling balls watched by little girl in hat, dress, and boots, 1960s . . . . . . . . . . . . . . . . . .    **25.00**

**Bradley's Telegraph Game,** Milton Bradley, educational, action game, 10⁵/₈ x 8", lid shows boy seated at table holding paper, messenger boy and third man looking on, includes wooden telegraph key, toy money, several telegram blanks, night letter blanks, cablegrams, and envelopes, c1905 . . . . . . . . . . .    **135.00**

**Bradley's Toy Town Post Office,** Milton Bradley, educational, action game, 8¹/₄ x 11", cover shows girl in hat and young boy in sailor–collared suit mailing letters, addressed envelopes flying in background, includes postman's mask, 2 cardboard sections and 2 wooden supports to create office, stamp, stamp pad, letters, envelopes, postcards, and toy stamps, ©1910. .    **175.00**

**Brady Bunch Game, The,** Whitman, TV/family comedy, board game, cover shows

pitched tent and family members in activities related to camping such as wood sawing, fishing, and campfire cooking, 1973 . . . . . . . . . . . . . . . . . .    **65.00**

**Brain Waves,** Milton Bradley, generic, strategy game, cover shows face with 3 lights in forehead emitting waves, 3 picture inset strip down right side, 1977    **15.00**

**Branded Game,** Milton Bradley, TV/western, board game, lid has running cowboy grabbing gun holster and sword cutting through boxed area with game name, 1966 *see illus* . . . . . . . .    **50.00**

**Break the Bank,** Bettye–B., TV/game show, cover promotes "Starring Bert Parks," picture of Parks in spotlight on left side, game name in blue box, mfg name in bottom right corner, 1955 *see illus*. . . . . . . . . . . . .    **45.00**

**Break the Bank,** Bettye–B., TV/game show, Series 2, cover shows Bert Parks on left with outstretched arms, 1955 . . . . . .    **40.00**

**Breaking Point,** Ideal, generic, skill game, lid shows 2 girls playing game, holding sticks, hanging blue balls, catch tray at bottom of game pc, 1976 . . . . .    **10.00**

**Breakthru,** 3M, generic, strategy game, cover shows 2 men playing game at table, 2 ships, waves, and dark clouds, 1965 . .    **20.00**

**Bridge for One, Charles Goren's Advanced**, Fine Edition, Milton Bradley, generic, card game, cover pictures the 4 card suits,

"Two Challenging Solitaire Games for Bridge Players," 1967    **10.00**

**Bridge for Three, Charles Goren's Cutthroat,** Fine Edition, Milton Bradley, generic, card, game, cover shows 4 card suits in individual cards with appropriate red and black colors, 1968. . . .    **10.00**

**Bridge For Two, Goren's,** Milton Bradley, generic, card game, cover has Goren's picture and signature, Ace, King, Queen and Jack playing cards, with "MB" on Ace of spade, 1964 . . . . . . .    **10.00**

**Bridge Keno,** Milton Bradley, generic, card/board game, cover shows playing board with faces of playing cards, 1930 . . . . . . .    **15.00**

**Broadside, American Heritage,** Command Decision Series, Milton Bradley, military (War of 1812), board game, lid shows storm scene at sea with American Revolution ships with flags, 5 stars in bottom right corner, contains plastic ships, 1962 . . . . . . . . . . . . . . . . . .    **45.00**

**Broadside, Gangway For Fun,** Transogram, TV/underwater adventure game, cover shows faces of 2 men and 1 woman in military hats on military vehicles, game name spread across 3 boxes, 1 next to each face, re-release of Transogram's Aquanauts game, 1964. . . . . . .    **28.00**

**"Brownie" Kick–In Top,** M.H. Miller Co., generic, skill game, $8^1/_2$ x $8^3/_4$ x $1^3/_8$", lid shows game pcs with game name on edge of metal bowl circular playing field, contains 2 pc spinning top and 5 wooden balls, c1910s. . .    **75.00**

**Bruce Force and the Treasure of Shark Island,** Ideal, adventure, board game, board has underwater scene of diver fighting off shark to reach open treasure chest, contains spinner and playing cards, 1963 . . . . . . . .    **30.00**

**Bruce Force—Lost In Outer Space,** Ideal, space, board game, cover shows diver using ray gun to fight off toothy creature, starry sky and earth planet

*Buck Rogers Game*

in background, 2 boys playing game in left corner inset, contains spinner and playing cards, 1963 . . . . . . . . . . . . . . . . . .    **50.00**

**Buccaneers, The,** Transogram, TV/sea adventure, board game, cover has picture of buccaneer with outstretched arm holding sword in right corner, encircled photo of Dan Tempest, 2 ships with cannons blasting smoke, and skull and crossbones flag, 1957 . . . . . . . . . . . . . . . . . .    **40.00**

**Buck Rogers Battle for the 25th Century,** TSR, space, contains gameboard, 16–page basic game book, 8–page advanced game book, cardboard counters, plastic chips, and 10–sided dice, 1988 . . . . . . . . . . . . . . . . . .    **15.00**

**Buck Rogers Game,** Milton Bradley, TV/space/comic strip character, board game, cover shows 2 rockets and 6 faces of the show's cast, 1979 *see illus.* .    **25.00**

**Buck Rogers Game,** Transogram, space/comic strip character, board game, cover shows 2 people in space gear chasing alien–type figures, promotes the "Adventure in the 25th Century Game," 1965 . . . . . . . . . . . . .    **50.00**

**Buckaroo The Cowboy Roundup Game,** Milton Bradley, western, board game, lid shows cowboys riding horses in cattle roundup, mountains in background, 1947    **35.00**

**Bucket of Fun,** Milton Bradley, generic, action game, lid shows 2 boys and 2 girls playing game, boy wearing green and white striped shirt, and the magic

*Game of Buffalo Bill*

*Bunco*

bucket "popping" out balls,
1968 . . . . . . . . . . . . . . . . . . .    **20.00**

**Buffalo Bill, Game of,** Parker
Brothers, western, board game,
15 x 9", lid shows rectangular
inset of cowboy and running
buffalos, round inset of man on
horse, Indian teepees in background, contains colored wood-
en counters and spinner, ©1898
*see illus* . . . . . . . . . . . . . . . . .    **75.00**

**Buffalo Hunt,** Parker Brothers,
western, board game (board on
bottom of box), 5¹/₄ x 5¹/₄ x 6³/₄",
lid shows 2 cowboys chasing
buffalo, mfg data in right bottom
corner, c1890s . . . . . . . . . . . .    **125.00**

**Bug–A–Boo Game,** Whitman,
generic, action board game,
cover shows 3 children playing
game, girl holding game pc,
boy in green and white striped
shirt, contains wind–up "bugs,"
1968 . . . . . . . . . . . . . . . . . . .    **15.00**

**Bugs Bunny Adventure Game,**
Milton Bradley, cartoon, board
game, cover shows Bugs Bunny
eating carrot in field, other cartoon characters in background
carrying net to catch flying
insects and animals, contains
playing pcs resembling
Hanna–Barbera favorites including Speedy Gonzales and Porky
Pig, 1961 . . . . . . . . . . . . . . .    **32.00**

**Bull in a China Shop,** Milton
Bradley, generic, skill game,
12" sq, lid shows bull with head
lowered among various china
dishes and vases, contains
8 wooden tenpins and metal
spring top, natural wood boxed

board has 8 affixed black pegs
and black circles on which to
stand pins, ©1906 . . . . . . . . .    **50.00**

**Bulls and Bears,** Parker Brothers,
business/stock market, separate
board and pcs box, 19" sq
board, 13¹/₂ x 6³/₄" matching
box, contains 2 dice, 6 wooden
counters, 6 metal chairs, 9 certificates, stock pool cards and
paper money, invented by
Monopoly's Charles B Darrow,
©1936 . . . . . . . . . . . . . . . . . .    **100.00**

**Bullwinkle and Rocky,** Ideal, cartoon, board game, cover shows
Rocky jumping in front of
Bullwinkle with outstretched
arms, mfg name in bottom right
corner, 1963 . . . . . . . . . . . . .    **60.00**

**Bullwinkle Hide 'N Seek Game,**
Milton Bradley, cartoon, board
game, full picture of Bullwinkle
on cover with letters of the word
"GAME" hanging by strings from
his antlers, Good Housekeeping
and Parents Magazine seals,
1961 . . . . . . . . . . . . . . . . . . .    **75.00**

**Bullwinkle Travel Adventure
Game,** Transogram, cartoon,
board game, lid shows
Bullwinkle and 3 insets of him
in travel activities including
going over waterfall in barrel
and being caught in quicksand,
1970 . . . . . . . . . . . . . . . . . . .    **50.00**

**Bunco,** Home Game Co., science,
card game, 5¹/₂ x 3⁷/₈ x 1", cover
shows game name, "patent
applied for," and asks "Have you

*The Game of Bunny Rabbit*

ever been Buncoed?", second cover shows 6 men in top hats smoking cigars, contains 115 cards, 1904 *see illus* . . . . . . .   **40.00**

**Bunker Poker,** Cadeaux (Milton Bradley), TV series character, card game of chance, came in cigar box, picture of Archie Bunker on box lid, 1972 . . . . .   **20.00**

**Bunny Rabbit, or Cottontail & Peter, The Game of,** Parker Brothers, book, board game, 9 x 17", lid shows rabbit carrying large carrot, wearing hat, jacket and bowtie, lid bottom has ship in circle in left corner, #91, and mfg info, c1928–29 *see illus*. . . . . . . . . . . . . . .   **150.00**

**Bunny Rabbit Game,** Parker Brothers, generic, board game, lid shows 2 rabbits, 1 carrying umbrella walking through field, contains spinner and bunny player pcs, 1961 . . . . . . . . . .   **25.00**

**Burger King Championship Checkers,** Commemorative Limited Edition, Burger King, advertising, strategy game, cover shows "Official Guinness Book

of World Records Challenge," Burger King logo, and a checker with a crown and "King Me!," 1988 . . . . . . . . . . . . . . . . . .   **10.00**

**Buried Treasure, The Game of,** Russell Mfg. Co., adventure, board game, lid shows pirate holding stick in right hand, large leaning tree, body of water in background, c1930s . . . . . . . .   **45.00**

**Burke's Law,** Transogram, TV/ mystery, board game, cover with show star Gene Barry on phone, 1964 . . . . . . . . . . . . .   **45.00**

**Burke's Law Target Game,** Transogram, TV/crime, action game, lid shows spinner, automobile with tires as targets, inset picture of show star Gene Barry, and strip down right side with silhouettes of men shooting guns, 1964. . . . . . . . . . . . . . .   **30.00**

**Burr Tillstrom's Kukla and Ollie A Game,** Parker Brothers, TV characters (No Fran), board game, cover shows Kukla and Ollie on each side of game name, 1962 . . . . . . . . . . . . . .   **35.00**

**Buy and Sell,** Whitman, business, board game, cover shows 2 women wearing hats, scarves, gloves, and jewlery with man in top hat and bowtie at table with gameboard, contains play money, 1953 . . . . . . . . . . . . . .   **15.00**

**By the Numbers,** Milton Bradley, TV/game show, word game, cover shows 2 couples on each side of the letter panel board with "You Build Words" spelled out, 1962. . . . . . . . . . . . . . . .   **10.00**

**– C –**

**Cabby,** Selchow & Righter, generic, board game, lid shows 5 cars, "Rules Made to be Broken!," contains metal cars and celluloid rings, 1938–40s . .   **60.00**

**Cake Walk Game, The,** Parker Brothers, 15 x 9", dance/Black collectible, board game, box reads "Anglo–American Game

Co., Montreal," lid shows 7 black people doing the "Cake Walk" dance, first man carrying cane, women in gowns, contains 4 playing pcs, and spinner, c1900s . . . . . . . . . . . . . . . .  **1,200.00**

**Call Kelly,** Games for Industry, advertisement, board game, lid shows man and woman on phones, woman seated at table with typewriter, inset strip of figures across lid bottom, "The New Game About Business Services," promotes Kelly Girls "Temp" services, 1966 . . . . . . .  **25.00**

**Call My Bluff,** Milton Bradley, TV/game show, board game, cover has 3 faces in circles, each holding numbered card, man in center wearing glasses, "The New TV Game" across lid bottom, 1965. . . . . . . . . . . . .  **30.00**

**Calling All Cars,** Parker Brothers, crime, board game, 16 x 8", cover shows 3 police cars and policeman at radio transmitter, contains green double spinner, 4 colored metal cars, board which folds in half, and instruction sheet, box bottom partitioned to hold metal cars, c1938 . . . . . . . . . . . . . . . . .  **45.00**
• Reissued – same cover, 1959 . .  **20.00**

**Calling Superman,** Transogram, superhero character, board game, lid shows Superman flying over city and crowds of people, inset of 4 faces, "A Game of News Reporting," 1954 . . . . . .  **100.00**

**Cam,** Parker Brothers, military, board game, cover shows game name surrounded by people engaged in various activities, "The Great Game," abbreviated version of Camelot, 1949 . . . . .  **20.00**

**Camel Game, The,** RJRTC, advertisement, dice game, cover shows package of Camel cigarettes, 1992 . . . . . . . . . . . . . .  **10.00**

**Camelot,** Parker Brothers, military, board game, lid shows 2 knights in armor with feathered plumes riding blanketed horses, "The Greatest of Modern Games, Quickly and Easily Learned," 1950s . . . . . . . . . . .  **30.00**

**Camelot,** Parker Brothers, Popular Edition, evolved from Chivalry, board game, box cover shows board, pcs box, and top of castle behind game name,1932 . . .  **40.00**

**Camelot, Legend of,** Hoyle, military, board game, cover shows battle, knights on horses carrying flags, castle and river in background, "An Adventure Game of Conquering Kingdoms," 1987 . . . . . . . . . . . . .  **20.00**

**Camouflage,** Milton Bradley, TV/ game show, skill game, c over shows 9 people of all sizes and ages in different clothing, 1961. . . . . . . . . . . . . . . .  **25.00**

**Camouflage, The Game of,** Parker Brothers, military, card game, $6^5/_8$ x $3^7/_8$", lid has game name on upward angle from left to right, contains cards and spinner, c1915-18 . . . . . . . . . . . .  **60.00**

**Camp Granada (Alan Sherman's),** Milton Bradley, camping, board game, cover shows camp tent and camper with large glasses holding pencil and letter, wearing camp shirt and peaked hat, 1965 . . . . . . . . . . . . . . . . . . .  **50.00**

**Camp Runamuck Game,** Ideal, TV/camping, board game, cover shows camp leader wearing hat with arrow through it, whistles on chain around neck, 3 men wearing sneakers, camp bunks, and campers, 1965. . . . . . . . . .  **45.00**

**Campaign,** Saalfield, military/Civil War, board game, lid shows Union and Confederate soldiers carrying flags, "The American 'Go' Game," 1961 . . . . . . . . . .  **32.00**

**Campaign,** Waddington, military/political strategy (Napoleon era), board game, lid shows sword, shield, 1971 . . . . . . . . .  **35.00**

**Campus Queen,** King–Sealey, generic, board game, cover pictures Queen carrying flowers with escort on lunch box game container, contains spinner and magnetic pcs, game printed on back of lunch box, 1967 . . . . .    **25.00**

**Can–Doo,** Aurora, advertisement, skill and action game, lid shows boy and man with flying cans of Campbell Soup, 4 circle insets along lid bottom, contains small plastic soup cans, 1970s. . . . . .    **15.00**

**Candid Camera,** Lowell, TV/generic, action game, cover pictures game host Allen Funt peeking out from behind curtain holding camera, 1963 . . . . . . .    **50.00**

**Candyland,** Milton Bradley, generic, board game, cover shows game name in peppermint stripes, boy and girl looking at gingerbread man, and gingerbread house with ice cream cone chimney, "A sweet little game for sweet little folks," 1955, 1962 . . . . . . . . . . . . . .    **30.00**

**Caper,** Parker Brothers, mystery, board game, lid shows burglar chiseling letters of game name with different tools, "The Great Jewel Robbery Game," 1970. . .    **35.00**

**Cap'n Crunch Island Adventure Game,** Warren, cartoon cereal character, board game, lid has large picture of Cap'n Crunch, "C" on hat, robot with gun, small inset picture bottom left, 1980s . . . . . . . . . . . . . . . . .    **18.00**

**Captain America,** Milton Bradley, comic book/superhero, board game, cover shows masked face with large "A" on head, half of a red and white shield, second picture of flying Captain America, in background, came with free comic book, 1966 . . .    **100.00**

**Captain America,** Milton Bradley, comic book/superhero, board game, cover shows flying figures, Captain America and The Falcon, "Featuring The Falcon and The Avengers," 1977 . . . . .    **30.00**

**Captain Caveman and the Teen Angels,** Milton Bradley, TV/animated series, board game, lid shows 3 women pointing at cartoon caveman holding club,

blonde in short skirt, brunette in long skirt, black woman in short skirt and boots, 1980 . . . . . . . .    **15.00**

**Captain Gallant of the Foreign Legion,** Transogram, TV/adventure, board game, cover shows men of Foreign Legion on horses, men dressed in Arabic clothing, camels, striped tent, and encircled photos of show stars, 1955 . . . . . . . . . . . . . . . . .    **45.00**

**Captain Kangaroo,** Milton Bradley, TV/generic, board game, picture of the Captain with mustache, wearing small blue hat at right side of lid, 1956 . . . . . . . . . . . . . . . . .    **75.00**

**Captain Kidd Junior,** Parker Brothers, adventure, board game, 10³/₄ x 12", cover shows boy dressed as pirate, feather in hat, walking blindfolded boy over plank leading to tub of water, dog and flag in scene, and "Walking the Plank" on wall, contains dice cup, 2 dice, and 24 colored wooden counters, instructions on back of box cover, 1926 . . . . . . . . . . . . . .    **75.00**

**Captain Video,** Milton Bradley, space, board game, cover shows 2 rockets in flight, planet, stars, and picture of Captain in circle, 1952 . . . . . . . . . . . . . . . . . . . .    **150.00**

**Capture Hill 79,** Hasbro, military, card game, cover shows soldier in helmet and camouflage jacket, facing pyramid–type hill, "G I Joe" in top left corner, contains playing cards, 1968 . . . . . . . .    **45.00**

**Car 54 Where Are You?,** Allison, TV/crime, cover shows 2 policemen, police car with "54" on door, NBC Television bottom left corner, and mfg name in shield at bottom right corner, 1962 . . .    **75.00**

**Car Travel Game,** Milton Bradley, generic, board game, cover shows station wagon, parents in front seat, boy and girl in back playing game, 1958 . . . . . . . .    **20.00**

**Careers,** Parker Brothers, educational, board game, 3 drawings across left side of lid (star, dollar sign, and heart), "Game of Fame, Fortune & Happiness," 1958 . . . . . . . . . . . . . . . . . .  **30.00**

**Careers,** Parker Brothers, educational, board game, star, dollar sign, and heart slanted top to bottom on right side of lid, "A Game of Optional Goals," varied color title letters, 1965 . . . .  **15.00**

**Cargo For Victory,** All–Fair, military, patriotism, board game, lid shows men carrying cargo to 2 ships, partial world map in background, 1943 . . . . . . . . .  **45.00**

**Cargoes,** Selchow & Righter, No. 42, business, board game, 16¼ x 9½", cover shows front of steamship with tug boat on each side, men on docks waving, city skyline in background, "SR" logo encircled in top left corner, contains 66 cards, die, and 4 metal ships, William Longyear illus, 1934, 1940s, 1950s . . . . . . . . . . . . . . . . .  **40.00**

**Carol Burnett's Card Game— Spoof,** Milton Bradley, TV/comedy, card game, cover shows Carol Burnett, "SPOOF" in large letters across bottom of lid, contains score pad, numbered playing cards, and divided card tray holder, 1964 . . . . . . . . . .  **25.00**

**Carrier Strike!,** Milton Bradley, military/naval strategy, board game, cover shows playing board and carrier ship with plane taking off, contains plastic aircraft carriers and airplanes, 1977 . . . . . . . . . . . . . . . . . .  **30.00**

**Cars N' Trucks Build–A–Game,** Ideal, generic, skill and action game, lid shows car and truck, pictures 4 people in assembly line tasks, mfg info and logo on right side, 1961 . . . . . . . . . . .  **50.00**

**Cascade,** Matchbox, action game, lid shows game apparatus and family of 4 playing, contains steel balls that drop from tower and bounce off drums to reach scoring area, "The Thump–A– Drum" game, 1972 . . . . . . . .  **15.00**

**Case of the Elusive Assassin, Ellery Queen's,** Ideal, mystery/

book, board game, cover shows bookmark stamped with pair of glasses in titled book, man with glasses smoking pipe, man with hat and mustache, man in uniform hat, man assisting men with turbans, back of man running with gun, Famous Mystery Classic Series, 1967 . . .  **30.00**

**Casey Jones Game Box,** Saalfield, TV/railroading, board game, lid shows Casey (Allen Hale) in striped engineer's outfit, steam locomotive and cargo cars in background, contains 3 games about railroading, 1959 . . . . . .  **50.00**

**Casino Electric Pinball,** Marx, generic, skill and action game, cover shows pinball game that works on 4 standard flashlight batteries, includes instant total Score–O–Meter Dial, 1971 . . . .  **30.00**

**Casper Electronic Adventure Game,** Tarco, cartoon, skill game, cover shows flying Casper, witch flying in full moon, rainbow, and haunted house, "Test Your Skill By Electronic Remote Control, Develop Your Coordination," 1962 . . . . . . . . . . . . . . . . . .  **25.00**

**Casper The Friendly Ghost,** Milton Bradley, cartoon, board game, lid shows Casper below game name at left and game board at right, 1959/1960s . . . .  **15.00**

**"Cat,"** Carl F. Doerr, sport/baseball, board game, 10½ x 5½", game name in large letters on lid center, "The Most Popular Game, Typically American" above game name, 2 batters on each side of lid, "All Rights Protected" and mfg info at center of lid bottom, contains 2 clay marbles, c1915 . . . . . . . . . . . . . .  **30.00**

**Cat and Mouse, Game of,** Parker Brothers, generic, board game, cover shows front of sitting cat with curved tail and head turned toward mouse on right side of lid, 1964 . . . . . . . . . . . . . . . .  **15.00**

**Catch Raffles,** unknown manufacturer, generic, board game, 14½ x 8½", cover has logo of

*Game of Catching Mice*

*The Cattlemen*

2 bees in oval with "New York,
Chicago, and St. Louis," lid
shows man in top hat and cape
with cane, contains spinner,
4 counters, and instruction
sheet, c1905–10 . . . . . . . . . .  **75.00**

**Catching Mice, Game of,**
McLoughlin Brothers, generic,
board game, gem series, 7³/₄ x
15¹/₂", lid shows cat and mice
on heart shaped cheese, words
of game name split above and
below cheese, ©1888 *see illus*  **250.00**

**Cattlemen, The,** Selchow &
Righter, western strategy, board
game, lid shows 2 men in cowboy hats, woman in hat, 1977
*see illus*. . . . . . . . . . . . . . . .  **15.00**

**Cavalcade,** Selchow & Righter,
horse racing, board game, lid
shows 2 jockeys riding #7 and
#8 horses, grandstand in back-
ground, 1950s . . . . . . . . . . . .  **40.00**

**Challenge the Yankees,** Hasbro,
sport/baseball, board game,
cover shows aerial view of stadium, inset strip down left side
shows 3 players in action shots,

"The Official Yankees Baseball
Game," 1964. . . . . . . . . . . . .  **250.00**

**Champion Road Race,** Champion
Spark Plugs, auto racing/adver-
tisement, board game, board
opens to 18 x 12", cover shows
racing car, waving fans, and
race starter, contains 2¹/₂ x 12"
strip on side of board with
cutout spinner and 6 cutout
race cars, unknown date . . . . .  **25.00**

**Championship Base Ball Parlor
Game,** Grebnelle Novelty Co.,
sport, board game, 22 x 9¹/₄",
"Played the Same as the Great
National Out–Door Game in
Every Detail," cover views baseball diamond, crowds in stands,
billboard with "Worlds and
National League Champions
Ball Park, Boston, 1914," contains 2 dice, 20 yellow and blue
players' position disks, photo of
1914 Boston Braves, booklet
listing players' names for all
16 leagues and 120 clubs, and
3 score cards, folding board
opens to 18 x 22", ©1914 . . . .  **1,250.00**

**Championship Golf, Gardner's,**
sport, action game, cover shows
swinging golfer with caddy
holding bag, 3 clubs shown,
one with #2 cover, "O" in word
Golf has smiling face, 1950s . .  **30.00**

**Champs: Land of Brawno,**
Selchow & Righter, sports game,
15¹/₂ x 15¹/₂ x 1¹/₂", cover shows
silhouettes of baseball player
with bat, dog, diver, and person
wearing boxing gloves, c1920s  **35.00**

**Charge, The,** E.O. Clark, No. 354,
military, board game,

*Charlie's Angels*

*Cheers*

19³/₈ x 10¹/₄", lid shows Rough Riders on horseback carrying flag charging Spanish fort, game is response to Spanish–American War, contains 26 playing pcs (2 kings, 24 soldiers), c1899 . . . . . . . . . . . . .   **200.00**

**Charge It!,** Whitman, shopping, card game, cover shows charge card with number, 1972. . . . . .   **20.00**

**Charlie McCarthy, Game of Topper, Edgar Bergen's,** Whitman Publishing Co., No. 2903, generic, board game, 8⁷/₈ x 8⁵/₁₆ x 1⁵/₈", lid shows face of Charlie McCarthy wearing top hat and monocle, another top hat in right bottom corner, contains 45 + pcs (8 wooden hats, score sheets, 36 cards, and stiff paper playing board 8¹/₂" sq), ©1938 by McCarthy Inc . . . . . . . . . . . .   **45.00**

**Charlie McCarthy Question And Answer Game, Edgar Bergen's,** Whitman Publishing Co., No. 3908, generic, card game, 8¹/₄ x 5¹/₂ x ⁷/₈", lid shows profile sketch of Charlie asking "Ask Me Another, Bergen, I've Got All The Answers," contains 22 question cards, 22 answer cards, instruction card, ©1938 by McCarthy Inc. . . . . . . . . . . .   **50.00**

**Charlie's Angels,** Milton Bradley, TV/detective, board game, cover shows 3 cast members (Kelly, Jill, and Sabrina), silhouette figures in background
• Farrah Fawcett cover, 1977 *see illus* . . . . . . . . . . . . . . . . . .   **35.00**
• Cheryl Ladd cover, 1978 . . . . .   **25.00**

**Chase, The,** Cadaco, nature, board game, lid shows bunny chased by 2 dogs, "A Nature Study Game," 1966 . . . . . . . .   **35.00**

**Checkered Game of Life, The,** Milton Bradley, generic, framed board game, 18" sq, red, black, and white litho cardboard, cover shows large "G" and "L" in game name, publishing info using Milton Bradley & Co. signature in bottom left corner, Bradley's first game, 1866. . . . .   **600.00**

**Checkline,** Crestline Mfg. & Supply Co., generic, board game, cover shows tiered playing area and playing pcs, "The Classic Space Tic–Tac–Toe Game," 1960s . . . . . . . . .   **8.00**

**Cheers,** Classic Games Inc., TV/comedy, trivia game, lid shows Cheers logo, horse and buggy scene, contains game board, plastic spinner, printed spinner board, character pawns, chips, wooden nickels, card tray, napkin trivia cards, "Normism" cards, "Cliffism" cards, ©1992 *see illus* . . . . . . .   **10.00**

**Cherry Ames' Nursing Game,** Parker Brothers, medical/book, board game, lid shows nurse carrying tray of medicines, 1959   **50.00**

**Chess Checkers & Acey Deucy Backgammon,** Milton Bradley, generic, board games, lid shows board and playing pcs, 1970 . .   **8.00**

*Cheyenne Game*

### Chess Checkers Backgammon

**Acey–Deucey,** Transogram, generic, board games, lid shows playing pcs, contains plastic chessmen and checkers, numbered playing book, 1960 . . . .  **10.00**

**Chestnut Burrs,** The Fireside Game Co., No. 1106, generic, board game, $2^3/_4$ x $3^3/_4$ x $^7/_8$", game name in lid center, "No. 1106" in upper right corner, copyright and mfg info at bottom, "New Game," ©1896  **40.00**

**Chevyland Sweepstakes,** Milton Bradley, advertisement/automobile, board game, left side of cover shows front of convertible, possibly dealers' promo, featured 1969 Corvette, Camaro, Impala Convertible, Impala Sedan, and Biscayne, 1968. . . . . . . . . . . . . . . . .  **50.00**

**Cheyenne,** Milton Bradley, TV/ western, new star, Ty Harding, shown standing on cover, 1958. . . . . . . . . . . . . .  **65.00**

**Cheyenne Game,** Milton Bradley, TV/ western, board game, lid shows cowboy aiming rifle leaning on rock, 1958 *see illus*  **55.00**

**Chicken, The Game of,** Schaper, generic, bingo type game, lid with sketch of chicken with open beak, 1957 . . . . . . . . . . .  **10.00**

**Chicklets Gum Village Game,** Hasbro, advertisement, board game, cover shows backs of heads of boy and girl holding balloons looking at village scene, small sketched figure in bottom right corner, contains small boxes of Chicklets, 1959  **30.00**

**Children's Hour,** Parker Brothers, generic, board game, lid shows Peanut the Elephant, elongated letters "l" and "h" in game name, "A Laugh A Minute," contains 3 games including "Porky the Pig," 1950s,1961 . . .  **30.00**

**Chinese Checkers,** National Games, Inc, No. 2005, generic, board game, lid shows Chinese man wearing pointed hat and Chinese clothing pulling Chinese man seated in cart, contains 18 marbles, 1940s . . .  **25.00**

**Ching Cong Oriental Checkers,** Samuel Gabriel Sons & Co., generic, board game (Chinese Checkers), box cover shows game name with oriental–style printing, 1930 . . . . . . . . . . . . .  **20.00**

**"Chips" Game**, Ideal, TV/crime, lid shows 2 uniformed patrol officers and 2 officers on motorcycles, 1981 . . . . . . . . . . . . .  **15.00**

**Chiromagica,** McLoughlin Brothers, generic, mechanical quiz game, $11^1/_2$" sq wooden box with slide cover which shows man with beard wearing long robe and pointed hat pointing to circle with game name, contains 3 answer sheets, 3 matching question disks, and mechanical hand pointer, c1870 . . . . .  **550.00**

**Chit Chat,** Milton Bradley, educational, word game (The Hugh Downs Game of Conversation), cover shows Downs with woman on one side, man on other, contains word cards and "Lucky Letters," 1963 . . . . . . . .  **18.00**

**Chitty Chitty Bang Bang,** Milton Bradley, movies, board game, cover shows the "flying car" with passengers over land and water, 1968 . . . . . . . . . . . . . .  **30.00**

**Chivalry,** George S. Parker & Co., military, strategy/skill board game, lid shows 2 knights on horses in battle, "The Greatest Modern Board Game of Skill," contains 40 pcs, 1888 . . . . . . .  **100.00**

**Chivalry, Game of,** Parker Brothers, societal, board game, $15^3/_4$" sq, lid depicts castles and men and women in regal clothing sitting on balcony with pillar posts filled with flowers, bowing man wearing striped pants holding hat, contains wooden pcs, favorite game invented by George S. Parker, although never successful, ©1855 . . . . . . . . . . . . . . . . .    **500.00**

**Choo Choo Charlie Game,** Milton Bradley, advertisement/ railroading, board game, based on Good n' Plenty candy mascot, cover shows locomotive, Good n' Plenty candy box railroad car with passenger and dog, and engineer wearing large hat, 1969 . . . . . . . . . . .    **40.00**

**Chop Suey Game,** Ideal, generic, board game, cover shows family of 4 playing, man in uniform hat holding chop sticks, 1967. .    **15.00**

**Chopper Strike,** Milton Bradley, military, 3–dimensional board game, "Two Level Land/Air Battle Game," cover shows gameboard, dice, and 2 players, contains miniature plastic anti–aircraft guns and helicopters, 1976 . . . . . . . . . . . .    **22.00**

**Christmas Goose,** McLoughlin Brothers, holiday, board game, 19½ x 10½", lid shows jester in high hat holding golden egg, reaching with cane to grab running goose, contains 12 wooden playing pcs, 24 markers, and large spinner, 1890 . . . . . . . .    **750.00**

**Chubby Checker's Limbo Game,** Wham–O, music/dance, action game, cover shows Chubby Checker with Limbo bar, second figure going under bar encouraged by 5 onlookers, dance verse in right bottom corner, contains Limbo bar and record with Limbo songs by "Kookie Joe," 1961 . . . . . . . .    **50.00**

**Chug–A–Lug,** Dynamic Games, generic, board game, "The Drinking Party Game," lid shows group of people playing game holding raised glasses, 1969. . . . . . . . . . . . . . . . . .    **10.00**

*Cinderella*

**Chuggedy Chug,** Milton Bradley, TV/children's show, board game, cover shows Paul Winchell as train engineer and Jerry Mahoney puppet riding in 2 cars, their names printed in railroad signal flags, 1955 . . . .    **45.00**

**Chute–5,** E.S. Lowe, generic, strategy dice game, lid shows family playing game and special playing dice chute, 1973 . . . . .    **8.00**

**Chutes and Ladders,** Milton Bradley, generic, board game, cover with checkerboard background, 1943. . . . . . . . . . . . . .    **25.00**

**Chutes and Ladders,** Milton Bradley, generic, board game, lid shows children on 3 ladders and 3 chutes, 1950s. . . . . . . . .    **20.00**

**Chutes and Ladders,** Milton Bradley, generic, board game, lid shows children going up and down sliding board, 1956 . . . .    **20.00**

**Chutzpah,** What–Cha–Ma–Call–It Inc, generic, board game, lid shows money and shopping bag, "$10, But for you...$5.95," 1967. . . . . . . . . . . . . . . . . . .    **50.00**

**Cinderella,** Milton Bradley, No. 4111, fairy tale, card game, lid shows long haired girl wearing long dress holding broom, background of high heeled slipper, "No. 4111" in bottom left corner, mfg info bottom right corner, c1921 *see illus* . . . . . . .    **50.00**

Cities

The Game of Cities

**Cinderella,** Milton Bradley, No. 4111, fairy tale, card game, 6³/₄ x 5¹/₂", lid shows barefoot girl with long hair, sitting on stool before fireplace and washtub, "No. 4111," in bottom left corner, mfg info bottom right corner, c1900 . . . . . . . . . . .    **25.00**

**Cinderella,** Parker Brothers, fairy tale, card game, 4 x 5¹/₂", cover shows gowned woman with long hair, Prince wearing cape, background circle of flowers, mfg info at bottom right corner, contains 25 multicolored litho cards and instruction sheet, ©1895 . . . . . . . . . . . . . . . . .    **15.00**

**Cinderella, Walt Disney's,** Parker Brothers, movie/fairy tale, board game, lid shows scenes from story including Cinderella trying on slipper and Prince at top of steps calling after gowned Cinderella, contains playing cards and glass slipper playing pcs, 1964 . . . . . . . . . . . . . . .    **35.00**

**Cinderella, Walt Disney's,** Parker Brothers, movie/fairy tale, board game, lid shows castle scene, pumpkin chariot with horses, and prince and Cinderella dancing, 1963 . . . . . . . . . . . .    **35.00**

**Cinderella or Hunt The Slipper,** McLoughlin Brothers, fairy tale, card game, 4¹/₂ x 6¹/₄", cover shows girl with long hair in long dress, copyright info along bottom left, "McLoughlin Bros.,

NY" bottom right corner, contains 43 cards and instruction sheet, ©1887 . . . . . . . . . . . . .    **60.00**

**Cinderfella,** Dot Records, movie/fairy tale, sound track album with its own road race game, album cover shows Jerry Lewis on bicycle passing a castle, waving to people in car and people at window with striped awning, contains gameboard, magic wand baton, tiara, and music stand with picture story and sing–along lyrics,1960 . . . .    **30.00**

**Citadel,** Parker Brothers, military, board game, lid shows knights on horses, contains wooden pcs, 1940 . . . . . . . . . . . . . . .    **35.00**

**Cities,** Alderman–Fairchild (All–Fair), No. 428, educational, card game, 5 x 4 x 1", cover shows city skyline and plane, contains playing cards, 1932 *see illus*. . . . . . . . . . . . . . . .    **35.00**

**Cities, Game of,** Parker Brothers, generic, card game, 5⁵/₈ x 4 x ³/₄", lid shows woman in long dress standing under tree, high–rise buildings in background, oval inset of waterfront buildings and gondola, copyright and mfg info in rect strip at lid bottom, ©1898 *see illus* . . .    **40.00**

**Cities Game, The,** Psychology Today, business/urban blight, board game, lid shows 4 walking figures against skyscraper background, 1970 . . . . . . . . . .    **25.00**

**City Life, Game of, or The Boys of New York,** McLoughlin Brothers, generic, card game, 5 x 6½", lid shows waving boy set in frame surrounded by leaves, 1889 . . . . . . . . . . . .    **40.00**

**Civil War, American Heritage Game of the,** Milton Bradley, military, board game, lid shows cannons, smoke from artillary fire, soldiers on horseback, mountain scene, and white horse, contains plastic soldiers, 1961 . . . . . . . . . . . . . . . . . .    **30.00**

**Clash of the Titans,** Whitman, movie/monster (based on Ray Harryhausen film), cover shows horseback rider holding sword attacking monster, 1981 . . . . . .    **25.00**

**Classic Games Chess Set,** Classic Games Co., generic, board game, bottom right corner of lid shows Roman figure holding flag, "Collector's Series," Ancient Roman figures as playing pcs, 1963 . . . . . . . . . . . .    **20.00**

**Clean Sweep,** Schaper, generic, action game, lid shows girl with braids and boy playing game and "pop up" trash can, contains over 100 "crazy pcs" including "trash" and plastic brooms, 1967 . . . . . . . . . . . .    **30.00**

• Second lid shows boy's face, players' hands, gears, and part of game board, 1967 . . . . . . .    **25.00**

**Click,** Akro Agates, generic, skill and action marble roll game, 7½ x 7½ x 1", cover shows 2 boys and girl shooting marbles into open box, one boy in sailor shirt and knee socks with marbles at his bent knee, mfg name and logo in circle, "Shoot Straight as a Kro Flies," c1930s    **45.00**

**Clock–A–Word,** Topper, educational, word game, cover shows clock playing pc that sets letters automatically, mfg name in oval at bottom left corner, 1966 . . . .    **10.00**

**Close Encounters of the Third Kind,** Parker Brothers, movie/space, board game, lid shows starry night, tracks leading to bright light, 1978 . . . . . . . . . .    **18.00**

*Clue*

**"Clue,"** Parker Brothers, mystery, board game with pcs box, lid shows strip of figures looking for clues, game name in quotes, "The Great New Sherlock Holmes Game!," contains moving pcs, dice, and cards, 1949    **50.00**

• Same lid design, "The Great Detective Game!," 1949 . . . .    **40.00**

• Reissued 1950 *see illus* . . . . . . .    **20.00**

**"Clue,"** Parker Brothers, mystery, board game, lid shows game name in quotes, magnifying glass over inset square on left side, "The Great Detective Game," 1956 . . . . . . . . . . . . .    **20.00**

**"Clue,"** Parker Brothers, mystery, board game, lid shows magnifying glass with game name in quotes in circle and figures in strip that form handle, "Parker Brothers Detective Game," 1963    **10.00**

**"Clue,"** John Waddington Ltd., mystery, board game, lid has game name in quotes, inset strip of people searching for clues, "The Great New Detective Game!," 1949 . . . . . . . . . . .    **40.00**

**Coast to Coast,** Ewing, educational/geography, radar action game, lid shows girl and 2 boys playing game, contains remote control and motorcycle playing pcs, 1955 . . . . . . . . . . . . . .    **25.00**

**Cold Feet,** Ideal, generic, skill and action game, lid shows game pcs and family of 4 playing game, boy squirting water at father, contains squirt gun, 1967    **25.00**

**College Football,** Milton Bradley, sport, board game, lid shows 2 teams playing game, crowds

*Columbo Detective Game*

in stands, "All the Plays of a
Real Game," 1930s . . . . . . . .    **100.00**
**Columbo Detective Game**,
Milton Bradley, TV/detective,
board game, lid shows Peter
Falk profile posed with hand in
his raincoat pocket, Columbo's
date book, and car, 1973 *see
illus* . . . . . . . . . . . . . . . . . .    **12.00**
**Combat!**, Ideal, TV/military,
board game, cover shows 1 soldier with binoculars, second
shooting rifle, both wearing
camouflage helmets, tank and
cityscape in background, "The
Fighting Infantry Game," 1963    **45.00**
**Combat! at Anzio Beachhead**,
Ideal, TV/military, board game,
cover shows 2 boys playing
game in bottom left corner,
encircled faces of 2 soldiers
wearing camouflage helmets,
soldiers, plane and artillery fire
in background, 1963 . . . . . . . .    **50.00**
**Combat! Card Game**, Milton
Bradley, TV/military, card game,
cover shows 2 soldiers aiming
and shooting guns in street
scene, 1964, reissued 1965 . . .    **30.00**
**Combat! Tank Game**, Magic
Wand, military, board game, lid
shows tank with soldier aiming
gun, red shield with picture of
tank in top left corner, from
game series, 1964 . . . . . . . . .    **25.00**
**Combination Board Games**,
Wilder Mfg Co., numbered 126
and 128 with patent number on
board, 8³/₄ x 17", generic, board
games, cover shows eagle flying
over bear, contains folding
board, 4 metal animal figures,

*Comic Conversation Cards*

dice cup, 5 dice, score sheets,
and Wilder adv pamphlet,
directions for 12 different games
on back of box cover, c1922 . .    **70.00**
**Comic Card Game**, Milton
Bradley, comics, card game, lid
shows game cards with faces of
comic strip characters including
Popeye, contains oversized
playing cards, 1972 . . . . . . . . .    **20.00**
**Comic Conversation Cards**, J.
Ottmann Lith. Co., card game,
lid shows black man and
woman playing cards, dog
under table, no date *see illus* . .    **70.00**
**Comical Game of Whip, The**,
Russell Mfg. Co., western, card
game, 6¹/₄ x 4³/₄", lid shows
cowboy on horse with whip,
1930–32 . . . . . . . . . . . . . . . .    **20.00**
**Comical Game of "Who," The**,
Parker Brothers, quiz, card
game, 6¹/₂ x 5", lid shows
man wearing monocle holding
cards and pointing to himself,
surrounded by adults and children, question in lower left corner, answer in lower right corner, mfg info centered at lid bottom, contains 60 printed cards
and instruction sheet, c1910. . .    **30.00**
**Comical Game: Sir Hinkle
Funny–Duster, The**, Parker
Brothers, generic, card game,
5¹/₄ x 6³/₄", lid shows man in

*Concentration*

*Connect Four*

knickers, high socks, and wig, one hand outstretched, other behind back, mfg info lower right corner, copyright info bottom left corner, contains 20 multicolored litho cards, ©1903 .... **25.00**

**Comical History of America,** Parker Brothers, educational, card game, $7^3/_8$ x $4^3/_4$ x 1", lid shows 4 people in colonial dress riding in car with skyscrapers background, c1920s .. **30.00**

**Commanders Of Our Forces,** E. C. Eastman, military (Civil War), card game, $4^1/_2$ x $3^1/_2$", lid shows marching soldiers holding flag, leader on horse, ships in background, contains 80 cards, 1863 ............. **100.00**

**Commerce,** J. Ottmann Lith. Co., business, $4^5/_8$ x $6^1/_4$ x 1", lid shows woman in print dress with lace–edged sleeves holding cards, one hand raised, chair and dishes in background, c1900 ................ **50.00**

**Concentration,** Milton Bradley, TV/game show, board game, 1st edition, cover shows profiles of man and woman looking at Rollomatic puzzle changer, "NBC" in upper right corner, 1958 *see illus* ............ **35.00**

**Concentration Game,** Milton Bradley, TV/game show, board game, 3rd edition, cover shows Rollomatic puzzle changer, 1960 ................. **20.00**

**Concentration Game,** Milton Bradley, TV/game show, board game, 9th edition, cover has arrow pointing at Rollomatic puzzle changer, 1964 ....... **15.00**

**Cones and Corns,** Parker Brothers, generic, skill game, $8^5/_8$ x $3^7/_8$", lid shows playing pcs, crossed sticks, "C & C" at center top, mfg info across lid bottom, and "An Entirely New and Novel Game," contains 8 colored wooden sticks, 4 colored wooden cone receptacles, and 18 colored wooden "acorn" pcs, ©1924 ............. **40.00**

**Conflict,** Parker Brothers, military/strategic war, board game, cover shows battle scene with ships and planes, "Land–Sea–Air," metal pcs, 1940 ........ **90.00**

**Conflict,** Parker Brothers, military, board game, cover has multicolored arrows above and below game name, 1960 .......... **60.00**

**Conflict,** Parker Brothers, military, board game, lid shows tank and bare trees, 1964 ........... **35.00**

**Confrontation,** Game–Science Corp., politics, economics, and conflict/strategy game, in envelope, lid shows globe, game name hyphenated with arrows, and "world strategy game," contains full color map board, no date .................. **18.00**

**Connect Four,** Milton Bradley, checkers game, box contains plastic vertical gameboard with slots, and red and black plastic checkers, 1974 *see illus* ...... **12.00**

**Conquest of the Empire,** Milton Bradley, Gamemaster series,

*Contack*

*Coon Hunt Game*

military, board game, lid shows
knight in armor on horse, totem
pole, ship, and circled faces,
contains plastic pcs, 1984 . . . .     **85.00**
**Conspiracy,** Milton Bradley, espionage, board game, lid shows
1 man carrying suitcase, other
wearing turban talking to third
man in hat, skyscraper back-
ground, 1982 . . . . . . . . . . . .     **9.00**
**Construction Game,** Wilder Mfg.
Co., No. 125, generic, board
game, 12$^1$/$_4$ x 7$^1$/$_2$", cover shows
stages of bridge construction,
1925. . . . . . . . . . . . . . . . . .     **85.00**
**Contack,** Parker Brothers, gener-
ic, domino type game, 6$^1$/$_2$ x 3$^7$/$_8$
x 1$^1$/$_4$", game name slanted
diagonally left to right across lid
and in smaller print in top left
corner, "Trademarks and Patents
Pending," contains 36 triangular
pcs, score cards, and red,
white, and blue chips, ©1939
*see illus* . . . . . . . . . . . . . . .     **10.00**
**Contack,** Parker Brothers, gener-
ic, skill game, name on lid in
diamond shape, "Triangle
Matching Game," 1930s . . . . .     **8.00**
**Continents and Products,**
unknown manufacturer, educa-
tional, card game, 4$^7$/$_8$ x 3$^7$/$_8$",
lid shows palm trees, house,
and fruits scattered on ground,
contains 5 yellow continent
cards, product cards, and
instruction sheet, c1895. . . . . .     **15.00**
**Controlling Interest,** American
Greetings, business, board
game, lid shows 4 men, one
talking on telephone and hold-

ing paper, ship and truck in
background, "The Business
Game That Corners the Market
on Fun," 1972 . . . . . . . . . . . .     **20.00**
**Convoy, The Naval War Game,**
Transogram, military, board
game, lid shows battleship and
2 people playing game, 1960s     **20.00**
**Coon Hunt Game, The,** Parker
Brothers, educational, board
game, 14$^7$/$_8$ x 9$^1$/$_2$", lid shows
dog and 4 black men in field,
1 man holding rifle, contains
2 colored wooden counters and
spinner, 1903 *see illus* . . . . . . .     **375.00**
**Cootie,** Schaper, generic, skill
and action dice game, lid shows
boy and girl looking at cootie,
game name across middle,
assembled cootie in bottom
third of lid, "The original exciting 'build a cootie bug' game
for boys and girls," 1960s. . . . .     **12.00**
**Cootie,** Transogram, generic, skill
and action dice game, lid shows
3 girls and 2 boys playing game,
"New and Exciting Way to Play
an Old Favorite," wooden play-
ing pcs, 1939. . . . . . . . . . . . .     **25.00**
**Cootie, Deluxe 6,** Schaper, gener-
ic, dice game, lid shows assembled cootie below game name,
mfg info at bottom, contains 6
cooties, 1950s . . . . . . . . . . . .     **30.00**
**Cootie, The Game of,** Schaper,
skill and action game, lid pictures 4 cooties, "another
Schaper plastic game" and
cootie in oval at bottom left cor-
ner, late 1950s. . . . . . . . . . . .     **25.00**

*The Game of Cootie*

**Cootie, The Game of,** Schaper, generic, skill and action dice game, cootie in center, name in top third, mfg info in bottom third, "The Game of 'Cootie' " on box edge, contains 4 multi-colored plastic pcs and dice, *see illus* . . . . . . . . . . . . . . . . 30.00

**Cootie Party Game,** Unique Novelty Co., generic, paper and pencil game, lid shows man and woman in Flapper era dress, ladybug in center, 1920s 30.00

**Corn & Beans**, E.G. Selchow & Co., quiz, card game, 5½ x 3½", lid shows 4 people seated at round table playing game, "The Funniest Game Out," contains 40 cards, question card, instruction sheet, 1875 . . . . . . 45.00

**Countdown**, E.S. Lowe, space, card game, lid shows rocket launch, letters of game name blocked down long side of lid, contains astronaut cards and plastic and wooden rockets, 1967. . . . . . . . . . . . . . . . . 60.00

**Countdown Space Game**, Transogram, space, board game, lid shows rocket plane with US flag printed on side, earth in background, "Force enemy rockets out of orbit...and Conquer outer Space," 1960. . . 50.00

**County Fair, The**, Parker Brothers, generic, card game, 6⅜ x 4⅝", lid shows partial scene of fair with tents and man in hat surrounded by 3 boys, contains 24 character cards, numbered price cards, and instruction sheet, ©1891 . . . . . . . . . . . . . 50.00

**Coup d'Etat**, Parker Brothers, military, card game, lid shows 2 figures shooting cannon balls on figure below, contains cards and metal daggers, 1966 . . . . . 15.00

**Courtroom**, W. Roy Tribble, law, board game, lid shows scales of justice in circle, "The American Game of Law," 1970s 15.00

**Cowboy Roundup**, Parker Brothers, western, board game, cover shows cowboy on horse rounding up cattle, game name on fence boards, trees in background, 1952. . . . . . . . . . . . . 35.00

**Cracker Jack Toy Surprise Game**, Milton Bradley, advertisement, candy, board game, cover shows traditional Cracker Jack box, boy and girl playing game in bottom right corner, contains boxes and toy surprises, 1976. . 22.00

**Crandall's Building Blocks**, Charles M. Crandall, Diamond Edition blocks, educational, skill and action game, 4¾" sq, cover shows boy sitting in chair pointing to lettered blocks and looking at seated girl, game name in blocks, contains grooved wooden letters, wooden dovetailed box, dated 1867 . . . . . . . . . . 230.00

**Crazy Car Race**, Steven Mfg., auto racing, skill and action game, pinball playing area shows 4 white marbles, 1 black marble, timers for Sand Hogs and Lap Dogs, 1972. . . . . . . . . 20.00

**Crazy Clock**, Ideal, generic, skill and action game, cover shows game pcs and man wearing beanie and green shirt, mfg info bottom right corner, sequel to Mouse Trap, 1964 . . . . . . . . 75.00

**Creature Castle Game,** Whitman, mystery, card game, lid shows sunset, barren trees, and castle, 1979 . . . . . . . . . . . . . . . . . .   **10.00**

**Creature Features,** Athol–Research Co., monster, board game, lid pictures creature faces, contains black and white photo cards . . . . . . . . . . . . . .   **30.00**

**Creature From The Black Lagoon Mystery Game, The,** Hasbro, mystery/monster, board game, picture of fanged Creature on dark background, "Enter the depths of The Black Lagoon," game name on left, 1963, . . . .   **185.00**

**Cribbage Board,** Milton Bradley, generic, board game, lid shows playing surface, 1960s . . . . . . .   **12.00**

**Criss Cross,** Ideal, generic, skill game, lid shows boy in short sleeved shirt with hand in front of face and girl with playing pc, 1971 . . . . . . . . . . . . . . . . . .   **15.00**

**Crosby Derby, The,** H. Fishlove & Co., horse racing, board game, cover shows jockeys riding horses Bing Crosby, 4 games in one, contains metal horses, win, place and show stubs, and money, 1947 . . . . . .   **110.00**

**Cross Country Marathon,** Milton Bradley, sports, lid shows marathon runner against country landscape with trees and mountains, unknown date . . . .   **65.00**

**Cross Up,** Milton Bradley, generic, crossword game, Lucille Ball with game on cover, 1974 . . . .   **25.00**

**Crossing the Ocean,** Parker Brothers, educational, board game, 14³/₄ x 8⁷/₈", lid shows 2 sailing ships, mfg info center bottom, contains 4 colored wooden counters, board depicts water surrrounded by famous world ports and has spinner in lower right corner, ©1893 . . . .   **120.00**

**Crow Hunt,** Parker Brothers, generic, skill and action game, 17¹/₂ x 15", lid shows crow in tree, silhouette of man in hat holding rifle, and scarecrow, comes with Daisy rifle, 1940s   **45.00**

**Crows in The Corn,** Parker Brothers, hunting, skill and action game, 13³/₄ x 12¹/₈", lid has border of crows, running man with gun, contains multicolored litho wooden and cardboard crows on fence target and gun with pellets, ©1930 . . . . . .   **100.00**

**Crusade,** Samuel Gabriel Sons & Co., military, board game, 14¹/₂" sq, cover shows armored knight on horse surrounded by shields, "Thrilling Game" at center bottom, unknown date . .   **25.00**

**Cuckoo,** J.H. Singer, generic, board game, cover shows large bird on tree branch, "A Society Game," "Patent Applied For," bottom left corner, mfg info bottom right corner, contains 6 gameboards, wooden dice cup, special die with colored sides, and wooden markers, 1891 . . . . . . . . . . . . . . . . . .   **35.00**

**Cut Up Shopping Spree Game,** Milton Bradley, shopping, action game, cover shows women and girls, some holding money, contains scissors, 1968   **15.00**

## –D–

**Dallas,** Southfork Dallas Collection, TV/western, board game, "Empire Building Strategy," lid shows partial view of Dallas newspaper referring to "Ewing Oil Empire...," 1985 . . .   **10.00**

**Dark Shadows,** Whitman, TV/soap opera/mystery, board game, cover shows moon behind game name and caped figure, "abc" in bottom right corner, contains large play mat with playing cards, 1968 . . . . .   **50.00**

**Dark Tower,** Milton Bradley, adventure, electronic game, lid shows the "Dark Tower" and armored man holding club, triangular inset picture with skull at point, "A Fantasy Adventure Born of Electronic Wizardry," 1981 . . . . . . . . . . . . . . . . . .   **60.00**

*The Deputy*

*Defenders of the Flag*

**Dastardly and Muttley in their Flying Machines,** Milton Bradley, movie, board game, lid shows 4 WW I aviators in pursuit of carrier pigeon, 1969–70 .... **55.00**

**Dating Game, The,** Hasbro, TV/game show, board game, lid shows 3 scenes from TV show including 3 men seated on stools, 1967 ............... **20.00**

**Davy Crockett Frontierland Game, Walt Disney's Official,** Parker Brothers, western, board game, lid shows standing Davy Crockett holding rifle and small inset picture of him looking at bear, crossed rifles below "Frontierland" at lower right corner, 1955 ............... **55.00**

**Davy Crockett Rescue Race, Walt Disney's Official,** Gabriel, TV/western, board game, lid shows fort, covered wagon, and kneeling Fess Parker wearing coonskin cap and holding rifle and compass, includes real compass, 1955 ........... **60.00**

**Day at the Circus, Game of,** McLoughlin Brothers, 23 x 6½", circus, board game, lid shows elephant, horse, acrobats, and other circus acts beneath striped awning, contains metal figure pcs and spinner, 1898 ....... **1,000.00**

**Dead Stop! Game,** Milton Bradley, generic, board game, lid shows gameboard and playing pcs, "use your deductive powers," 1979 ............. **30.00**

**Dealer's Choice,** Parker Brothers, automobile, card game, lid shows woman and man looking at car with "special" on window, "Wheeling Dealing Used Car Game," 1972 .............. **15.00**

**Dear Abby Game,** Ideal, celebrity, based on celebrity columnist, card game, lid shows man with loosened tie holding cards with game name, woman with arm around him, 1972 .......... **20.00**

**Decathalon Game, Bruce Jenner,** Parker Brothers, sports, action game, lid shows Jenner wearing "USA" shirt, "Compete in 10 Exciting Events," 1979 ....... **20.00**

**Decoy,** Selchow & Righter, duck hunting, board game, lid shows duck with spread wings looking at decoy, "A Game of Chance," contains 40 small plastic ducks and decoys, 1956 ........... **40.00**
• Wooden version ............ **70.00**

**Deduction,** Ideal, strategy, board game, lid shows man wearing peaked checkered hat and vest holding pipe and playing game, inset circle shows gameboard setup, "The Game That Makes Thinking Fun," 1976 ........ **7.00**

**Defenders of the Flag,** Noble and Noble Publishers, Inc., military, card game, 8¼ x 6⅛ x ¾", lid shows card sized pictures of uniformed soldiers from various wars and branches of service, c1922 *see illus*. ............ **40.00**

**Deputy, The,** Milton Bradley, western, board game, lid shows 2 men in cowboy hats and vests, one wearing deputy badge, and

*Dewey at Manila*

*Dick Tracy Detective Game*

partial shot of third man's hand
and holster, 1960 *see illus* . . . .    **50.00**

**"Derby Day,"** Parker Brothers,
horse racing, card game,
2¹/₂ x 3³/₄", lid shows jockey on
horse framed by horseshoe with
game name, "The Unique Race
Game," mfg info at bottom,
contains 48 multicolored litho
cards, instruction booklet, and
red and black numbered card-
board chips, c1900 . . . . . . . .    **35.00**

**Derby Day,** Parker Brothers, horse
racing, action game, lid shows
2 jockeys riding #2 and #4 horses, fence in foreground, jockey
#2 wearing checked jacket
matching horse's face cover,
"indoor horse race game with
hurdles," 1940s . . . . . . . . . . .    **24.00**

**Derby Downs,** Great Games,
horse racing, board game, lid
shows group of racing horses on
track, 2 towers in background,
comes with record, 1973 . . . . .    **25.00**

**Derby Steeple Chase, The,**
McLoughlin Brothers, horse racing, board game, 10³/₄ x 10¹/₄",
lid shows 2 horses with riders
leaping obstacle, mfg info at
bottom, contains 4 wooden
counters, 18 wooden chips, and
spinner, ©1890 . . . . . . . . . . .    **95.00**

**Destroy Death Star Game, Star
Wars,** Kenner, movie/space,
board game, lid shows spaceship, inset picture of 2 cast
characters, 1978 . . . . . . . . . .    **20.00**

**Detectives, The,** Transogram,
TV/detective, board game, lid
shows man seated in car reaching for phone, "An Exciting
Game of Deduction," and part
of newspaper article with headline "Body of Socialite
Found...," 1961 . . . . . . . . . . .    **45.00**

**Dewey at Manila,** Chaffee &
Selchow, Starry Flag Series, military, card game, 6¹/₂ x 5", lid
pictures Dewey in oval, ship
battle background, contains
52 cards, 1899 . . . . . . . . . . . .    **55.00**

**Dewey's Victory,** Parker Brothers,
military strategy, board game,
16¹/₂ x 14¹/₂", lid shows ship battle scene, man in cap in oval,
"Never Beaten" on striped background, contains 7 yellow and
6 blue round cardboard disks,
spinner, ©1900 . . . . . . . . . . .    **300.00**

**Diamond Game, The,** McLoughlin
Brothers, sport/baseball, board
game, 4 x 8¹/₄", cover shows
spinner surrounded by 4 base-
balls, c1885 . . . . . . . . . . . . . .    **75.00**

**Dick Tracy Crime Stopper Game,**
Ideal, detective/comic strip character, battery operated board
game, lid shows Tracy pointing
to gameboard with spinner,
"Dick Tracy" in circle above hat,
contains clue decoder, 1963 . . .    **90.00**

**Dick Tracy Detective Game,**
Whitman Publishing Co.,
No. 3065, detective/comic book
character, board game, 13 x 6¹/₂
x 1", lid shows Tracy reading
note and holding magnifying
glass and handcuffs, contains
spinner with 2 number rings, 16
markers, and small cardboard

*Dick Tracy Playing Card Game*

squares, ©1937 by Chester
Gould, licensed by Famous
Artist Syndicate *see illus* . . . . . . **55.00**
**Dick Tracy Marble Maze,** Hasbro,
detective/comic book character,
skill game, lid shows circle
maze playing board, strip with
game name and face of Dick
Tracy runs across picture, 1966 **60.00**
**Dick Tracy Master Detective
Game, The,** Selchow & Righter,
TV/detective, comic book character, animated series, board
game, lid shows Tracy at desk
looking at watch, 4 animated
figures including man in sombrero, man in glasses, and
policeman on right side of lid,
1961 . . . . . . . . . . . . . . . . . . **45.00**
**Dick Tracy Playing Card Game,**
Whitman Publishing Co.,
No. 3071, detective/comic book
character, card game, 5 x 6½",
lid shows Tracy reading "finger
print record," Junior watching,
police shield in background,
contains 35 multicolored cards,
©1934 by Chester Gould . . . . . **55.00**
**Dick Tracy Playing Card Game,**
Whitman Publishing Co.,
No. 3071, detective/comic book
character, 5 x 6½ x ⅞", cover
with Tracy holding flashlight,
Junior at his side, ©1937 by
Chester Gould *see illus* . . . . . . **45.00**

**Dick Van Dyke Game,** Standard
Toykraft, TV/comedy, board
game, lid shows 2 women and
2 men from cast playing game,
Van Dyke holding card with
Mary's picture, "A Game of
Family Fun with Dick Van Dyke
and his TV Friends," 1962–64 . . **90.00**
**Dig,** Parker Brothers, wealth,
action game, 10⅞ x 7⅜ x 1⅜",
lid has game name in large
letters, Rich Uncle Pennybags
carrying pick in upper right corner, "The Pick Does The Trick,"
contains pile of letters, 4 picks,
calling cards, shares, and gold
bars, ©1940 . . . . . . . . . . . . . . **35.00**
• Same cover, reissued, "Lively
Action Game," 1950s . . . . . . . **15.00**
**Dig,** Parker Brothers, wealth,
action game, lid shows hands
with picks reaching for lettered
cards, "The Pick Does the Trick,"
1950s . . . . . . . . . . . . . . . . . **12.00**
**Dig,** Parker Brothers, educational,
card game, letter picking game,
lid shows lettered cards and
4 people sitting at table with
hands on pile of letter cards,
one man with raised arm, 1959 **10.00**
**Dig,** Parker Brothers, educational,
card game, inset on lid shows
family playing game, 1968 . . . . **10.00**
**Diner's Club Credit Card Game,
The,** Ideal, advertisement/busi-
ness, board game, lid shows
uniformed man with gloved
hand, entrance canopy, and
evening street scene, 1961 . . . . **45.00**
**Dino the Dinosaur Game, The
Flintstones Present,** Transogram,
TV/cartoon, board game, lid
shows amusement park rides,
Flintstones riding in open vehicle, ferris wheel, and Dino
wearing blanket inscribed
"Game," 1961 . . . . . . . . . . . . **65.00**
**Diplomacy,** Games Research, Inc.,
military/negotiation, board
game, "The Exciting Game of
International Intrigue," lid shows
map, rule book, playing area,
and pcs, 1971 . . . . . . . . . . . . **30.00**
• Original Edition, blank lid, game
name top left corner, 1971 . . . **20.00**

**Director's Choice,** Direct Broadcast Programs, Inc., movie trivia, board game, lid shows dice, "Watch the Movie, Play The Game, The Ultimate Game for Movie Lovers," includes video tape, 1984 . . . . . . . . . .  **10.00**

**Disk,** The Madmar Quality Co., generic, board game, lid shows long board with center container and launching stick on each side, contains 6 green and 6 red 1$^{11}/_{16}$" cardboard disks with points, 2 snappers, and playing pcs, "The Famous American Game," c1900 . . . . . . . . . . .  **35.00**

**Disneyland,** Whitman, amusement park, board game, lid shows 2 people on airplane ride, park scene at bottom, features "Magic Whirl" spinner, 1965 . . . . . . . . . . . . . . . . .  **40.00**

**Disneyland Game, Walt Disney's,** Transogram, Disney, board game, lid has 4 inset scenes of the "New Park, as Seen on TV and in the Movies," 1950s . . . .  **45.00**

**Disneyland "It's A Small World" Game,** Parker Brothers, Disney, board game, lid shows globe with flags and 8 costumed children representing different countries, 1965 . . . . . . . . . . .  **35.00**

**Disneyland Monorail Game,** Parker Brothers, Disney, card game, lid shows monorail on track with park scenes in background, 1960. . . . . . . . . . . . .  **35.00**

**Disneyland Monorail Game,** Parker Brothers, Disney, card game, lid shows monorail, can–can girl, elephant, castle, train, and plane in background, 1960s . . . . . . . . . . . . . . . . .  **40.00**

**Disneyland Pirates of the Caribbean Game,** Parker Brothers, Disney, board game, lid shows pirate holding sword, 2 others wearing kerchiefs on heads, 1 with knife in mouth, pirate ship and several tropical buildings in background, 1965  **35.00**

**Disneyland Riverboat Game,** Parker Brothers, Disney, board game, lid shows riverboat with

*Doc Holliday Wild West Game*

smokestacks and paddle wheel, Indians and animals beneath tree, 1960s. . . . . . . . . . . . . .  **30.00**

**District Messenger Boy, Game of The,** McLoughlin Brothers, morality, board game, lid shows uniformed messenger carrying letter, street scene with spires in background, "Game of The Telegraph Boy" inset bottom right corner, contains wooden pawns and spinner, 1904 . . . . .  **100.00**

**Diver Dan,** Milton Bradley, generic, tug–o–war action game, lid shows underwater scene of diver struggling with octopus for treasure chest and mermaid and fish, 1961 . . . . . . . . . . . . . .  **45.00**

**Divine Right,** TSR, role playing/ fantasy, board game, lid shows horses and armored knights battling on mountain and cloaked figure with pointed hat, 1979 . .  **15.00**

**Doc Holliday Wild West Game,** Transogram, western, board game, lid shows kneeling man in hat and holster holding gun, 2 men on horseback, and man on ground with gun at side, 1960 *see illus.*. . . . . . . . . . . . .  **45.00**

**Doctor Dolittle,** Mattel, musical show, board game, lid with show star Rex Harrison in top hat, parrot on shoulder, 1967 . .  **45.00**

**Doctor Dolittle Card Game,** Post, muscial show, card game, cover shows parrot head and monkey scratching his head, contains playing cards with animal pictures and Rex Harrison Doctor Dolittle card with parrot on top hat, 1967 . . . . . . . . . . . . . . .  **15.00**

*Dog Race*

**Doctor Dolittle's Magic Answer Machine,** Apjac, lid shows Dolittle pointing to chart and horse wearing glasses, 1967 . . .    **20.00**

**Doctor Dolittle's Marble Maze,** Hasbro, lid shows Dolittle at ship's wheel, marble maze playing area background, 1967 . . . .    **45.00**

**Doctors and The Quack, The,** Parker Brothers, medical, card game, 6½ x 4⅞", lid shows man in hat holding whip and riding in horse–drawn chariot, "Q" in Quack has flower design in center, publishing info bottom right corner, c1887 . . . . . . . . . . . .    **40.00**

**Dodging Donkey, The,** Parker Brothers, generic, skill game, 7⅛ x 13¾", lid shows donkey looking out barn window and cats, chicks, and sunflowers, contains hanging mulitcolored litho donkey in barn target with 4 colored balls, c1924 . . . . . .    **65.00**

**Dog Race,** Toy Creations, No. 1213, dog racing, board game, 14⅝ x 10⅝ x 1⅜", lid shows 4 racing dogs in separate lanes chasing rabbit, #2, #1, and #4 visible on dogs' coats, "New Racing Game Sensation," 1937 . . . . . . . . . . . . . . . . . .    **30.00**

• Reissued by Transogram, same cover, 1938 *see illus* . . . . . .    **25.00**

**Dog Sweepstakes,** Stoll & Eisen Games, Inc., (Playjoy), racing, action game, 10½ x 20 x 1¼", lid shows 8 bulldogs chasing rabbit, "Hilarious Party Contest," gates with flags in background, 1935 . . . . . . . . . . . . . . . . . .    **60.00**

**Dogfight, American Heritage,** Milton Bradley, Command Decision Series, military, board game, lid shows WWI biplanes in air battle, contains plastic planes, 1962 . . . . . . . . . . . . .    **60.00**

**Dollar A Second,** Lowell, TV/stunt show, action game, lid shows money surrounding host Jan Murray and 2 insets of people doing stunts, contains "56 games, stunts, penalties, events complete with timing device and full set of props," ABC show, 1956 . . . . . . . . . . . . . .    **55.00**

**Dollar Bill Poker,** E.S. Lowe, game of chance, board game, lid with gameboard and Tony Randall and Jack Klugman as Odd Couple, contains playing pcs and cards, 1974 . . . . . . . . .    **10.00**

**Dolly and Daniel Whale,** Milton Bradley, generic, board game, lid shows ice scene of bear and 4 cartoon characters, 1 atop whale's head peering through water opening, and 1 wearing Eskimo clothes, 1964 . . . . . . . .    **40.00**

**Domination,** Milton Bradley, strategy, board game, lid shows playing pcs, gameboard, and hand moving pcs, 1982 . . . . . .    **15.00**

**Domino's Pizza Delivery Game,** Wortquest USA, Inc., advertising/business, lid shows Domino logo box, delivery car, and driver carrying pizza, "$9.00" in red inset, "It's Pizza Party Time" on sign, 1989 . . . . . . . . . . . .    **10.00**

**Dondi Prairie Race,** Hasbro, western, board game, cover shows boy wearing cowboy hat and striped shirt riding in wagon and pulling horse's reins, "Prairie Race Game," 1960 . . . . . . . .    **35.00**

**Donkey Kong,** Milton Bradley, generic, board game, based on arcade game, lid shows gorilla carrying blonde woman, 1981    **15.00**

*Down You Go*

*Donkey Party*

**Donkey Party,** Whitman, pin the
tail on the donkey game, contains paper tails and pins, game
rules and instruction booklet, no
date *see illus* . . . . . . . . . . . .    **25.00**

**Donny–Brook Fair,** Noves, Snow
& Co., generic, card game,
6¼ x 5¼", lid shows man and
woman dancing, man on stool
clapping, tent with flags, mfg
name bottom left corner, and
"Boston & Worcester" bottom
right corner, contains 65 small
yellow squares, 7 animal cards,
and 31 people cards, 1877. . . .    **35.00**

**Don't Bug Me,** Hasbro, generic,
skill and action game, lid shows
boy and girl playing game and
net and bug playing pcs, "The
game that will drive you buggy,"
1967. . . . . . . . . . . . . . . . . .    **10.00**

**Don't Go Overboard,** Schaper,
generic, skill and action game,
lid shows boy and girl playing
game, contains ship playing
area and magnetized sailors,
1971. . . . . . . . . . . . . . . . . .    **10.00**

**Don't Go To Jail,** Parker Brothers,
generic, dice game, lid shows
3 dice and man with mustache
and hat behind locked bars,
"The Monopoly Dice Game,"
1991. . . . . . . . . . . . . . . . . .    **10.00**

**Double Exposure,** Ideal, TV/quiz,
skill game, lid shows TV host
pointing to 2 jigsaw puzzle pcs,
backs of man and woman,
based on CBS program, 1961 . .    **25.00**

**Double or Nothin',** Remco,
generic, action game, lid shows
boy in striped shirt pointing to
2 children on fence and one
who has fallen, "The Follow the
Leader Game," 1958 . . . . . . . .    **15.00**

**Double Trouble Super Puzzle
Game,** Whitman, generic, puz-
zle/action game, lid shows
group of people assembling
puzzle on floor, 1968 . . . . . . . .    **10.00**

**Down and Out,** Milton Bradley,
generic, skill game, 9½ x 7½",
lid shows game pcs and game
name at top center, checkerboard background, contains red
metal ringed tower and 4 steel
balls, target board has numbered depressions for balls and
2 holes to insert in tower,
c1928–30 . . . . . . . . . . . . . .    **35.00**

**Down the Pike with Mrs. Wiggs
at the St. Louis Exposition,**
Milton Bradley, educational,
card game, 7½ x 5½", cover
shows game name slanted up to
right, contains small phrase
cards, 1904 . . . . . . . . . . . . . .    **25.00**

**Down You Go,** Selchow &
Righter, TV/generic, action
game, game name letters in
blocks on lid, "The Newest Party
Game..." on circular inset, "Play
the famous Television Show..."
on arrow pointing to game
name, 1954 *see illus* . . . . . . . .    **20.00**

**Dr. Busby,** J. Ottmann Lith. Co.,
medical, board game, 6⅜ x
8⅝", lid shows doctor in long
coat and vest with glasses on
forehead, man in bathrobe seat-

Dr. Kildare

Dukes of Hazzard Game

ed in chair with feet in tub, St.
Nicholas Series . . . . . . . . . . .    30.00
**Dr. Kildare,** Ideal, TV/medical,
board game, lid has picture of
hospital and show star Richard
Chamberlain in medical jacket
with stethoscope, "Medical
Game for the Young," contains
doctor cards and medical ana-
lyzer, 1962 *see illus* . . . . . . . .    40.00
**Dracula Mystery Game,** Hasbro,
mystery, board game, cover
shows Dracula, flying bat,
"deaths" in inset, and arrow
pointing down, 1963 . . . . . . . .    115.00
**Drag Strip,** Milton Bradley, car
racing, skill and action game,
lid shows 2 racing cars above
and below game name, 1965 . .    25.00
**Dragnet, The Game of,**
Transogram, TV/detective, lid
shows series star Jack Webb in
hat, 4 policemen chasing man
in suit and tie, 1955 . . . . . . . .    50.00
**Dream Date,** Transogram,
No. 3897, originally titled "Girl
Meets Boy," generic, magnetic
plastic playing surface with
plastic spinner, lid shows 3 girls
playing game and playing board
and describes contents, 1963 . .    30.00
**Dream House TV Home Game,**
Milton Bradley, TV/generic/
home, board game, lid shows
ABC program host and 2 contestant couples, game name set
house shaped frame, 1968 . . . .    20.00
**Dubble Up,** Samuel Gabriel Sons
& Co., generic, board game, lid
shows 6 circles with pictures of
star, anchor, bell, and crown,
"Let's Play a New Game," . . . . .    20.00

**Dude Ranch Game, Gene Autry's,**
Built Rite, western, board game,
lid shows 2 horses with riders
and 3 people roping calf,
includes stock car race game,
1956 . . . . . . . . . . . . . . . . . . .    50.00
**Dudley Do–Right's Find Snidely
Game,** Whitman, cartoon characters, board game, lid shows
cartoon man in Ranger outfit
leading horse wearing blanket
and hat, large–nosed man in top
hat behind tree, "Be the First
Dudley to Find Snidely and
Win," 1976 . . . . . . . . . . . . . .    15.00
**Dukes of Hazzard Game,** Ideal,
TV/crime, lid shows 2 police
cars, convertible, and show
stars, 1981 *see illus* . . . . . . . .    10.00
**Dunce,** Schaper, generic, skill and
action game, lid shows boy
wearing dunce cap on stool,
globe, game name and math
problems on blackboard, and
bell and apple on desk, 1955 . .    20.00
**Dunce, Let's Play,** Schaper, generic, cover shows boy on stool
with dunce cap, box inset with
spinning top and dunce figures
in each corner, Parents
Magazine seal, 1955 . . . . . . . .    18.00
**Dune,** Avalon Hill, book, board
game, cover shows cornucopia
shaped form and small figures in
right corner against sand back-
ground, 1979 . . . . . . . . . . . . .    12.00
**Dune,** Parker Brothers, movie/
adventure, board game, lid
shows monster hand emerging
from underground, "A Parker
Brothers Adventure Game,"
1984 . . . . . . . . . . . . . . . . . . .    15.00

**Dungeon Dice,** Parker Brothers, generic, dice game, lid shows people playing game, small figure in bottom right corner, 2 figures above game name, 1977 . .    **6.00**

**Dungeons & Dragons,** Tactical Studies Rules, military/role playing, board game, "Original Collector's Edition," one of first role playing games, lid shows medieval figure in brick doorway, "playable with pencil and paper and miniature figures," 1974 . . . . . . . . . . . . . . . . . .    **20.00**

**Duran Duran Game,** Milton Bradley, music group, board game, "Into the Arena," lid shows music group and "D" in circle, contains 3 sets of cards, and 4 plastic pawns, 1985 . . . .    **18.00**

**Dynamite Shack,** Milton Bradley, generic, action game, lid shows exploding game shack and "Bang," 1968 . . . . . . . . . . . . .    **15.00**

–E–

**E. T., The Extra–Terrestrial,** Parker Brothers, movie/space, board game, lid shows E.T.'s face and 4 bicycles with riders, 1982 . . .    **8.00**

**Easy Money,** Milton Bradley, business, board game, 19 x 10", pcs box, folded board shows game name in semi–circle across top third of lid, coins, and "Milton Bradley Company" on bottom third, light background, contains dice, multicolored buildings, wooden counters, and cards, patent issued by Parker Brothers, 1936 . . . . . . . . . . . . . . . . . . . . .    **25.00**
• Red background, 1936 . . . . . . .    **20.00**
• Board and pcs box with name in larger letters on dollar bill, "MB" logo left corner, coins in right corner, 1940s . . . . . . . .    **20.00**

**Easy Money, The Game of,** Milton Bradley, business, board game, cover shows game name in large letters on dollar bill, coins at bottom right corner, 1950s *see illus* . . . . . . . . . . . . . . . .    **18.00**

*The Game of Easy Money*

**Easy Money Game,** Milton Bradley, business, board game, lid shows gameboard, playing pcs, and "A Game of Buying and Selling," mfg logo and info down left side, 1974 . . . . . . . .    **12.00**

**Easy on the Ketchup Game,** Lakeside, generic, action game, Ketchup bottle container shakes out plastic "Ketchup" drops, "Lunch Bunch," 1975 . . . . . . . .    **10.00**

**Ed Wynn, The Fire Chief,** Selchow & Righter, celebrity, board game, 4¼ x 9", lid shows Wynn wearing glasses and fire chief hat, smoke coming from house in background, contains dice cups, dice, colored wooden counters, knobbed sticks, and tin pans, c1937 . . . . . . . . . . .    **25.00**

**Eddie Cantor's Automobile Game "Tell it to the Judge,"** Parker Brothers, celebrity, card game, cover shows Cantor in circle, hand outstretched receiving money, 1930s . . . . . . . . . . . . .    **30.00**

**Eddie Cantor's Game,** Parker Brothers, celebrity, board game, lid shows 5 cards, numbers 7, 1, and 2 visible, "Back Seat Driver" on one card, "Tell It To the Judge" on black strip near sketch of Cantor, 1950s . . . . . . . . . . .    **25.00**

**Eddie Cantor's New Game "Tell It to the Judge,"** celebrity/legal, separate board and pcs box, 19¾" sq box, 4⅞ x 10¾" matching pcs box containing wooden counters, "Judge" label, dice, cards, and paper "fine" money, cover shows Cantor holding 5 cards, inset picture of judge and

*Electronic Detective*

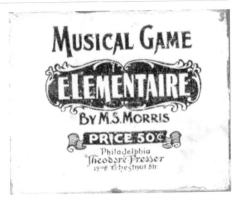

*Elementaire*

man with outstretched hands,
©1936 . . . . . . . . . . . . . . . . . .     **35.00**
• Reissued 1959 . . . . . . . . . . . . .     **30.00**
**Egg Race Game,** Ideal, generic,
skill and action game, lid shows
children doing stunts with eggs,
2 children running with eggs on
spoons, 1968 . . . . . . . . . . . . .     **18.00**
**'84 L.A. Games Monopoly,** AGK
Games, monopoly/sports, board
game, lid shows dice, part of
round playing surface, and
sports figure drawings along lid
bottom, unauthorized knockoff
pulled from shelves, 1984 . . . .     **25.00**
**Election '68,** Createk, politics,
board game, lid shows White
House, 3 politicians holding
signs, elephant, and donkey,
1967 . . . . . . . . . . . . . . . . . .     **22.00**
**Electra Woman and Dynagirl
Game,** Ideal, superheroines,
board game, cover shows
blonde and brunette women,
1977 . . . . . . . . . . . . . . . . . .     **18.00**
**Electric Baseball,** Electric Game
Co, sports, board game, lid
shows batter, fielder, pitcher,
catcher, and referee, arrows
point to different areas of gameboard, money back guarantee in
lower right corner, "Jim Prentice
Brings You, True To Life Action,"
contains steel balls, 1940s . . . .     **60.00**
**Electric Football,** Electric Game
Co, sports, board game, cover
shows player carrying ball, second player with #35 on shirt,
football stadium background,

"Electric" in flag banner, "A Jim
Prentice Game," 1940s . . . . . .     **50.00**
**Electronic Battleship,** Milton
Bradley, military, board game,
"A Computer Memory Game
with Live Action and Sound," lid
shows 2 players and playing sur-
face, 1979 . . . . . . . . . . . . . . .     **25.00**
**Electronic Detective,** Ideal, mys-
tery, board game, lid shows
computer and Don Adams in
question mark with woman's
face, "Computerized
Who–Done–It Game," comes
with 45–rpm record explaining
game rules, 1979 *see illus.* . . . .     **25.00**
**Electronic Radar Search Game,**
Ideal, military, board game, lid
shows playing surface and man
with glasses and 2 boys playing
game, 1969 . . . . . . . . . . . . . .     **18.00**
**Elementaire,** Theodore Presser,
music, board game, 4½ x 3½ x
⅞", lid reads "A Musical Game,"
by M.S. Morris, gives price and
mfg name and address, 1896
*see illus* . . . . . . . . . . . . . . . . .     **20.00**
**Eliot Ness and the Untouchables
Game,** Transogram, TV/mystery,
cover shows Ness and several
other men with guns and falling
figure in car, 1961 . . . . . . . . .     **60.00**
**Emergency Game, The,** Milton
Bradley, TV/fire fighting, board
game, lid shows fire engine, firemen with hoses, and 3 inset triangular pictures, 1973–74 . . . .     **15.00**

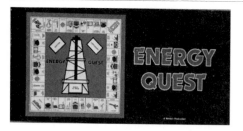

*Energy Quest*

*The Errand Boy or Failure and Success*

**Emily Post Popularity Game,** Selchow & Righter, celebrity/etiquette personality, board game, cover shows 5 people beneath tree, "Win a Circle of Friends," 1970 . . . . . . . . . . . . . . . . . . **18.00**

**Enemy Agent,** Milton Bradley, espionage, board game, lid shows running man in hat carrying leather satchel chased by 3 armed guards, "The Game of Foreign Intrigue," contains unique "Passport Scanner," 1976 **18.00**

**Energy Quest,** Weldon Productions, business/oil search/Monopoly, board game, lid shows playing surface and game name, 1977 *see illus* . . . . . . . . **15.00**

**Engineer,** Selchow & Righter, railroading, railroad track game, lid shows train wreck, signal flag, 2 engineers with striped caps, and third engineer on ground reaching for cap, 1957 . . . . . . . **22.00**

**Ensign O'Toole — U.S.S. Appleby Game,** Hasbro, military, board game, lid shows Ensign, destroyer at sea, "Have Fun Aboard the Navy's Wackiest Destroyer," 1963 . . . . . . . . . . **38.00**

**Errand Boy or Failure and Success, The,** McLoughlin Brothers, generic, board game, 14½ x 15", lid shows boy in hat carrying 2 packages, man talking to barefoot boy, package on ground, and woman in hat, "An Amusing Game," ©1891 *see illus*. . . . . . . . . . . . . . . . . **400.00**

**Escape From New York, The Game,** TSR, generic, simulation game, cover shows 2 running men, 1 carrying briefcase, brick wall and skyscapers in background, 1980 . . . . . . . . . . . . . **12.00**

**Escape from Death Star Game, Star Wars,** Kenner, movie/space, cover has inset pictures of 6 characters, game name extends as border around cover, 1977 . . **18.00**

**Espionage,** Transogram, spy, board game, magnetic action game, lid shows boy with game, 1963 . . . **40.00**

**Excursion to Coney Island,** Milton Bradley, generic, card game, lid shows woman in hat in circle, ocean swimmers, "Excursion to" in banner in top left corner, and mfg info in ribbon strips in top right corner, contains printed cards and reading booklet, copyrighted but undated, c1885 **30.00**

**Executive Decision,** 3M, business management, board game, lid shows 4 men, 1 with hand on globe holding paper, 1 with phone, 1971 . . . . . . . . . . . . . **15.00**

**Exports and Transportation, Game of,** Mills Games Mfg. Co., business, lid shows aerial view of globe, "Exports" in center of lid and board, narrow box with trade cards, 1936 . . . . . . . . . . **12.00**

**Express Monopoly Card Game,** Parker Brothers, generic, card game, lid shows game cards and "Go" underlined with arrow, Parker Brothers, 1993 . . . . . . . . **5.00**

*Eye Guess*

**Eye Guess,** Milton Bradley,
TV/quiz, third edition, "Bill
Cullen's TV Game," lid shows
Cullen holding glasses, 1960s. .    **20.00**
• Same cover, "new" fourth edi-
tion see illus . . . . . . . . . . . .    **18.00**

–F–

**F Troop,** Ideal, TV/military, board
game, lid shows 3 troopers
around cannon, fort and battle
in background, 1965 . . . . . . . .    **110.00**
**F Troop Card Game,** Ideal, TV/
military, "mini–board" card
game, lid shows cartoon drawings of Indians attacking fort,
troopers peering from fort
watching Indians climb ladder,
1965 . . . . . . . . . . . . . . . . . .    **40.00**
**F.B.I. Crime Resistance Game,**
Milton Bradley, detective/crime,
board game, lid shows FBI
shield, 2 men huddled together,
woman with raised hands, running man with raised arm, and
boy in left bottom corner watching, "Crime Resistance Manual
Included, Don't be a Victim,"
1976 . . . . . . . . . . . . . . . . . .    **25.00**
**F.B.I. Game, The,** Transogram,
detective/crime, board game, lid
shows 2 men in shirts and ties
with camera focused out window at 2 men on street, Capitol
building in background, based
on Random House's Landmark
Book series, 1961 . . . . . . . . .    **45.00**
**Face The Facts,** Lowell Mfg.,
TV/legal, played exactly "as
played on the CBS Television
Network," lid pictures panel of

*Fairyland Game*

3 judges and table with defen-
dant and plaintiff, Lowell, 1961    **35.00**
**Fairies' Cauldron Tiddledy Winks
Game, The,** Parker Brothers,
generic, skill game, 7¼ x 4¼",
lid shows cauldron and fairies
with wands, contains felt pcs,
sticks, base, bone winks and
black wooden bucket to make
cauldron, c1925 . . . . . . . . . . .    **30.00**
**Fairway Golf,** Trio, sports, board
game, lid shows Billy Maxwell
and 4 golfers and caddy with
bags, "It's new! It's Fun! It's For
Everyone!," title word "Golf" in
golf ball, 1954 . . . . . . . . . . . .    **30.00**
**Fairyland Game,** Milton Bradley,
generic, board game, 11¼ x
11¼ x ⅞", lid shows children
looking at fairy holding large
wand pointing at castle, c1880s
*see illus* . . . . . . . . . . . . . . . .    **50.00**
**Fame and Fortune,** Whitman,
generic, board game, lid shows
bucket of gold coins, 2 faces in
upper right corner, 1962 . . . . . .    **18.00**
**Familiar Quotations,** McLoughlin
Brothers, educational, card
game, 3¼ x 4¼", lid shows
bearded man in circle above 2
books surrounded by leaves and
flowers, "Popular Authors," con-
tains playing cards, c1890 . . . .    **22.00**
**Familiar Quotations From
Popular Authors, Game of,**
McLoughlin Brothers, educational, card game, 4 x 5", lid

*Family Feud*

*Farmer Electric Maps*

shows bearded man, contains
cards, c1888 . . . . . . . . . . . . .    **20.00**
**Family Feud,** Milton Bradley,
TV/quiz, new 2nd edition, lid
shows 2 panels of contestants,
one cheering and being congrat-
ulated by show host, scoreboard
in background, 1977 *see illus.* .    **12.00**
**Family Game, The,** Dynamic
Design Inc., generic, 3 framed
photographs above game name,
"Insight and Understanding,"
1971 . . . . . . . . . . . . . . . . . .    **10.00**
**Famous Men, Game of,** George
S. Parker & Co., educational,
card game, $5^5/_8$ x 4", lid corners
show pictures of Napoleon,
Washington, Beethoven, and
Shakespeare, game name in
script, contains printed cards,
c1887 . . . . . . . . . . . . . . . . .    **20.00**
**Famous Rook,** Rook Card Co.,
Division of Parker Brothers,
generic, card game, lid shows
bird with open beak on branch
holding playing cards, both
Rook Card Co. and Parker
Brothers info, patented March
22, 1910 . . . . . . . . . . . . . . . .    **15.00**
**Fan–Tel,** O. Schoenhut, Inc.,
generic, skill game, $2^1/_2$ x 6",
cyclindrical container with flat
wooden sticks, ©1937 . . . . . . .    **18.00**
**Fang Bang,** Milton Bradley, generic, action game, lid shows snake
heads, inset of children playing
game, "Balloon Breakin' Action
Game," 1967 . . . . . . . . . . . . .    **18.00**
**Fangface,** Parker Brothers, TV/car-
toon, board game, lid shows

werewolf Fangface in cloud hovering above 4 people in convert-
ible, 1979 . . . . . . . . . . . . . . .    **15.00**
**Fantastic Four Game, The New,**
Milton Bradley, comic book
character, board game,
"Featuring Herbie the Robot,"
lid shows man–like creature,
man and woman, and Herbie in
white cloud, "Join the Fantastic
Four As They Battle the Evil
Doctor Doom," 1978 . . . . . . . .    **15.00**
**Fantastic Voyage,** Milton Bradley,
TV/movie/space, board game,
lid with inset pictures of lady
grabbing purse from creature,
man carrying child, and man
wearing turban, spacecraft in
background, 1968 . . . . . . . . . .    **25.00**
**Fantasy Island,** Ideal, TV, board
game, Ideal, lid has 2 circles
with show stars and names
"Roarke" and "Tattoo," house on
island in background, 1978 . . .    **18.00**
**Fantasy Land Game, Walt
Disney's,** Parker Brothers,
Disney, board game, lid shows
Snow White and other Disney
characters flocking toward cas-
tle, 1950s–60s . . . . . . . . . . . .    **35.00**
**Farmer Electric Maps,** J.M.
Farmer, educational, $18^3/_{16}$ x 11
x $11^3/_{16}$", lid shows bolt of
electricity, "Educational, Enter–
taining," contains 6 stiff board
maps, ©1938 *see illus* . . . . . . .    **45.00**
**Farmer Jones' Pigs,** McLoughlin
Brothers, Popular Series
No. 406, farming, board game,
$8^1/_2$ x $14^1/_2$", lid shows farmer

*Fart The Game*

chasing pigs with stick, contains
wooden counters and spinner,
c1885 . . . . . . . . . . . . . . . . .    **120.00**

**Fart The Game,** Baron Scott
Enterprises, generic, board
game, box contains game
board, plastic paper coupons,
4 plastic playing pieces, die,
and whopee cushion, *see illus*    **15.00**

**Fascination,** Remco, generic, skill
game, battery operated, lid
shows boy and girl with ponytail playing game, "the electric
maze game," 1961 . . . . . . . . .    **30.00**

**Fascination,** Remco, generic, skill
game, battery operated, lid
shows boy and girl with braids
holding mazes, 2 adults and
2 children in background playing game, "Play the Triple Maze,
Play the Circle Maze, The
Electric Maze Game," 1968 . . .    **25.00**

**Fascination,** Selchow & Righter,
generic, skill game, 6" sq, contains wooden board and top
and red marbles, directions on
back of box, c1890 . . . . . . . .    **25.00**

**Fascination Checkers, The
Original Game of,** Remco,
generic, board game, lid shows
playing board and hand holding
pc with eyes and mouth, 1962    **25.00**

**Fast Eddie,** Mattel, generic, skill
and action marble game, lid
shows plastic boy playing pc
shooting marbles into playing
ring, 1970 . . . . . . . . . . . . . .    **10.00**

**Fast Mail, The,** Milton Bradley,
postal, board game,

$20^5/_8$ x $10^5/_8$", wooden box, lid
shows steam locomotive on
tracks in oval inset, contains colored wooden counters and spin-
ner, c1900 . . . . . . . . . . . . . .    **650.00**

**Fast 111's,** Parker Brothers, auto
racing, lid shows multicolored
cars on track, drivers' heads visible, "The Car–Racing Board
Game," 1981 . . . . . . . . . . . .    **15.00**

**Fastest Gun, The,** Milton Bradley,
western, board game, lid shows
hand reaching for holstered gun,
"3–D Wild West Game," 1974    **30.00**

**Fat Albert and the Cosby Kids,**
Milton Bradley, cartoon/black
collectibles, board game, lid
shows Fat Albert bending over
and 7 black children, 1 child
wearing scarf with hand on
Albert's back, 1973 . . . . . . . . .    **25.00**

**Fearless Fireman,** Hasbro, firefighting, board game, lid shows
firemen on fire truck, fire station, and girl pointing to smoke
coming from windows,
"Thrilling Game and Toy,"
1955–57 . . . . . . . . . . . . . . . .    **95.00**

**Feed the Elephant,** Cadaco,
generic, action game, lid shows
2 children tossing peanuts at
elephant wearing clown hat,
1952 . . . . . . . . . . . . . . . . . .    **30.00**

**Feeley Meeley,** Milton Bradley,
generic, action game, lid shows
girl in sailor collar shirt and
3 others playing game, contains
cards and large box with hole
on each side, "The Game That
Gives You a Funny Feeling!,"
1967 . . . . . . . . . . . . . . . . . .    **15.00**

**Felix the Cat,** Milton Bradley,
generic, board game, lid shows
black cat holding 3 balloons,
"Fun" and "New" on balloons,
1960 . . . . . . . . . . . . . . . . . .    **40.00**

**Ferrilude or Game of Beasts,**
West & Lee Game Co., educational, card game, $2^7/_8$ x 4", lid
shows monkey and other animals around bench, mfg info
below, contains animal cards,
1873 . . . . . . . . . . . . . . . . . .    **32.00**

**Ferry Command,** Milton Bradley,
military, board game, lid shows

Fire Department

*Fibber McGee and the
Wistful Vista Mystery*

4 planes in clouds, game name
at lid bottom, 1943 . . . . . . . .   **30.00**
**Fess Parker Trail Blazers Game,**
Milton Bradley, TV/western,
board game, lid shows Parker in
3 action shots including fighting
with Indian and aiming rifle at
bear, spinner in upper right corner, includes Trail Blazers Club
membership application, "From
the Daniel Boone T.V. Show,"
1964 . . . . . . . . . . . . . . . . .   **40.00**
• Second cover shows Parker
  fighting 2 Indians, 1 holding
  tomahawk, third Indian with
  bow and arrow, 1964. . . . . . .   **38.00**
**Feudal,** 3M, military, board game,
lid shows knights in armor playing pcs on checkerboard sur-
face, 1969 . . . . . . . . . . . . . .   **18.00**
**Fibber McGee,** Milton Bradley,
No. 4561, radio/celebrity, board
game, 7⁷/₁₆ x 5³/₈ x 1⁵/₈", lid
shows old radio microphone,
"By Arrangement With The
National Broadcasting Co. Inc.,"
©1936. . . . . . . . . . . . . . . . .   **20.00**
**Fibber McGee and the Wistful
Vista Mystery,** Milton Bradley,
No. 4768, radio/celebrity/mys-
tery, board game, 7³/₈ x 5³/₈ x 2",
Fibber and Molly in circle on
right, "The Merry Fibber McGee
and Molly Game," contains
cards, colored disks, and story
booklet, published by arrangement with National
Broadcasting Company and

Needham, Louis, & Brorby, Inc,
©1940 *see illus* . . . . . . . . . . .   **25.00**
**Finance,** Parker Brothers, busi-
ness, board game, lid shows
houses, dice, playing pcs, and
game name letters in circles,
1956 . . . . . . . . . . . . . . . . . .   **10.00**
**Finance and Fortune,** Parker
Brothers, business, board game,
lid shows man in top hat
exchanging house for money
from man in hat and woman
with folded hands, 1936, 1962   **30.00**
**Finance and Fortune, The Game
of,** Parker Brothers, business,
board game, lid shows coins,
currency, and deed, city build-
ings background,1955 . . . . . . .   **25.00**
**Fire Department,** Milton Bradley,
firefighting, board game, 10¹/₄ x
6¹/₄ x ⁷/₈", lid shows 3 children
and fire truck, contains spinner
and colored wooden chips,
c1920 *see illus*. . . . . . . . . . . .   **35.00**
**Fire Department, Game Of,**
Milton Bradley, No. 4247, firefighting, board game, lid shows
3 men standing on rear of fire
engine with whitewall tires and
bell on front passing skyscrapers, contains 4 large wooden
markers and spinner, c1930 . . .   **80.00**
**Fire Fighters,** Milton Bradley, firefighting, board game, 8¹/₈ x
14¹/₄", lid shows horse–drawn
steam fire engine driven by fireman, contains round colored
wooden counters and spinner,
©1909 . . . . . . . . . . . . . . . . .   **115.00**
**Fireball XL5,** Milton Bradley,
space, board game, lid shows
spaceship marked "XL5," 1964   **90.00**

*Game of Fish Pond*

**Firehouse Mouse,** Transogram, firefighting, action game, lid shows children playing game, boy holding cards, and girl with bow in hair, "A 5 Alarm Fun Filled Riot!," 1967 . . . . . . . . . .    **30.00**

**Fish Bait,** Ideal, generic, action, game, lid shows playing surface and complex playing pc with several balls traveling down obstacle course, 1965 . . . . . . .    **55.00**

**Fish Pond, Game of,** Wescott Bros, No. 12, fishing, 12¼ x 3¼ x 1⅜", lid shows boy wearing hat sitting alone fishing, 4 children seated near pole with hooked fish, unknown date *see illus*. . . . . . . . . . . . . . . . .    **65.00**

**Fish Pond, The Game of,** McLoughlin Brothers, fishing, skill game, 19½ x 10¼", lid shows girl and boy in rowboat, contains wooden fish poles and numbered cardboard fish, 1890    **125.00**

**Fish Pond, The Game of,** Milton Bradley, fishing, action game, 21 x 12¾", lid shows man in pointed hat with beard fishing in pond, contains 2 fishing poles and numbered fish, c1895    **125.00**

**Five Hundred, Game of,** Home Game Co., generic, card game, lid shows banner with word "Standard," game name underlined, and price and mfg info, contains "full set ivory enamel playing cards," c1990s . . . . . . .    **15.00**

**Five Spot, Bradley's,** Milton Bradley, sports/pool, lid shows boy and girl and pool table with balls, "A Novel Game of Pool," 1931 . . . . . . . . . . . . . . . . . .    **15.00**

**Five Wise Birds, The,** Parker Brothers, generic, skill game, lid shows boy wearing cowboy hat holding rifle aimed at 5 birds on fence and girl holding note pad, 1954 . . . . . . . . . . . . . . . . . .    **45.00**

**Five Wise Birds, The,** unknown manufacturer, generic, skill game, 17½ x 8¼ x 1¼", lid shows 5 birds on fence, c1920s    **40.00**

**Flag Game, The,** McLoughlin Brothers, educational, card game, 8½ x 4½", lid shows George Washington surrounded by flags, contains flag cards and tickets, ©1887 . . . . . . . . . . . .    **50.00**

**Flags, Game of,** Cincinnati Game Co., No. 1111, educational, card game, 2⅞ x 3¾", lid shows 4 flags surrounding globe, "Crown Card" below game name, mfg info and "Copyrighted, 1896 by Fireside Game Co." at bottom, includes cards and "Crown" card, ©1896 . . . .    **45.00**

**Flags, Game of,** McLoughlin Brothers, educational, card game, 5½ x 7½", lid shows youngster wearing triangular hat carrying flag, ©1896. . . . . . . . .    **75.00**

**Flagship Airfreight,** Milton Bradley, transportaion/aviation, board game, lid shows cargo being loaded onto plane, "The Airline Cargo Game," 1946. . . .    **55.00**

**Flap Jack,** Remco, generic, action game, lid shows girl with frying pan and boy in chef's hat holding pancakes, "The Flip–Flop Game," 1958 . . . . . . . . . . . . .    **20.00**

**Flapper Fortunes,** The Embossing Co, generic, board game, 3⅝ x 2½", game name, copyright, and mfg info in square at lid center, circles, squares, stars, and quarter moons border, ©1929. . . . . . . . . . . . . . . . .    **18.00**

**Flash Gordon Game,** Game Gems/T. Cohn, comic strip hero, board game, lid shows Gordon wearing holster belt and holding gun, woman inset bottom left corner, rocket, man and woman in background, 1965 . . . . . . . .    **75.00**

**Flash, Justice League of America,** Hasbro, superhero, board game, lid shows superhero attacking robot, "POW" and strip of 7 faces in upper right corner, 1967    **150.00**

*Flinch*

**Flash: The Press Photographer Game,** Selchow & Righter, photography, action game, lid shows man holding camera with flash bulb, "Press" and "Flash," 1956 . . . . . . . . . . . . . . . . .   **50.00**

**Flea Circus,** Mattel, generic, action game, contains tightrope and other circus stunt apparatus on which magnetic fleas perform, 1964 . . . . . . . . . . . . . .   **25.00**

**Flight Captain,** E.S. Lowe, transportation, board game, lid shows 4 planes in flight, 4 players and game surface inset, 1972 . . . . . . . . . . . . . . . . .   **20.00**

**Flight Round the World, A,** Spears, transportation/aviation, board game, lid shows plane flying over waterfall, contains metal planes, 1928 . . . . . . . .   **45.00**

**Flight To Paris, The,** Milton Bradley, 17 x 8¾", air transportation, board game, lid shows prop plane, contains colored metal planes and spinners, ©1927. . . . . . . . . . . . . . . . .   **155.00**

**Flinch,** Flinch Card Co., generic, card game, lid has game name in top half, mfg info and price in bottom half, 1913 . . . . . . . .   **10.00**

**Flinch,** Flinch Card Co., generic, card game, game name in lid center above small sphere, mfg info below, 1935 . . . . . . . . . .   **9.00**

**Flinch,** Parker Brothers, generic, card game, "New Edition," name in banner across top half of lid, Flinch Card Co and Parker Brothers info at bottom,1938. . . . . . . . . . . . . . .   **7.00**

**Flinch,** Parker Brothers, generic, card game, lid has name across middle, "Registered...U.S. Patent Office" and Parker Brothers info at bottom, 1940s *see illus* . . . . .   **5.00**

• Reissued in alternate color, "Reg. U.S. Patent Office,"1940s. . . . . . . . . . . .   **50.00**

**Flinch,** Parker Brothers, generic card game, "New Edition, Millions Play It!," vertical lines above and below game name at lid center, 1940s. . . . . . . . . . .   **5.00**

**Flinch,** Parker Brothers, generic, card game, lid has game name at top and numbered cards, "Numerical Card Game," 1951   **5.00**

**Flinch,** Parker Brothers, generic, card game, lid shows man, woman, and child playing game, child looking at cards, "The Famous Card Game," 1963 . . . .   **4.00**

**Flintstones Game, The,** Milton Bradley, cartoon, board game, lid shows Flintstones on camping trip, Fred diving, tent, palm trees, and women sunning beneath umbrella, 1971 . . . . . .   **25.00**

**Flintstones Just For Kicks,** Transogram, cartoon, action game, lid shows playing surface with different animal face targets and bottom catch tray, contains multicolored balls, 1962 . . . . . .   **60.00**

**Flintstones Mitt–Full,** Whitman, cartoon, skill and action game, lid shows Fred Flintstone and friends, hand holding mitt with Flintstone face, 1962 . . . . . . . .   **60.00**

**Flinstones Present Dino the Dinosaur** *see Dino the Dinosaur Game*

**Flinstones Stoneage Game, The,** Transogram, 1961, cover shows Fred and friends, "The Game That Rocked Bedrock!," 1961 . .   **40.00**

**Flip For Fun,** Parker Brothers, generic, board game, lid shows boy and girl seated in car holding game boards, "Play in the Car With Seat Belts Buckled," 1966 . . . . . . . . . . . . . . . . . .   **15.00**

*The Flying Nun Game*

*The Fonz Hanging Out At Arnolds*

**Flip It: Auto Race and Transcontinental Tour,** De Luxe Game Corp., transportation/automobile, board game, 11³/₈ x 9³/₈ x 1", lid shows game track with name in center, "Two Games in One," lid serves as second gameboard, contains metal cars, c1920s . . . . . . . . . . . . . . . . .    **45.00**

**Flip–It Jackpot,** Aurora, TV/celebrity, endorsed by Flip Wilson, action game, lid shows Wilson, 2 adults, and 2 children with jackpot machine, contains chips, 1973 . . . . . . . . . . . . . .    **25.00**

**Flipper Flips,** Mattel, TV/cartoon, board game, lid shows boy wearing goggles riding Flipper, boat in background, contains small plastic dolphins, 1965 . . .    **45.00**

**Flitters,** The Martin Co., generic, skill game, 6 x 9", lid shows woman with long hair playing game, boy in sailor collar shirt, and round table, contains wooden striker, wooden button, wooden dowels, and multicolored tissue paper disks (flitters), ©1899. . . . . . . . . . . . . . . . . .    **30.00**

**Flivver Game,** Milton Bradley, automobile/transportation, board game, separate board and 6¹/₄ x 4¹/₄" pcs box, lid shows side view of old car, game name in rectangle at top, and mfg info in smaller rectangle at bottom, c1923–24 . . . . . . . . . . . . . .    **180.00**

**Flying Nun Game, The,** Milton Bradley, TV/comedy, lid shows 4 boys waving to flying nun, 1968 *see illus*. . . . . . . . . . . . . . . .    **30.00**

**Flying Nun Marble Maze Game,** Hasbro, 1967, TV/comedy, marble game, lid shows flying nun and banner strip in center with game name, circular playing surface background, 1967. . . . .    **35.00**

**Flying The Beam,** Parker Brothers, transportation/aviation, board game, lid shows plane flying through clouds, game name in banner angled from mid–center left to top right corner, 1941    **75.00**

**Flying The United States Air Mail,** Parker Brothers, postal, board game, 18 x 14¹/₂", lid shows prop plane, contains colored metal airplanes, dice cup, dice, and white printed cards, ©1929    **190.00**

**Foil,** 3M, educational, word game, lid shows man standing against enlarged card with "g," woman with arm on patterned card, cards with letters "e" and "f," 1969 . . . . . . . . . . . . . . . .    **12.00**

**Fonz Hanging Out At Arnolds, The,** Milton Bradley, TV/comedy, platform board game, lid with show star Henry Winkler, Jefferson High School banner, and people eating and dancing, 1978 *see illus*. . . . . . . . . . . . .    **15.00**

**Foolish Questions,** Wallie Dorr Co., generic, card game, 5¹/₂ x 3³/₄", Rube L. Goldberg lid illus, mfg info at bottom, 1924–26. . .    **18.00**

**Foot Race, The,** Parker Brothers, generic, board game, 5³/₈" sq, lid shows 4 running boys, house and towered building in background, mfg info bottom right corner, and ribbon border, contains round colored wooden counters, spinners, c1900 . . . . .    **18.00**

**Football, The Game of,** George A. Childs, sports, board game, 11³/₄ x 8³/₄", lid shows pile of players, tower flying flag, and copyright 1895, contains wooden bench team cards and affixed spinner, 1895 . . . . . . . .    **150.00**

**Fore,** Artcraft Paper Products, sports, action game, lid shows #19 flag marker, "O" in game name is golf ball, large tee, and boy with striped shirt and socks carrying golf bag, 1954 . . . . . .    **30.00**

**Foreign Exchange,** Avalon Hill, international/business, board game, lid shows hand dropping coins, "The International Money Game," 1979 . . . . . . . . . . . . .    **10.00**

**Forest Friends,** Milton Bradley, generic, board game, lid shows 3 squirrels, "A Cute Little Folks Animal Game," 1956–1962 . . .    **12.00**

**Formula–1,** Parker Brothers, auto racing, lid shows cars numbered 2, 3, 4, 5, and 6 above game name, 1963 . . . . . . . . . . . . . .    **50.00**

**Formula 1,** Parker Brothers, auto racing, board game, lid shows race cars coming down hill, trees in background, 1964 . . . .    **45.00**

**Fortress America,** Milton Bradley, Gamemaster Series, military, board game, lid shows soldiers, helicopters, and pre–Desert Storm Saddam Hussein picture, 1986 . . . . . . . . . . . . . . . . . . .    **35.00**

**Fortune 500, The Business Game,** Pressman, business, board game, lid shows man holding briefcase standing in middle of gameboard showing dice and cards, 1980 . . . . . . . . . . . . . .    **25.00**

**Fortune Telling Game, The,** Parker Brothers, fortune telling, card game, 4³/₄ x 6¹/₄", lid shows woman and witch seated before fireplace, quarter moon, mfg info bottom left corner, contains 30 cards, c1890 . . . . . . . . . . .    **18.00**

**Forty Niners,** National Games, western, board game, lid shows bearded man wearing hat and neckerchief and horseback riders chasing covered wagon, 1950s . . . . . . . . . . . . . . . .    **20.00**

**"49ers," The,** National Games, western, board game, lid shows covered wagon holdup, horses, and man with rifle, "Game of Risk and Rescue," 1950s . . . . . .    **25.00**

**Foto–Electric Football,** Cadaco–Ellis, sports, board game, wooden box version, side view of running player carrying ball, 1941 . . . . . . . . . . . . . . . . .    **30.00**

**Foto–Electric Football,** Cadaco, sports, board game, lid shows front view of football player in running pose carrying ball, 1950    **12.00**

**Foto–Electric Football,** Cadaco, sports, board game, lid shows 3 players, ball carrier being tackled, "National Pro Football Hall of Fame Game,"1965 . . . .    **15.00**

**Foto–Electric Football,** Cadaco, sports, board game, lid shows 3 running players,1 wearing #17 and 1 carrying ball, "Professional Football Hall of Fame Game," 1971 . . . . . . . .    **8.00**

**Foto–Finish Horse Race,** Pressman, horse racing, name of game superimposed over horse race photos on lid,1940 . . . . . .    **25.00**

**4 Cyte,** McGraw Hill Book Co., Original Edition, educational, word game, lid has large #4 with elongated cross line and game letters in blocks, "the championship word game," 1963 . . . . . . . . . . . . . . . . . .    **9.00**

**4 Cyte,** Milton Bradley, Twin Set Table Model, educational, word game, lid shows couple playing game at beach and couple playing game at table, individual playing surface for each player, 1967 . . . . . . . . . . . . .    **12.00**

**Four Games, (Noodle Soup, 2nd Series; Scrambles, 11th Series; Scrambles, 12th Series; Wordlets, 3rd Series),** Frederich H. Beach, generic, party/parlor game, 9 x 11¹/₂ x 1¹/₈", lid lists game names, "For Individual & Group Play," 1936 . . . . . . . . .    **22.00**

**Four Puzzled Pigs, The,** unknown manufacturer, generic, 6³/₄ x 6³/₄ x 1¹/₄", lid shows game name in circles, c1880s . . . . . . . . . . .    **40.00**

*Fox Hunt*

**Fox and Hounds, Game of,** Parker Brothers, sports/fox chase, board game, lid shows mounted hunters jumping stone wall after hounds chasing fox, contains metal pcs, 1948 . . . . . . . . . . .     **25.00**

**Fox Hunt,** Milton Bradley, sports/fox chase, board game, 16¼ x 11¼", lid shows mounted hunter and hounds chasing fox, contains round colored wooden counters, ©1905 *see illus.* . . . . . . . . . . . . . . . . . .     **50.00**

**Frankenstein Horror Target Game,** Hasbro, horror, action game, lid shows bats and 2 white circles around Frankenstein face, moon with flying bat, 1964 . . . . . . . . . . .     **115.00**

**Frankenstein Mystery Game,** Hasbro, mystery/horror, board game, lid shows Frankenstein's face, hand, lightning, 4 arrows, and game name in left top corner, "Find the Lurking Monster," 1963 . . . . . . . . . . . . . . . . . .     **110.00**

**Frantic Frogs,** Milton Bradley, generic, action game, lid shows 4 frog drawings and windup key, playing surface inset bottom right corner, "Action Wind–Up Game," contains tin windup frogs, 1965 . . . . . . . .     **20.00**

**Free Parking,** Parker Brothers, monopoly, board game, lid shows back of car, parking meter, and policeman chasing

man with a cane and a hat flying, "Feed the Meter Game," 1988 . . . . . . . . . . . . . . . . . .     **10.00**

**Freefall,** Hasbro, generic, action game, lid shows 3 children looking at playing pc, "One of the tallest games in the world!," 1968 . . . . . . . . . . . . . . . . . .     **15.00**

**Frisko,** The Embossing Co., No. 701, generic, dice game, 10⅞ x 8 x 2¼", lid shows dice, money, and crossed pistols, "The Roaring Game of the Barbary Coast," contains tiles numbered 1 through 6, die, die cup, and chips, ©1937 . . . . . . . . . . . . .     **25.00**

**Frog Pond,** unknown manufacturer, generic, board game, 18 x 10", lid shows 8 frogs on lily pads, "Made in U.S.A.," bottom right corner, contains metal frogs and fishing poles, 1895–97 . . . . . . . . . . . . . . .     **45.00**

**Frog Who Would A–Wooing Go, The,** The United Games Co., generic, lid shows frog in colonial dress with high socks and lacy cuffs holding hand to head, unknown date . . . . . . . . . . .     **60.00**

**Frontier Fort Rescue Race,** Gabriel, western, board game, lid shows backs of soldiers shooting at Indians approaching fort, 1956. . . . . . . . . . . . . . .     **30.00**

**Frontierland Game, Walt Disney's Official,** Parker Brothers, Disney, board game, lid shows man holding rifle riding horse along side covered wagon, 1955–56. .     **40.00**

**Fu Manchu's Hidden Hoard,** Ideal, mystery, board game, lid shows book with game title "By Sax Rohmer," several action scenes, and Manchu with mustache and round hat, 1967 . . . .     **45.00**

**Fugitive,** Ideal, crime, board game, lid shows man being chased by men and dogs, other dogs, moon, and trees, 1964. . .     **125.00**

**Fun at the Circus,** McLoughlin Brothers, generic, board game, 16¾" sq, wooden frame, lid shows circus performers including giraffe, dog on stool, and monkey pulling cart on tightrope, contains 4 turned wooden pawns and themed spinner, 1897 . . . . . . . . . . . . . . . . . . **500.00**

**Fun At The Zoo: A Game,** Parker Brothers, generic, board game, 21 x 11", lid shows elephant with drum and clown in cart, contains colored wooden markers and spinner, ©1902 . . . . . . **220.00**

**Funky Phantom Game, The,** Milton Bradley, horror, board game, lid shows 3 people and dog looking at Phantom leaning on clock, open trunk holding book and clothes, 1971 . . . . . . **18.00**

**Funny Bones,** Parker Brothers, generic, action game, lid shows jester holding bone, "A Game for People Who Love To Laugh," 1968 . . . . . . . . . . . . . . . . . . **10.00**

**Funny Finger Game,** Ideal, generic, action game, lid shows 4 laughing players with fingers in playing pcs, 1968. . . . . . . . . **16.00**

**Funny Fortunes,** unknown manufacturer, fortune telling, board game, 10$^1/_2$ x 10$^3/_4$", lid shows cat in center of game name, contains teetotum and counters, unknown date . . . . . . . . . . . **40.00**

–G–

**G.I. Joe Combat Infantry! Game,** Hasbro, toy/doll/military, action game, lid shows soldiers with rifles wearing helmets in battle, planes in sky, 1964–65 . . . . . . . **25.00**

**G.I. Joe Commando Attack Game, Official,** Milton Bradley, toy/doll/military/cartoon series, board game, lid shows 4 commandos, star in name, and 2 boys at large gameboard, "A Real American Hero," 1985 . . . **10.00**

**G.I. Joe Marine Paratroop! Game,** Hasbro, toy/doll/military, action game, lid shows soldiers parachuting from planes and soldiers who have landed carrying rifles, 1965. . . . . . . . . . . . **40.00**

**G–Men,** Milton Bradley, mystery, card game, 5$^1/_2$ x 4 x $^7/_8$",

*Game of the States*

No. 4641, Carolyn Wells writer, lid shows game name above 5 picture insets including one of man wearing hat, 1936. . . . . . . **25.00**

**Gambler,** Parker Brothers, game of chance, board game, lid shows hand holding "Lottery" card and 4 gambling cards, "Moment of Madness, Off to the Races, Sweepstakes," and "Even Steven," 1977. . . . . . . . . . . . . **7.00**

**Gamblers Golf,** Gammon Games, sports, board game, lid shows 2 golfers, one wearing peaked hat holding tee flag, 1975 . . . . . **12.00**

**Game of the States,** Milton Bradley, educational, board game, lid shows color illustration of the US, box contains colored paper money, cards, plastic and wooden playing pieces, 1975 *see illus.* . . . . . . . . . . . . . **8.00**
*see also The States, Game of*

**Games People Play Game, The,** Alpsco, book, board game, lid shows book cover by Eric Berne and 6 circles with 2 crossed lines, 1967. . . . . . . . . . . . . . . **15.00**

**Gang Way For Fun Game,** *see Broadside, Gang Way For Fun*

**Gardner's Championship Golf,** *see Championship Golf, Gardner's*

**Garfield,** Parker Brothers, comic strip character, board game, lid shows 3 comic strip scenes, 1981 . . . . . . . . . . . . . . . . . . **8.00**

**Garroway's Game of Possessions,** Reco, TV celebrity/educational, board game, lid shows Garroway and bowtie, US map bottom right corner, and "NBC"

*Gavitt's Stock Exchange*

bottom left corner, endorsed by
Dave Garroway, 1955 . . . . . . .    **40.00**
**Gavitt's Stock Exchange,**
W.W. Gavitt Printing and
Publishing Co., business/Wall
Street, card game, $3^1/_2$ x $2^1/_2$ x
$^3/_4$", "The Great College and
Society Card Game...Corner the
Burlesque Stock Market," letter-
ing on lid includes copyright
and patent dates, mfg name,
and address as "Three Buildings,
Topeka, Kansas, USA," ©1903
*see illus* . . . . . . . . . . . . . . . . .    **15.00**
• Reissued, lettering on lid
includes trademark and copy-
right info ©1904 . . . . . . . . . .    **12.00**
**Gene Autry's Dude Ranch Game,**
*see Dude Ranch Game*
**General Hospital, The Game of,**
Cardinal, TV/soap opera/med-
ical/role playing, board game,
lid shows hospital, 1982 . . . . . .    **18.00**
**Genuine Streamer Quoits,** Milton
Bradley, sports, skill game,
$13^1/_2$ x $7^1/_4$", lid shows game
name in grid, game pcs, and
wavy lines background, contains 2 wooden bases, 2 wood-
en 4" poles, and 8 rope quoits,
c1924 . . . . . . . . . . . . . . . . . .    **20.00**
**GEO–Graphy World Wide,**
Cadaco–Ellis, educational,
board game, lid shows men and

women holding sticks on shapes
representing geographical parts
of the world, spinner, timer, and
game name across top, "A
Cadaco–Ellis Educational
bottom right corner, contains
spinner and timer, 1954 . . . . . .    **18.00**
**GEO–Graphy, World Wide,**
Cadaco, educational, board
game, cover shows men and
women holding sticks on shapes
representing geographical parts
of the world, spinner, timer, and
game name in small box top
right hand corner, contains spin-
ner and timer, 1958 . . . . . . . .    **15.00**
**Geographical Cards, Improved,**
Peter G. Thomson, educational,
card game, $5^3/_4$ x $4^3/_4$ x $1^1/_2$", lid
has game name and mfg info in
rectangular shapes and small
circle in bottom left corner,
©1883 . . . . . . . . . . . . . . . . . .    **15.00**
**Geography Game,** A. Flanagan
Co., educational, card game,
$5^3/_4$ x $4^1/_{16}$ x $1^1/_{16}$", lid shows
woman in long dress pointing to
globe and 3 small children
standing, by Harriet B. Rogers,
c1910s . . . . . . . . . . . . . . . . . .    **20.00**
**Geography Up To Date,** Parker
Brothers, educational, card
game, $6^3/_4$ x $5^1/_4$", lid shows
3 buildings, 3 men, and cow,
game name in cloud at top,
contains 48 cards, c1890 . . . . .    **15.00**
**George of the Jungle,** Parker
Brothers, generic, board game,
Tarzan spoof, lid shows character drawings of Tarzan tackling
alligator and other animals and
woman, 1968 . . . . . . . . . . . . .    **50.00**
**George Washington's Dream,**
Parker Brothers, generic, reading
game, $7^1/_2$ x $4^5/_8$", lid shows oval
inset with man in colonial dress
pushing elevator button, profile
head of man in colonial hat
outside inset, "A Reading
Game," contains colored printed
cards, advertising card, and
instruction and reading booklet,
c1899 . . . . . . . . . . . . . . . . . .    **20.00**

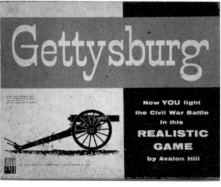

*Gettysburg*

**Ges–it Game,** Knapp Electric, Inc.
(Division of P.R. Mallory),
educational, board game, cover
shows numerous figures in dif-
ferent activities and dress, "The
Where Are They...What Are
They...What Do They
Do...Game," c1894–1929 . . . .    **40.00**

**"Get Smart" Mini Board Card
Game,** Ideal, TV/spy comedy,
board card game, lid shows
man with legs up holding gun,
woman seated with one shoe
off, and dog with smoking
bomb in mouth, 1965 . . . . . . .    **25.00**

**"Get Smart" The Exploding Time
Bomb Game,** Ideal, TV/spy
comedy, board game, lid shows
man wearing belted coat and tie
talking on phone and holding
rifle, roadster and exploding
building in background, 1965. .    **75.00**

• Second lid shows 4 men in different hats and outfits, time
bomb split in half next to
game name, and strip on right
with inset of man talking on
phone and time bomb over-
head, 1965 . . . . . . . . . . . . .    **75.00**

**Get That License,** Selchow &
Righter, automobile, board
game, lid shows license plates
from various states including
Vermont and Wyoming, "The
License Plate Game," 1955. . . .    **30.00**

**Get The Message,** Milton Bradley,
TV/quiz, board game, lid shows
1 messenger boy with bike and
second messenger boy and
woman with apron carrying
signs with game name and mes-
sages, striped background,
"Another Great TV Home
Game," 1964 . . . . . . . . . . . . .    **12.00**

**Getaway Chase Game,** DX (AMF),
auto racing, combination slot
car racing action and board
game, lid shows 2 old autos
with large headlights on city
street and 2 youngsters playing
game, contains 41 pcs, 1970s    **65.00**

**Gettysburg,** Avalon Hill, board
game, educational, box contains
fold–out gameboard, die, cards,
battle manual, counters, and
instructions, 1958 *see illus* . . . .    **25.00**

**Ghost Gun,** Hasbro, mystery,
action game, lid shows boy
holding Ghost Gun and loaded
target strip flashing ghost target
on wall, 1974. . . . . . . . . . . . .    **55.00**

**Ghosts!,** Milton Bradley, mystery,
quiz game, lid shows flying
ghosts and bats, "Creepy, Sneaky
Guess Who Game," 1985 . . . . .    **8.00**

**Giant Wheel Cowboys 'N Indians,**
Remco, western, lid shows game
name in rope framed oval and 3
game players, 1 wearing cowboy hat and holster, spinner on
left side, 1958 . . . . . . . . . . . .    **42.00**

**Giant Wheel Thrills & Spills
Horse Race Game,** Remco,
sports, lid shows 3 children with
playing surface on the floor,
3 horses on race track, and spin-
ner on left, 1958 . . . . . . . . . .    **55.00**

**Gidget Fortune Teller Game,**
Milton Bradley, TV/fortune
telling, card game, lid shows
Gidget talking on phone and
picture cards of woman dressed
in gown, ice skater, cheerleader,
and surfer, 1966. . . . . . . . . . .    **30.00**

**Gilligan, The New Adventures of,**
Milton Bradley, TV/comedy,
board game, 3–dimensional
board, lid shows Gilligan on
shoulders of man wearing hat
surrounded by group of people,
"A Set Up and Play Game,"
playing surface inset bottom
right corner, 1974. . . . . . . . . .    **20.00**

**Gilligan's Island Game,** Game
Gems/T Cohn, TV/comedy,
board game, lid shows 2 men
and Gilligan in floating tub, fish
at base of tub, 1964 . . . . . . . .    **75.00**
• Same cover dated 1965 . . . . . .    **150.00**
**Go Back,** Milton Bradley, generic,
action floor game, lid shows
boys and girls on game squares
with horseshoe pictures, contains indoor/outdoor vinyl pads,
1967 . . . . . . . . . . . . . . . . . .    **12.00**
**Go Bang,** Milton Bradley,
No. 4162, generic, board game,
$8^7/_8$ x $8^7/_8$ x $^5/_8$", lid shows girl in
hat watching dynamite explode,
c1890s . . . . . . . . . . . . . . . . .    **35.00**
**Go For Broke,** Selchow & Righter,
business, board game, lid shows
man with top hat and monocle
in circle throwing money,
"$" signs in top 2 corners,
Money" in bottom 2 corners,
"The Game of Spend A Million,"
1965 . . . . . . . . . . . . . . . . . . .    **12.00**
**Go For The Green!,** Time Inc.,
sports, action  game, lid shows
golfers on golf course, sand
traps, ocean, sandy beach, and
mountains, "Sports Illustrated"
at top, 1973 . . . . . . . . . . . . . .    **20.00**
**Go To The Head of The Class,**
Milton Bradley, Series 7, educational, board game, lid shows
rolled diploma, graduate's hat,
and blackboard with game
name, 1955 . . . . . . . . . . . . . .    **10.00**
• Series 10, cover reissued, 1957.    **18.00**
**Go To The Head of The Class,**
Milton Bradley, New Series 17,
educational, board game, lid
shows man, woman, boy, and
girl at gameboard, 1967 . . . . . .    **8.00**
**Goat, Game of,** Milton Bradley,
No. 4728, generic, card game,
$5^1/_2$ x 4", lid shows goat's head
in circle, "Play It and Be Glad,
Made in USA," game number at
bottom left corner, and mfg info
bottom right corner, contains
60 cards, ©1916 . . . . . . . . . . .    **15.00**
**Godfather Game, The,** Family
Games, book/movie, board
game, Original Edition came in

violin case with name on pic-
ture resembling gun, 1971 . . . .    **45.00**
• Second version in rectangular
box with game name on gun
within violin shape, "An Adult
Game," 1971 . . . . . . . . . . . . .    **8.00**
**Godzilla Game,** Ideal, movie
monster, board game, lid shows
fire–breathing monster and
burned out city, 1963 . . . . . . . .    **250.00**
• Same cover, 1964. . . . . . . . . .    **175.00**
**Godzilla Game,** Mattel, monster,
board game, lid shows monster
with spaceship in mouth and
inset of 3 youngsters playing
game, 1978 . . . . . . . . . . . . . .    **35.00**
**Going! Going! Gone!,** Milton
Bradley, auction, action game,
lid shows items for sale at flea
market, 1975 . . . . . . . . . . . . .    **15.00**
**Going Hollywood,** Hollywood
Game Co., celebrity, board
game, "2 Games in One," lid
shows game name and camera
in circles and Hollywood pho-
tographs, 1943 . . . . . . . . . . . .    **35.00**
**Going to Jerusalem,** Parker
Brothers, religious, board game,
"Bible Game Based on the
New Testament," 2–tone lid
shows biblical pictures and
sights, 1955 . . . . . . . . . . . . . .    **20.00**
**Going to Market,** Beech–Nut
Packing Co., advertising, card
game, lid advertises Welch's
products, shows punch bowl
and ingredients for Welch
Punch, contains 52 cards with
product logos and advertise-
ments, ©1915 . . . . . . . . . . . .    **110.00**
**Gold Hunters, The,** Parker
Brothers, adventure, board
game, $13^3/_4$" sq, circle at bottom
left of lid shows 3 men, tools,
and tent, 1 man pointing, 1 sift-
ing for gold, circle wreath at top
right corner shows man with
gun and dog, middle of lid
shows mountains and river, "A
Game of Adventure," contains
colored wooden counters and
spinner, c1902 . . . . . . . . . . . .    **190.00**
**Gold Trail,** Hasbro, generic, skill
game, lid shows circular playing

*Game of Golf*

area, inset of kneeling cowboy
with cactus and mountains in
background, 1966 . . . . . . . . .    **15.00**
**Goldfinger, James Bond 007
Game,** Milton Bradley, movie,
board game, "Goldfinger" in
black letters against gold background over 10 inset pictures,
1966 . . . . . . . . . . . . . . . . . .    **40.00**
**Golf, Game of,** McLoughlin
Brothers, sports, board game,
13$^1/_2$ x 15$^1/_2$", lid shows
3 women wearing hats and long
dresses with lace collars carrying golf clubs, contains wooden
playing pcs, round wooden
counters, and spinner, wooden
box, ©1896 *see illus* . . . . . . . .    **900.00**
**Golf, The Game of,** Clark &
Sowdon, sports, board game,
Tokalon Series, No. 352,
19 x 10$^1/_2$", lid shows men and
women in long skirts playing
game, 1 woman swinging club,
1 with hand on hip, men wearing hats and high boots, contains wooden counters and
cardboard spinner, c1905 . . . . .    **200.00**
**Golf, The Game of,** J.H. Singer,
sports, board game, lid shows
man wearing hat, knickers, and
high socks swinging golf club,
flag in background, c1898 . . . .    **120.00**
**Golliwogg,** Milton Bradley, book,
card game, lid shows hairy
black character wearing bowtie
and long jacket bending over
while standing on wooden plat-

form, contains 39 cards, based
on character in books by Bertha
Upton, rare black collectible,
1907 . . . . . . . . . . . . . . . . . . .    **175.00**
**Gomer Pyle Game,** Transogram,
TV/military comedy, board
game, lid shows Pyle, soldier in
jeep, and sergeant with hands
on hips looking at soldier hold-
ing mop, 1964 . . . . . . . . . . . .    **35.00**
**Gong Show, The,** American,
TV/quiz, action game, lid
shows game name in starburst
design, 4 inset pictures including woman, man in hat, and
man wearing a tuxedo, 1977 . .    **20.00**
**Good Ol' Charlie Brown,** Milton
Bradley, comic strip, board
game, lid shows Charlie Brown
with outstretched arms, 1971 . .    **18.00**
**Good Old Aunt, The,** McLoughlin
Brothers, generic, pooling game,
10$^1/_2$" sq, lid shows game name
in horseshoe framing woman's
face wearing old fashioned night
cap and curled locks, "A
Pleasing Game," contains spinner, 40 white counters, and 20
red counters, ©1892 . . . . . . . .    **150.00**
**"Goodbye, Mr Chips" Game,**
Parker Brothers, movie, board
game, lid shows man wearing
graduate's hat and gown running
in front of campus buildings,
1969 . . . . . . . . . . . . . . . . . . .    **28.00**
**Gooses Wild,** Co-5 Co., game of
chance, dice game, lid shows
flying goose, dice, numbered
cards, and "Pot," 1966 . . . . . . .    **5.00**
**Grab A Loop,** Milton Bradley,
generic, action game, lid shows
5 laughing shoeless players,
"The Game That Really Grabs
You" in circle held by hand at
top, 1968. . . . . . . . . . . . . . . .    **15.00**
**Grand National,** Whitman, horse
racing, board game, lid shows
jockeys on horses, "A Sweepstakes Game of Chance" and
currency, contains dice, money,
and counters, 1937 . . . . . . . . .    **30.00**
**Grand National Steeple Chase,
The,** Spears Games, horse racing, board game, lid shows
2 horses in horseshoe frame,

1 white horse with rider in striped shirt, "Edition De Luxe," 1920s . . . . . . . . . . . . . . . . .    **30.00**

**Grand Slam, The Game of (And Many Other Games),** Whitman Publishing Co., generic, card game, lid shows deck of cards and pencil, "54 Cards of Playing Card Quality," c1930–32 . . . . .    **15.00**

**Grand Slam Game,** Ideal, generic, skill and action game, lid shows 2 boys and 2 girls playing game, 3 players on knees, 1 boy with hands on head, 1969    **22.00**

**Grande Auto Race,** unknown manufacturer, auto racing, board/track game, board has game name in middle of oval track, racing cars in 4 corners, unknown date . . . . . . . . . . .    **15.00**

**Grandma's Game of Useful Knowledge,** Milton Bradley, No. 4931, educational, quiz game, 6¼ x 8¼", lid shows man smoking pipe seated in chair with feet above kettle, number and "Made in U.S.A." in bottom left corner, contains 100 question cards, c1910 . . . . . . . . . .    **22.00**

**Grandmama's Improved Arithmetical Game,** McLoughlin Brothers, educational, card game, 4½ x 6¼", lid shows elderly woman wearing cap seated in chair, 1 girl on lap, other wearing dunce cap seated on stool, and boy writing at blackboard, 1887 . . . . . . . . . .    **35.00**

**Grandmama's Improved Geographical Game,** McLoughlin Brothers, educational, card game, 6¼ x 4½", lid shows people watching woman holding Egyptian geography picture, "The World of McLoughlin Bros N.Y.," 1887 . . . . . . . . . . . . . .    **30.00**

**Grandmama's Sunday Game: Bible Questions, Old Testament,** McLoughlin Brothers, religious/educational, quiz game, 4½ x 6¼", lid shows man

with long hair atop beast with paws on tree, contains 100 cards and answer booklet, ©1887 . . . . . . . . . . . . . . . .    **30.00**

**Gray Ghost,** Transogram, TV/military, board game, lid shows Confederate soldier and flag and uniformed men on horses, 1958    **50.00**

**Grease,** Milton Bradley, movie/musical, board game, lid shows records and movie's stars in square inset, 1978 . . . . . . . . .    **40.00**

**Great Escape, The,** Ideal, generic, action/board game, lid shows 2 boys and girl playing game, 2 players holding cards, 1967 . .    **18.00**

**Great Grape Ape Game, The,** Milton Bradly, TV/comedy, board game, 3–dimensional board, lid shows clothed ape with stripes on sleeves looking at smaller character, 1975 . . . . .    **20.00**

**Green Acres Game, The,** Standard Toykraft, TV/western comedy, board game, lid with show's stars, man holding briefcase leaning on fence, and mailbox, 1965 . . . . . . . . . . . . . . . . . .    **45.00**

**Green Ghost Game,** Transogram, mystery, board game, lid shows players at large playing surface and playing pcs, contains raised glow–in–the–dark gameboard, 1965 . . . . . . . . . . . . . . . . . .    **80.00**

**Green Hornet Quick Switch Game,** Milton Bradley, mystery, board game, lid shows man in raincoat and hat with gun, 5 action pictures, 2 arrows form circle around "Quick Switch Game," 1966 . . . . . . . . . . . . .    **250.00**

**Guess Again,** Milton Bradley, generic, electric quiz game, lid shows girl with playing surface and boy holding card, "Lights Show Whether You Guess Right or Wrong," 1967 . . . . . . . . . .    **15.00**

**Guided Missile Navy Game,** Milton Bradley, military, board game, lid shows ships at sea, air battle, 1964 . . . . . . . . . . . . . .    **15.00**

*Gunsmoke*

**Gumby and Pokey Playful Trails,** Co–5, animated character, board game, lid shows cartoon Gumby wearing hat and riding horse, 1968 . . . . . . . . . . . . . . . **55.00**

**Gumby Game, The,** Milton Bradley, animated character, board game, lid shows Gumby and friends in open car with 1 friend peeping out from behind bushes, 1988 . . . . . . . . **12.00**

**Gunsmoke,** Lowell, TV/western, board game, lid with show star James Arness with gun, covered wagon, mountains, and cactus in background, 1958 *see illus.* . **55.00**

**Guru,** E.S. Lowe, strategy, board game, "The Think Game for Swingers of All Ages," lid shows game name, gameboard, and playing pcs in circle, 1969 . . . . **22.00**

**Gusher,** Carrom Industries, business/oil industry, board game, lid shows gusher surrounded by coins and currency, "Win A Million," mfg info bottom strip, "Made In USA," 1946 . . . . . . . **75.00**

**Gypsy Fortune Teller, Game of,** Milton Bradley, No. 4271, fortune telling, board game, $6^3/_4$ x $5^1/_2$ x 1", lid has game name in circle surrounded by 8 smaller circles, ribbon border, c1922 . . . . . . . . . . . . . . . . . **10.00**

**–H–**

**H.R. Pufnstuf Game,** Milton Bradley, TV/children's action show, board game, lid has inset pictures of woman wearing pointed hat with umbrella, man

*The Hand of Fate*

in boat wearing hat, and boy surrounded by cartoon characters, 1971 . . . . . . . . . . . . . . . **20.00**

**Hair Bear Bunch Game, The,** Milton Bradley, TV/cartoon, board game, lid has cartoon drawings of 2 men watching animal coming over wall and 2 animals emerging from manhole, 1971 . . . . . . . . . . . . . . . **20.00**

**Halma,** E.I. Horsman, strategy, board game, separate board and pcs box, $5^1/_2$ x 4", lid shows gladiator with armor and sword in circle, copyright info center bottom, contains 64 wooden pawns, 19 each of 2 colors and 13 each of 2 colors, forerunner of Chinese Checkers, G.H. Monks inventor, pat May 29, 1888, ©1885 . . . . . . . . . . . . . **40.00**

**Halma, The Famous Game of,** Parker Brothers, strategy, board game, pcs box has picture of gladiator with sword and shield, mfg info and address at bottom right, 1915 . . . . . . . . . . . . . . . **30.00**

**Halma, The Famous Game of,** Parker Brothers, generic, board game, lid has rectangle on left side with spiral strip holding part of game name, "Halma" in large letters, 1938 . . . . . . . . . . **25.00**

**Hand of Fate, The,** McLoughlin Brothers, fortune telling, board game, cover shows bats, black cats, owl, and figure with point-

ed hat holding book, 1901
*see illus.* . . . . . . . . . . . . . . . . . . **1,000.00**

**Hand of Fate, The,** Parker
Brothers, fortune telling, board
game, 13¹/₄ x 11¹/₂ x 1¹/₄", lid
shows tree, woman on her
knees holding hand of woman
wearing hat with feather, and
third woman looking on, lighthouse and ship in background,
c1910 . . . . . . . . . . . . . . . . . **55.00**

**Hands Down,** Ideal, generic,
action game, cover shows 4 sets
of hands pressing levers on
playing pc, the
"Slam–O–Matic," 1964 . . . . . . **15.00**

**Hands Up Harry,** Transogram,
western, action game, lid shows
target of cowpoke with mustache holding 2 guns, cactus
and cowpoke with hat blown
off and gun in the air background, "Showdown at the
Circle T," "Sturdy Plastic and
Masonite With Western Gun
and Safety Darts!," 1964. . . . . . **45.00**

**Hang on Harvey! Game,** Ideal,
board game, cover shows
boy playing game, placing
peg in clear playing surface to
make Harvey scale down wall,
1969 . . . . . . . . . . . . . . . . . . **20.00**

**Hangman,** Milton Bradley, gener-
ic, word game, cover has
Vincent Price holding noose,
"A Classic American Game for
Two," 1976 . . . . . . . . . . . . . **10.00**

**Happiness, Game of,** Milton
Bradley, generic, board game,
cover shows 3 players and playing surface with currency,
"Mod" art, and plastic pcs, and
woman wearing turtleneck shirt,
1972 . . . . . . . . . . . . . . . . . . **10.00**

**Happy Days,** Parker Brothers, TV/
comedy, board game, cover
shows The Fonz and friends,
motorcycle, and banner with
letter "J," 1976 . . . . . . . . . . . **15.00**

**Happy Face,** Milton Bradley,
generic, board game, lid shows
6 children holding 6 cards with
smiling, sad, hiding, funny, crying, and happy facial expres-

sions, game name in mask
shape, 1968 . . . . . . . . . . . . . . **15.00**

**Happy Landing,** Transogram, aviation, board game, lid shows circle inset of family playing game
and prop plane with game name
on wing flying over airport,
1938 . . . . . . . . . . . . . . . . . . **25.00**

**Happy Little Train Game, The,**
Milton Bradley, railroading,
board game, lid shows dressed
rabbit watching toy train with
smiling face engine traveling on
curved track, 1957 . . . . . . . . . **10.00**

**Hardy Boys Game, The,** Milton
Bradley, TV/book, board game,
lid shows square insets of
4 male faces, 1 Afro–American,
and 4 square insets of underwater diver with harpoon, musical
group with dancing girl, 2 men
and ship, and man with lantern
looking at big treasure chest,
1970 . . . . . . . . . . . . . . . . . . **20.00**

**Hardy Boys Treasure Game, Walt
Disney's,** Disney, book, board
game, cover shows 2 boys wearing checkered shirts with rolled
up sleeves looking at bag of
treasure, 1957 . . . . . . . . . . . **20.00**

**Harlem Globetrotters Game,**
Milton Bradley, TV/sports/black
collectibles, board game, lid
shows Globetrotters basketball
team running with the ball,
1971 . . . . . . . . . . . . . . . . . . **15.00**

**Harpoon,** Gabriel, sports/spear
fishing, board game, lid shows
men rowing boat and man with
harpoon aimed at jumping
whale, ship in background, contains miniature whales, 1955 . . **25.00**

**Hashimoito–San Game,** Transogram, 1963, TV/cartoon characters, Hector Heathcote Show,
board game, lid shows mice,
2 Japanese women, 1 with fan,
and mice, 1 in Japanese clothes,
"The Japanese House Mouse,"
1963 . . . . . . . . . . . . . . . . . . **30.00**

**Hats' Off,** Kohner, generic, action
game, lid shows family flipping
hats into 4–section playing sur-
face, 1967 . . . . . . . . . . . . . . **15.00**

*Have Gun Will Travel*

**Hats Off Bowling Game,**
Transogram, sports, action
game, outdoor scene on cover
shows 4 children, bowling
alley, bowling ball, and bowling
pins with clown hats, game
name alongside bowling alley,
1944 . . . . . . . . . . . . . . . . .     **28.00**

**Haunted House,** Ideal,
horror/treasure hunt, board
game, lid shows flying bats and
moon, "Thrills—Chills—Exciting
Play for Hidden Treasure," playing surface is house with trap
doors, secret passages, and
jewel in attic, 1962 . . . . . . . .     **60.00**

**Haunted Mansion Game, Walt
Disney World,** Disney, board
game, 3–dimensional, lid shows
3 youngsters playing game at
table, haunted house, flying
bats, ghosts, and gravestone in
background, Walt Disney World
logo lid top, 1980s. . . . . . . . .     **35.00**

**Have Gun Will Travel,** Parker
Brothers, TV/western, board
game, cover shows Richard
Boone in cowboy hat at top of
signature card with game name
and "Wire Paladin, San
Francisco," desert scene with
cactus, 1959 *see illus* . . . . . . .     **60.00**

**Have–U "It?,"** Selchow & Righter,
celebrity/film, card game,
7³/₄ x 5³/₄ x 1", based on Clara
Bow, the "IT" girl from film *IT*,
lid has "IT?" in quotation marks
and very large letters, copyright
info bottom left corner, mfg info
below letter "T," ©1924 . . . . . .     **22.00**

**Hawaiian Eye,** Lowell, TV/detec-
tive, board game, lid shows
3 men's faces in circles, wooden

sculpture mask at left, "Every
Play a Challenge of Wits and
Skill," mfg info and logo bottom
right corner, faces of man and
woman wearing graduate hats
and age recommendation in top
right corner, 1963 . . . . . . . . . .     **80.00**

**Hawaiian Punch Game,** Mattel,
advertising, board game, cover
shows sketch of man wearing
flowered shirt, fruit drink mascot holding glass of punch,
youngsters playing game inset,
1978 . . . . . . . . . . . . . . . . . . .     **12.00**

**Headache,** Kohner, generic, dice
game, lid shows multicolored
domes with sketch drawings of
smiling faces, arms, and legs,
includes Pop–O–Matic for
rolling dice, sturdy plastic game
board, 1968 . . . . . . . . . . . . . .     **8.00**

**Hearts,** Parker Brothers, generic,
letter game, lid shows dice
spilling from cup, letters of
game name in individual hearts,
1940 . . . . . . . . . . . . . . . . . . .     **7.00**

**Hearts,** Parker Brothers, generic,
letter game, lid shows 3–dimensional blocks with letters of
game name, 6 small hearts on
either side of mfg name, 1960. .     **5.00**

**Hector Heathcote Game,** Transogram, cartoon, board game,
lid shows running cartoon character wearing large hat looking
at pocket watch and carrying
rifle, and 3 marching men
in high boots carrying rifles,
1963 . . . . . . . . . . . . . . . . . . .     **70.00**

**Hee Haw,** Dooley Fant, Inc.,
TV/ comedy, board game, lid
shows game name on wooden
board, and playing surface,
1975 . . . . . . . . . . . . . . . . . . .     **15.00**

**Heidi Elevator Game,** Remco,
TV/doll/book, board game, lid
shows Heidi Pocketbook Doll in
front of "Up" and "Down" ele-
vators, elevator man in "Up"
car, 1965 . . . . . . . . . . . . . . . .     **20.00**

**Helps to History or Historical
Games With Cards,** A. Flanagan,
educational, card game,
4¹/₈ x 3⁵/₈ x 1", lid info includes
"On the History of the United

*Heroes of America*

States, by D. Eckley Hunter,"
mfg info, and publisher, 1885 . .    **22.00**

**Hen That Laid the Golden Egg,
The,** Parker Brothers, generic,
board game, 14$^1/_2$ x 16$^1/_2$", lid
shows 3 hens and nest of eggs
in fence, contains spinner, 4
hens, and 24 eggs, wooden box,
©1900. . . . . . . . . . . . . . . . . .    **250.00**

**Hendrik Van Loon's Wide World
Game,** Parker Brothers, travel,
board game, lid shows planes,
ships, and mountain, mfg info in
small rectangle at bottom, based
on famous author, 1933 . . . . . .    **45.00**

**Heroes of America,** Paul
Educational Games, education-
al, board game, lid shows
American Flag, "Games of the
Nations," mfg info, and
Wyoming and Ohio, c1920s
*see illus*. . . . . . . . . . . . . . . . .    **25.00**

**Hexagons,** Clement Toy Co.,
generic, puzzle game, lid shows
2 men seated at table playing
game, woman watching, fireplace in background, mfg info
at lid top below game name,
contains 18 moveable wooden
puzzle parts in oak frame and
instruction sheet, 1924 . . . . . . .    **50.00**

**Hexed,** Tryne Games, mystery,
puzzle game, lid shows game
name in banner held by ghost,
1960 . . . . . . . . . . . . . . . . . . .    **10.00**

**Hey Pa, There's A Goat on the
Roof,** Parker Brothers, generic,
board game, 3–dimensional,
cover shows goat on barn roof,
1965 . . . . . . . . . . . . . . . . . .    **30.00**

**Hi–Ho Cherry–Ho,** Whitman,
generic, board game, lid shows
2 seated girls and boy playing
plastic cherry–picking game,
single and multi–stem cherries
border, 1960 . . . . . . . . . . . . .    **5.00**

**Hi–Ho Santa Claus Game,**
Whitman, holiday, board game,
cover by Sarah Winship shows
Santa pointing to multicolored
game spinner, "It's Fun" on toy
spinner top, contains plastic
ornaments, 1962 . . . . . . . . . .    **8.00**

**HI–Q,** Kohner, brain twister,
board game, lid shows game
playing surface with circle insets
in corners, arrows pointing to
holes for jumping pcs, "The
New Game Craze," 1960s . . . .    **35.00**

**HI–Q,** Tryne, brain twister, puzzle
game, lid shows "A Puzzle
Game" above rectangle with
game name in quotation marks,
mfg info at bottom, 1950s . . . . .    **25.00**

**Hialeah Horse Racing Game,**
Milton Bradley, horse racing,
board game, lid shows 4 jockeys
riding horses, numbers 2, 4 and
5 visible on blankets, red and
white striped tower in back-
ground, 1940s . . . . . . . . . . . .    **35.00**

**Hickety Pickety,** Parker Brothers,
generic, board game, 10$^3/_4$ x
12", lid shows 4 circular nests
and 3 hens, "A Game" in center
ring, contains spinner, 24 wood-
en eggs, 6 each yellow, red,
blue, and green, 1924 . . . . . . .    **40.00**

**Hickety Pickety,** Parker Brothers,
generic, board game, lid shows
2 hens and 4 circles resembling
nests with eggs, contains wood-
en eggs, 1954 . . . . . . . . . . . .    **30.00**

**Hidden Titles,** Parker Brothers,
generic, card game, 6$^1/_8$ x 5$^1/_8$ x
1", cover shows game name and
mfg info including Salem, Mass.,
New York, and London loca-
tions, c1910s . . . . . . . . . . . . .    **15.00**

**Hide N' Thief,** Whitman, generic,
action game, lid shows thief
with large eyes wearing checkered hat carrying bag with "$"
sign, 2 thieves with money bags,
1 other thief, and 2 houses, inset

*High Bid*

in bottom right corner shows
game players, "Surprise Game
of Hide & Seek," 1965 . . . . . . .    **10.00**

**High Bid,** 3M, auction, board
game, lid shows auctioneer
behind lectern pointing to bidding item held by another man,
backs of seated bidders, and
woman with raised hand, auction goods in background, 1965
*see illus* . . . . . . . . . . . . . . . .    **10.00**

**High Gear Game,** Mattel, generic, board game, lid shows playing surface, cogs of "mechanical
maneuver game," and 5 players
including man in vest and child
in overalls standing on tiptoes,
"You Can Tell Its Mattel...It's
Swell," 1962 . . . . . . . . . . . . .    **20.00**

**High Spirits With Calvin And The
Colonel, Game of,** Milton
Bradley, generic/animated characters, board game, lid shows
3 drawings of animated chara-
caters atop letters "I" in game
name, 1 on left laughing with
arms outstretched, 1962 . . . . .    **42.00**

**Highway Patrol,** Bell, TV/detec-
tive, board game, lid with show
star Broderick Crawford wearing
hat and holding wired microphone, police car in chase, and
helicopter, 1959. . . . . . . . . . .    **40.00**

**Hill's Spelling Blocks,** S.L. Hill,
No. 4A, educational, block
game, wooden box with slide

cover, 6" sq, lid shows group of
women, 2 small girls, toy house
in bottom left corner, and game
number in lid center, contains
16 litho wooden blocks with
pictures and letters, first patent
issued 1858, 1872 . . . . . . . . .    **370.00**

**Hip Flip,** Parker Brothers, generic
action game, group of boys and
girls playing game on cover, balloons in background, wavy
game name letters, "Swinging
Game for Swinging People,"
1968 . . . . . . . . . . . . . . . . . .    **10.00**

**Hippety–Hop,** Corey Games,
generic, board game, lid shows
group of characters including
dog running past sign post with
game name, "A New Children's
Game," 1940 . . . . . . . . . . . .    **32.00**

**Hippodrome, The,** E.O. Clark,
Tokalon Series, circus, board
game, 19¹/₂ x 10¹/₄", lid shows
circus acts including ballerina
standing on horse, clown juggling balls, and elephant wearing hat, 3 masks at bottom center, contains 3 tiddledys and
winks, c1900 . . . . . . . . . . . . .    **60.00**

**Hippopotamus,** Remco, generic,
electric puzzle game, lid shows
two hippos face–to–face, mfg
name at top center, 1961 . . . . .    **20.00**

**History Up To Date,** Parker
Brothers, educational, card
game, 6³/₈ x 5¹/₄", lid shows soldiers with cannons, battle scene,
1 standing soldier pointing with
left hand, c1904 . . . . . . . . . .    **22.00**

**Hit the Beach, American
Heritage,** Milton Bradley,
Command Decision Series, military, board game, lid shows soldiers on beach, bursts of gunfire,
trees at left, and circle of 5 stars
bottom right corner, 1965 . . . . .    **35.00**

**Hobbit Game, The,** Milton
Bradley, TV/book, board game,
lid shows 4 youngsters playing
game, "MB" logo top left corner,
"The Adventures of Bilbo in
Middle–Earth" from "The Lord of
the Rings," 1978. . . . . . . . . . .    **18.00**

**Hocus Pocus,** Transogram, magic,
action game, lid shows 4 players

*Hollywood Movie Bingo*

watching rabbits pop from hat, "Glows in the Dark," 1968 . . . .    **40.00**

**Hogan's Heroes Bluff Out Game,** Transogram, TV/military, board game, cover shows saluting soldiers in various uniforms, 1 soldier pointing and smiling, 1966 . . . . . . . . . . . . . . . . . .    **65.00**

**Hokum,** Parker Brothers, generic, card game, 8¼ x 6¼", cover shows jester with playing board and pcs, "A Great Fun Making Game," Bingo type game, trademark and patent number below game name, contains numbered cards, numbered yellow disks, and round red markers, ©1927 . . . . . . . . . . . . . .    **15.00**

**Hold The Fort,** Parker Brothers, military strategy, board game, 15¼ x 13", lid shows Civil War scene, soldiers attacking fort and carrying flag, soldier inset top right corner, ©1895 . . . . . .    **250.00**

**Hold Up On The Overland Trail Game,** Transogram, TV/western, board game, cover with show stars William Boyd and Doug McClure, background of Indians watching cowboys on horseback going through pass, 1960 . . . . . . . . . . . . . . . . . .    **45.00**

**Holly Hobbie Wishing Well Game,** Parker Brothers, greeting card character, board game, woman's bonnet on cover, 1976 . . . . . . . . . . . . . . . . . .    **12.00**

**Hollywood Movie Bingo,** Whitman Publishing Co., movie stars, card game, 9½ x 6⅝ x 1", No. 3046, Bingo type game, lid shows film projectors and backs of 2 seated men, "The Game of the Movie Stars," contains spinner, cards, and disks, 1937 *see illus* . . . . . . . . . . . . . . . . .    **40.00**

**Hollywood Squares,** Ideal, TV/game show, quiz game, lid shows people seated behind panels in 9 squares, smiling male with logo on jacket pocket on right, 1974 . . . . . . . . . . . .    **10.00**

**Hollywood Squares, The,** Whitman, TV/game show, quiz game, lid shows 9 squares, 5 with faces, "X's" and "O's" on right, 1967 . . . . . . . . . . . . . . . . . .    **12.00**

**Hollywood Stars, The Game of,** Whitman, quiz game, cover shows game name in show production board with striped shutter, man on horseback, 2 women in  gowns, and man in uniform jacket and high boots, ribbon spiral running across lid, 1955 . . . . . . . . . . . . . . . . . .    **10.00**

**Home Fish Pond, The,** McLoughlin Brothers, fishing, skill game, 12" sq, lid shows boy and girl with fishing pole on pond bank and fish in pond, game directions inset at upper right corner, contains 4 wooden poles and numbered fish with wooden supports, c1890. . . . . .    **100.00**

**Home Games,** The Martin Co., generic, 7 game assortment, 12½ x 10", lid shows 2 men, woman in long dress, and child in collared shirt, game name on angle in upper left corner, contains 83 pcs including 2 paper balloons, 15 round wooden lettered disks, 14 wooden colored sticks, metal cup, tape with 2 supports, wooden dice cup with 6 wooden lettered dice, wooden cup, 2 wooden and cardboard paddles, 16 celluloid winks, 4 metal disks, 2 bubble blowers, 4 cardboard rings, and 4 wooden pegs, envelope contains 7 instruction sheets, c1900–05 . . . . . . . . . . . . . . .    **140.00**

*Hop–Over Puzzle*

*Hopalong Cassidy Game*

**Home History Game,** Milton
Bradley, educational, card
game, 5⅝ x 6¾", lid shows
3 men in colonial outfits,
2 playing drums and 1 playing
fife and man on ground with
raised hand, contains white
cards with historical dates,
c1909 . . . . . . . . . . . . . . . . . .                18.00

**Home Team Baseball,** Selchow &
Righter, sports, board game,
lid shows player sliding into
base, catcher on knees, and
umpire, 1974. . . . . . . . . . . . .                12.00

**Honey Bee Game,** Milton
Bradley, generic, board game,
12¼" sq, lid shows boy and dog
running from bees flying from
hive, fence, fields, and buildings
in background, contains
24 round colored metal disks,
large revolving metal disk, and
magnet, c1913. . . . . . . . . . . . .                40.00

**Honey West,** Ideal, detective,
board game, "The Girl Private–
Eye Game," cover shows battling man and woman, seated
man holding head, and 2 figures
in lighted window, mfg logo
bottom right corner, 1965. . . . .                65.00

**Hoopla, The Game of,** Ideal,
generic, skill game, lid shows
players around playing pcs and
hoops on ground, multicolored
"Hoopla" letters, "Fun Filled
Contest of Skill, Suspense and
Action," 1966 . . . . . . . . . . . .                35.00

**Hoot!** Saalfield Publishing Co.,
generic, card game, lid has
game name in center, "Thornton
W. Burgess, Author Bedtime
Stories" top left corner, animal
character cards based on
Burgess stories, contains
52 animal cards and Hooty
card, c1926–28 . . . . . . . . . . .                40.00

**Hop–Over Puzzle,** J. Pressman &
Co., Inc., No. 2992, generic,
skill and strategy game,
6⅝ x 6⅝ x 1½", lid shows numbers 1 through 9 and 2 frogs on
lily pads, mfg info, contains
black and white marbles,
c1930s *see illus* . . . . . . . . . . .                20.00

**Hop–Pop Game,** Schaper, gener-
ic, board game, lid shows
4 children playing game,
"A Lively Game of Funny
Animals Ready to Stalk and
Capture," 1968. . . . . . . . . . . .                15.00

**Hopalong Cassidy Game,** Milton
Bradley, TV/western hero, board
game, cover has man in cowboy
hat on horse holding gun and
wearing sheriff's badge, 1950 . .                60.00

**Hoppity Hooper,** Milton Bradley,
cartoon, board game, lid shows
truck with striped roof, 1 cartoon character holding sign
"Prof Waldo A Big Fake," and
second cartoon character playing horn in front of group with
trees in background, 1965 . . . .                70.00

**Hoppy The Hopparoo, The
Flinstones,** Transogram, TV/car-
toon, board game, lid shows
rabbit carrying present followed
by 5 Flinstone characters,
1965 . . . . . . . . . . . . . . . . . . . .                60.00

**Horse Racing Game, The,** Milton Bradley, horse racing, board game, lid shows 2 jockeys riding horses, 1 horse wearing #4, 1936 . . . . . . . . . . . . . . . .    **40.00**

**Hot Potato,** Remco, generic, action game, cover shows 4 children passing potato and timer on stand, 1959–60s . . . . .    **22.00**

**Hot Property! The Board Game,** Take One Games, film industry, board game, came in film canister with game name in center, "Make the Deals That Make the Movies," 1985 . . . . . . . . . . . .    **18.00**

**Hot Spot, 1–2–3 Game!,** Parker Brothers, generic, board game, lid has 2 circles, 3 dice, and diagonal stripes, 1961 . . . . . . .    **18.00**

**Hot Wheels Wipe–Out Race Game,** Mattel, toy/auto racing, board game, lid shows racing cars, "Hot Wheels" top left , 3 circles in strip on left, 1968 . .    **25.00**

**Hotels,** Milton Bradley, business/ real estate, board game, lid shows game track with highrise buildings, 3–dimensional game of land development and "High Rises and High Stakes," 1987 . .    **18.00**

**Hoth Ice Planet Adventure, Game, Star Wars,** Kenner, movie, board game, lid shows space battle, based on *The Empire Strikes Back,* 1977 . . . .    **12.00**

**Houndcats Game, The,** Milton Bradley, cartoon, board game, lid shows 4 cartoon characters riding in convertible chasing character wearing sombrero riding in basket attached to blimp–shaped plane, grass, flowers, and snow capped mountains background, 1973 . .    **12.00**

**House That Jack Built, The,** McLoughlin Brothers, nursery ryhme, card game, 3$^1/_4$ x 4$^3/_8$ x 1$^1/_8$", cover shows 3 barrels in front of 2 story house with lamp posts on upper deck, c1890 *see illus.* . . . . . . . . . . . . . . . .    **25.00**

**House That Jack Built, The,** Parker Brothers, nursery rhyme, board game, lid shows boy sawing wood plank set on wooden

*House That Jack Built*

horses, mfg info bottom right corner, contains 16 multicolored litho cards, c1890 . . . . . . . . .    **20.00**

**How Silas Popped the Question,** Parker Brothers, generic, card game, 6$^1/_2$ x 5", cover shows man and woman on sofa, gentleman in striped jacket and high collar, "A Game" on sofa back, no logo on box cover, two Parker Brothers, Inc. ads in box, c1915 . . . . . . . . . . . . . .    **30.00**

**How To Succeed in Business Without Really Trying,** Milton Bradley, Broadway musical show, board game, lid shows game name on stand surrounded by 4 rectangles labled with business activities "Advertising Office, Coffee Break, Conference Room," and "Executive Suite," "This is not a Serious Game," 1963 . . . . . . . . . . . . .    **12.00**

**Howdy Doody's Electric Doodler Game,** Harett–Gilmar, TV/puppet, activity games, lid shows Howdy Doody wearing neck scarf, sparks around letter "E," 4 small character drawings down right, 1951 . . . . . . . . . . .    **40.00**

**Howdy Doody's T.V. Game,** Milton Bradley, TV/puppet, board game, lid shows Howdy Doody with clown and duck wearing hat, "A Visit to Howdy's Own TV Studio," 1953 . . . . . . .    **40.00**

**Huck Finn, Adventures Of,** Transogram, TV/book, board game, cover shows Finn wearing hat and vest standing with man and woman, genie lamp, and genie in turban with chains on wrists, "As Seen On TV," 1969 . . . . . . . . . . . . . . . . .   **30.00**

**Huckle Chuck, Huckleberry Hound's,** Transogram, cartoon character, action games, cover shows 3–foot spring activated replica of Huckleberry Hound with target belly, contains rings, beanbags, and darts, 1961 . . . .   **40.00**

**Huckleberry Hound,** Milton Bradley, cartoon character, board game, lid shows dog chasing Huckleberry carrying postman's bag, letters flying from bag, 1981 . . . . . . . . . . .   **15.00**

**Huckleberry Hound "Bumps" Game,** Transogram, cartoon character, board game, lid shows Huckleberry and friends in picture frame, 1961 . . . . . . .   **35.00**

**Huckleberry Hound Western Game,** Milton Bradley, cartoon character, board game, lid shows playing board and Huckleberry wearing cowboy hat and gun holster holding slate with game name, 1959. . .   **30.00**

**Huff 'N Puff Game,** Schaper, generic, action game, lid shows boy wearing turtleneck and girl wearing headband looking at playing surface with a spring–loaded wolf, 1968 . . . . . . . . .   **15.00**

**Huggin' The Rail,** Selchow & Righter, auto racing, board game, cover shows racing cars and curved fence, 1948 . . . . . .   **50.00**

**Hullabaloo Electric Teen Game,** Remco, TV show, quiz game, cover shows multicolored game name and 3 women and man in bottom left corner, "More than 200 Questions and Answers," 1965 . . . . . . . . . . .

**Humpty Dumpty Marble Game,**   **65.00** Hasbro, nursery rhyme charac-

ter, skill and action game, lid shows Humpty sitting on wall holding marble in right hand and 4 marbles bouncing from left hand, castle background, 1966 . . . . . . . . . . . . . . . . . .   **12.00**

**Hunch,** Happy Hour, generic, marble game, 3–dimensional plastic board, cover shows game name in elongated letters and 3 small multicolored ovals, "Fascinating New Game in Sculptured Plastic," 1956 . . . . .   **15.00**

**Hungry Henry Game,** Ideal, generic, balancing game, lid shows man and 2 children putting game pcs into mouth of large bird, smaller bird flying over game name, 1969 . . . . . . .   **15.00**

**Hunting, The New Game of,** McLoughlin Brothers, sports, board game, 16$^{1}/_{2}$" sq, lid shows boy carrying rifle and caught "game," dog, brook, and trees, contains colored lead dogs, spinner, arrow, and round litho "game" pcs, wooden box, ©1904 . . . . . . . . . . . . . . . . .   **350.00**

**Hunting The Rabbit,** Clark & Sowden, #326, hunting, board game, 15 x 7$^{1}/_{2}$", lid shows 2 hunters with rifles aimed at rabbit running across field, c1890–95 . . . . . . . . . . . . . . .   **60.00**

**Hurdle Race,** Milton Bradley, sports, board game, 16$^{1}/_{4}$ x 11$^{1}/_{2}$", lid shows park setting, clothed elephant kicking man over hurdle, and on–lookers including man in checkered pants and flying jacket and policeman waving club, "It Is Great Sport," contains round colored wooden counters and spinner, ©1905 . . . . . . . . . . .   **100.00**

–I–

**"I Don't Know,"** Milton Bradley, social, card game, 5$^{1}/_{4}$ x 4$^{1}/_{4}$", cover shows man and woman

*I'm George Gobel
and Here's The Game*

*I've Got A Secret*

seated at table, man with
crossed legs holding papers,
flower print upper right corner,
box bottom with Pitch–a–Ring
Junior and Magic Hoops Junior
advertising, contains 35 cards,
c1903 . . . . . . . . . . . . . . . . . .    **15.00**

**I Dream of Jeannie Game**, Milton
Bradley, TV series, board game,
lid shows seated Jeannie with
folded arms, trail of smaller
Jeannies flying, dancing, chasing
man, and with palm tree and
man on island, 1965 . . . . . . . .    **30.00**

**"I Spy" Game,** Ideal, TV/mystery,
lid shows 2 men holding guns
pointed at space rocket, 1965. .    **55.00**

**"I Spy" Mini–Board Card Game,**
Ideal, TV/mystery, card game,
lid shows 2 men fighting off
man with bare legs and towel
hanging from belt, open briefcase bottom right corner,
"Starring Robert Culp and Bill
Cosby," 1966 . . . . . . . . . . . . .    **25.00**

**"I'm A Millionaire,"** Parker
Brothers, generic, card game,
"A Laughable Game," lid shows
tied money bag with "$" sign,
1907 . . . . . . . . . . . . . . . . . . .    **12.00**

**I'm George Gobel, and Here's
The Game,** Schaper, celebrity,
card game, lid shows Gobel
saluting, 7 cards, and movie
camera bottom right corner,
contains playing movie camera
shaped pcs, 1955 . . . . . . . . . .    **45.00**

**I've Got A Secret,** Lowell, TV/
game show, board game, lid
shows host Garry Moore with
hand holding, "America's No. 1
TV Panel Show" in bottom right
corner, 1956 . . . . . . . . . . . . .    **40.00**

**I.D.,** Milton Bradley, generic,
board game, lid has game name
in center square, "The identity
Game," 1988 . . . . . . . . . . . . .    **10.00**

**Illya Kuryakin Card Game,** Milton
Bradley, TV/mystery, card game,
lid shows man holding rifle,
buildings and 3 battling figures
in background, "The Man From
Uncle" top right corner,
1965–66 . . . . . . . . . . . . . . . .    **30.00**

**Image,** 3M, generic, trivia game,
lid shows bearded man wearing
sombrero with feather, and faces
of famous people including
Einstein, Geronimo, and De
Gaulle, "the who, what, when
and where game," 1972 . . . . . .    **10.00**

**In–Side Golf,** John M. Hall
Enterprises, sports, board game,
cover shows golf club, "o" in
game name is golf ball on tee,
1967 . . . . . . . . . . . . . . . . . . .    **15.00**

**In the Chips,** Tega, business/
investments, lid has Silicon
Valley landscape, "Local investment game of the Santa Clara
Valley (Silicon Valley)," 1980 . .    **10.00**

**In The White House,** Cincinnati
Game Co., No. 1115, educational, card game, 2³/₄ x 3³/₄", lid
has picture and mirror reflection
of White House in 2 ovals with
2 Capitol domes on each oval,
pictures are separated by
2 Capitol domes placed side-
ways, dotted background, contains 44 cards with blue and
white White House backs, faces

depict presidents and their
accomplishments, ©1896 . . . . . **25.00**

**Incredible Hulk Game, The,**
Milton Bradley, comic superhero, board game, cover shows
running Hulk followed by Fan-
tastic Four, 1978 . . . . . . . . . . . **15.00**

**India,** Whitman, generic, board
game, Parcheesi type game, lid
shows Indian temples, elephant
with howdah, and 2 uniformed
figures holding long spears,
1950s . . . . . . . . . . . . . . . . . **10.00**

**India, An Oriental Game,**
McLoughlin Brothers, generic,
board game, Parcheesi type
game, 14¹/₂ x 15", cover shows
man wearing turban and robe
riding camel, contains 16 round
wooden counters and spinner,
wooden box, c1890–95 . . . . . **110.00**

**India, Game of,** National Games,
No. 2003, generic, board game,
lid shows elephant wearing turban and jacket holding roped
animal prisoner followed by 3rd
animal wearing hat and belted
coat, background buildings
include Indian temple roof,
no date . . . . . . . . . . . . . . . . . **40.00**

**India Bombay,** Cutler & Saleeby
Co., No. 4020, generic, board
game, 22 x 10", cover shows
2 tigers attacking elephant, contains wooden markers and
2 dice, c1910 . . . . . . . . . . . . **25.00**

**India Bombay,** Cutler & Saleeby
Co., No. 4023, generic, board
game, 10¹/₄ x 6", cover shows
roaring tiger, c1920 . . . . . . . . **30.00**

**Indiana Jones From Raiders of
the Lost Ark,** Parker Brothers,
movie/adventure, board game,
cover shows Jones with mustache and hat, truck in back-
ground, 1982 . . . . . . . . . . . . . **15.00**

**Indoor Golf Course, Arnold
Palmer's,** see Arnold Palmer's
Indoor Golf Course

**Inflation,** Charles Joseph–
Carpenter Game Products, business, board game, cover has
currency below game name,

"Buy, Sell and Trade Your Way
to $1,000,000," 1974 . . . . . . . . **10.00**

**Inside Golf, Arnold Palmer's,** see
Arnold Palmer's Inside Golf

**Inspector Gadget Game,** Milton
Bradley, TV/cartoon, board
game, lid shows 2 hands on
right reaching for man wearing
glove, hat, and coat, and
woman in striped shirt, 1983 . . **10.00**

**Intercept,** Lakeside, military,
board game, lid shows 2 hands
on playing surface, plane, and
moon, mfg name and logo bot-
tom right corner, 1978 . . . . . . . **15.00**

**International Airport Game,**
Magic Wand, aviation/travel,
board game, metal, cover shows
plane with pilot pointing the
way, boy with outstretched arms,
and figure wearing goggles on
wing, airline logos down left
side, contains 4 magnetic jets
and spinner, 1975 . . . . . . . . . . **12.00**

**International Game of Stake, The,**
Marks Brothers Co., generic,
skill and action game, 14 x 10 x
2³/₄", cover shows 2 men and
2 women seated at table with
4 cones, and "STAK" in circle,
1937 . . . . . . . . . . . . . . . . . . . **28.00**

**International Grand Prix,** Magic
Wand, auto racing, board game,
metal, cover shows #2 race car
and national flags down left,
contains 6 magnetic racing cars,
1964 . . . . . . . . . . . . . . . . . . . **25.00**

**Interpol Calling,** Bell, TV/espi-
onage/mystery, lid shows tower
with "Bell's" banner flying at
top, dotted lines connecting
major international cities, and
inset of man's face, 1959 . . . . . **40.00**

**Interpretation of Dreams,** 3M,
TV/mystical, board game, lid
shows rectangle in upper right
corner with NBC logo and man
with 3 women, 1 woman wearing long gown, 1 wearing headband, came with "Dream
Dictionary," 1969 . . . . . . . . . . **15.00**

**Interstate Highway,** Selchow &
Righter, travel, board game,

*Ivanhoe*

cover shows 2 highways with
vehicles, buildings in background, "Interstate 54" shield,
and mfg logo in circle at bottom
right corner, 1963 . . . . . . . . .  **35.00**

**Intrigue,** Milton Bradley, mystery,
board game, cover shows ship,
dock, and city buildings, contains wooden satchels and metal
keys, 1955. . . . . . . . . . . . . .  **35.00**

**Inventors, The,** Parker Brothers,
generic, board game, cover
shows 4 men wearing hats,
"Patent Attorney" on office door
and man standing in doorway,
1974. . . . . . . . . . . . . . . . . .  **15.00**

**Ipcress File, The,** Milton Bradley,
movie/mystery/espionage, board
game, lid shows gun next to
oval with game name, man with
glasses, and woman with folded
arms holding gun, 1966 . . . . . .  **38.00**

**Ironside,** Ideal, TV/mystery/detec-
tive, board game, lid shows
Ironside in wheel chair, man
falling, and man running, ceme-
tery background, 1967 . . . . . . .  **90.00**

**It's About Time,** Ideal, TV
series/generic, board game, lid
shows astronauts in space capsule, Stone Age people, and
dinosaur, 1965. . . . . . . . . . . .  **45.00**

**Ivanhoe,** George S. Parker & Co.,
book, board game, 6½ x 4½
x1", cover shows knight's armor
and heraldic crosses border,
1890 *see illus* . . . . . . . . . . . .  **20.00**

# –J–

**J. Fred Muggs 'Round The World
Game,** Gabriel, TV/travel, lid
shows *Today TV* show chimp
dressed in jacket and shirt carrying camera case and girl and
boy at gameboard, plane and
map outline in background,
1955 . . . . . . . . . . . . . . . . . .  **60.00**

**Jack and the Beanstalk,**
Transogram, book, board game,
lid shows Jack wearing feathered
hat and carrying harp and goose
being chased by Giant,  bean-
stalk on left, 1957 . . . . . . . . .  **35.00**

**Jack and the Beanstalk, Game of,**
National Games, book, board
game, lid shows Jack climbing
beanstalk toward castle, 1941 . .  **40.00**

**Jack and The Bean Stalk, The
Game of,** McLoughlin Brothers,
book, board game, 20½ x 19¾",
cover shows Jack wearing feathered cap carrying harp, jumping
over bush, and running from
Giant carrying club, 1898 . . . . .  **500.00**

**Jack & Jill,** Milton Bradley, nursery rhyme, board game,
8 x 15½", cover shows Jack tum-
bling down hill with pail, nursery rhyme printed in rectangular
box, house in background, contains round colored wooden
markers and spinner, ©1909 . . .  **55.00**

**Jack And Jill Jacks Game,** Hasbro,
generic, skill and action game,
lid shows Jack and Jill holding
playing pcs, sketch of boy inset
at top left corner, right side
shows Jack and Jill falling down
hill, spilling pail, and "Jack"
playing pcs on track leading to
well, 1966 . . . . . . . . . . . . . . .  **15.00**

**Jack Straws,** Milton Bradley,
generic, skill game, 6 x 5", cover
shows girl with lacy cuffs and
bow at neck looking at sticks on
table, contains 2 hooks and
multicolored wooden sticks,
c1900 . . . . . . . . . . . . . . . . . .  **15.00**

**Jack Straws, The Game of,** Parker
Brothers, generic, skill game, lid

has scrolled border around
game name and mfg info, 1900s    **20.00**

**Jackie Gleason's "And AW–A– A–
AY We Go!,"** Transogram,
TV/comic celebrity, board game,
lid shows 5 differently dressed
Gleason images in row with
outstretched arms, 1956 . . . . . .    **100.00**

**Jackson Five,** Shindana, musical
group, action game, lid shows
6 cards with band members'
pictures and 3 circles with "J5"
in heart shaped insets, 1972 . . .    **45.00**

**James Bond 007 Card Game,**
MIlton Bradley, movie/spy, lid
shows Bond wearing shirt,
bowtie, and gun holster, standing with hand on belt, and piles
of money chips, 1964–66 . . . . .    **30.00**

**James Bond 007 Thunderball
Game,** Milton Bradley,
movie/spy, board game, lid
shows action shots including
helicopter, woman in wide–
brimmed hat, and Bond with
scuba diver, 1965 . . . . . . . . . .    **30.00**

**James Bond Message from "M"
Game,** Ideal, movie/spy,
board game, cover shows inset
of Bond with gun, 5 people
against background of large
"007" imprint, "Message From
M Game," contains plastic villains and movie weapons,
1965–66 . . . . . . . . . . . . . . . . .    **125.00**

**James Bond Secret Agent 007,**
Milton Bradley, movie/spy, lid
shows Sean Connery hitting
man with hand on letter, open
safe, woman with gun, and win-
dows, 1964 . . . . . . . . . . . . . . .    **25.00**

• Second version with same cover
but different Bond character,
1964 . . . . . . . . . . . . . . . . . .    **25.00**

**Jan Murray's Charge Account,**
Lowell, TV/business, word
game, lid shows Murray, round
checkered cylinder, small
squares letter chips, and
2 cards, 1961 . . . . . . . . . . . .    **30.00**

**Jan Murray's Treasure Hunt,**
Gardner, TV/adventure, board
game, lid shows seated Murray
holding currency, open currency
boxes, plane, and car, 1959 . . .    **20.00**

*Jetsons Fun Pad*

**Jaws, The Game of,** Ideal, movie,
board game, lid has open shark's
mouth above hand holding stick
putting pcs into open mouth of
shark game pc, 1975 . . . . . . . .    **15.00**

**Jean Dixon's Game of Destiny,**
Milton Bradley, fortune telling,
card game, lid shows numbers
and figures representing astrology signs against target background, "A Card Game of
Numerology and Astrology,"
1968 . . . . . . . . . . . . . . . . . . .    **10.00**

**Jeopardy,** Milton Bradley, 1st
Edition, TV/generic, quiz show,
lid shows game name in oval,
"Players Are Given the Answers
and Asked to Come Up With the
Questions," 1964 . . . . . . . . . .    **12.00**

• 13 subsequent editions . . . . . .    **10.00**

**Jet Race Game,** Built–Rite, aviation, speed board game, lid
shows jet plane taking off and
mfg info in triangle, contains
large US map gameboard, jet
markers, fair weather flight
cards, and speedy spinner dial,
1960s . . . . . . . . . . . . . . . . . .    **15.00**

**Jetsons Fun Pad,** Milton Bradley,
cartoon, action balancing game,
lid shows Jetsons in "space
ship," 1963 *see illus* . . . . . . . .    **65.00**

**Jetsons Game, The,** Milton
Bradley, cartoon, lid shows
Jetsons and cartoon animals in
space ship, 1985 . . . . . . . . . .    **10.00**

**Jig Chase,** Game Makers, dog racing, jigsaw puzzle game, lid
shows race dog chasing rabbit

above game name letters and flying checkered flag, flag atop tower in bottom right corner, strip of running dogs along bottom, contains multiple puzzles, 1940s . . . . . . . . . . . . . . . . .   30.00

**Jig Race,** Game Makers, horse racing, jigsaw puzzle game, 2 strips of racing horses run diagonally across cover, checkered flag behind game name, tower with flag in bottom right corner, contains jigsaw track for each player, 1940s . . . . . . . . . . . . .   30.00

**Jimmy The Greek Odds Maker Poker–Dice,** Aurora, celebrity/gambling, dice board game, lid shows 3 women and 2 men around gameboard with dice, game name across top and down right side of lid, 1974 . . .   12.00

**Jingo,** Cadaco–Ellis, generic, jigsaw puzzle game, lid shows face of pirate, fox, and turkey, pirate wearing earrings and hat with skull and crossbones, 1941 . . . . . . . . . . . . . . . . . .   18.00

**John Drake Secret Agent,** Milton Bradley, TV/mystery/espionage board game, lid shows man holding rifle falling over wall after being hit by man carrying briefcase, inset with game name, man's face, and target body with bullet holes in top right corner, 1966 . . . . . . . . .   40.00

**Johnny On The Pony,** Remco, generic, board game, lid shows boy on bucking horse and woman with raised arms, "The On Again, Off Again Game," 1959 . . . . . . . . . . . . . . . . . .   32.00

**Johnny Ringo,** Transogram, TV/western, board game, lid shows cowboy wearing vest and sheriff's badge leaning against tree, stagecoach and mountains in background,1960 . . . . . . . .   90.00

**Johnny's Historical Game,** George S. Parker & Co., military/educational, board game, $5^{1}/_{16}$ x $6^{9}/_{16}$ x 1", cover shows soldiers on horses, in boat, and

marching, game name printed above flag, ©1890 . . . . . . . . .   22.00

**Joker Joker Joker,** Milton Bradley, TV/children's quiz show, quiz game, lid shows 3 harlequin joker cards, 1979 . . . . . . . . . .   8.00

**Jolly Faces Game, The,** Ideal Book Builders, educational, puzzle game, $7^{3}/_{4}$ x $8^{1}/_{4}$", cover shows clown wearing feathered hat and ruffled collar, patent info bottom left corner, #300 bottom center, mfg info bottom right corner, contains 4 multicolored cardboard faces, paper packet with 16 mouth, eye, and nose puzzle pcs, 1912 . . . . . . . . . .   35.00

**Jolly Old Maid, The,** Parker Brothers, generic, card game, $4^{3}/_{4}$ x 6", cover shows woman with glasses wearing bonnet and coat, c1910 . . . . . . . . . . .   20.00

**Jolly Tumblers,** Milton Bradley, generic, board game, 22 x $9^{1}/_{2}$", cover shows 2 clothed animals on seesaw and 2 in chase in front of houses, contains 4 aluminum cylinders each containing steel ball and target board, c1895 . . . . . . . . . . . . . . . .   95.00

**Jollytime Dominoes,** Milton Bradley, generic, dominoes game, cover shows girl and boy with picture dominoes, "3 Games in 1," Color Dominoes, Regular Dominoes, Picture Dominoes," 1955 . . . . .   12.00

**Jonny Quest Game,** Transogram, TV/cartoon, board game, cover shows fighting scuba diver on boat and boy holding radio, boat in background, boy's face in "Q" of game name, strip of 4 faces and dog in bottom left corner, 1964 . . . . . . . . . . . .   600.00

**Journey to the Unknown Game,** Remco, TV/mystery, board game, lid shows monster eye beside lightning bolt, "Based on the ABC Television Program," 1968 . . . . . . . . . . . . . . . . .   95.00

**Jubilee,** Cadaco–Ellis, generic, tile game, lid shows 4 people playing game at table and numbered tiles, strip down left shows game being played in 4 different settings, 1954 . . . . . . . . . . . .    **20.00**

**JumPin,** 3M, generic, board game, lid shows face behind game name looking at game pcs, contains metal pawns, 1964 . . . . . . . . . . . . . . . . .    **18.00**

**Jumping D.J. Surprise Action Game,** Mattel, TV, action card game, lid shows Dishonest John dressed in black, circle with Beany & Cecil, and partial playing card with Beany wearing hat, contains cartoon face playing cards, 1962 . . . . . . . . . . .    **35.00**

**Jumping Frog, Game of,** J.H. Singer, nursery rhymes, card game, 5 x 4", cover shows dressed frog, water background, contains 20 cards depicting pairs of 10 nursery rhymes, c1890 . . . . . . . . . . . . . . . . .    **20.00**

**Jungle Book Game, Walt Disney presents Rudyard Kipling's,** Parker Brothers, Disney, board game, lid shows boy sitting on baboon's stomach, with girl and other cartoon animals watching, 1966 . . . . . . . . . . . . . . . . .    **18.00**

**Jungle Parts,** Wolverine Supply & Mfg. Co., generic, board game, 21⁵/₈ x 21¹/₂", board has ape in large center circle surrounded by animals including alligator, elephant, leopard, and zebra, small circles in each corner, no date. . . . . . . . . . . . . . . . . . .    **40.00**

**Jungle Skittles,** American Toy Works, action game, lid shows cougar running among skittles, monkey throwing ball, and palm tree, 1950s . . . . . . . . . .    **45.00**

**Junior Combination Board,** Milton Bradley, generic, board game, 12 different games, 17 x 8³/₄", lid shows people sitting on blanket, pyramids, man in long robe holding stick, ship, and 2 camels, contains 20 checkers, 32 wooden counters, and spinner, ©1905 . . . . . . . .    **50.00**

**Junior Executive, The Money Game of,** Whitman, business, board game, cover shows office scene with secretary at executive's desk, policeman with raised hand, dog, and house in left bottom corner, jagged edged circle top left corner, 1960 . . . .    **12.00**

**Junior Executive, The Money Game of,** Whitman, business, board game, cover shows boy and girl seated at table with gameboard, 3 zigzag strips run from bottom left to top right of board, 1963 . . . . . . . . . . . . . .    **12.00**

**Junior Quarterback Football Game,** Built–Rite, sports, miniature bookshelf game, cover shows silhouette of player in throwing position with ball in right hand, football background, 1960s . . . . . . . . . . . . . . . . . .    **10.00**

**Junior Table Top Bowling Alley,** Merit, sports, action/skill game, lid shows bowling alley playing surface, player bowling strike, boy, and girl, "A Game of Fun and Skill For The Whole Family," contains 10 bowling pins, 3 bowling balls, Jr Bowling League application, official scoring pad, 1961 . . . . . . . . . . . . .    **15.00**

**Junk Yard, The,** Ideal, skill and action game, lid shows 2 hands operating flippers on playing surface, "A Target Game With Pin Ball Action," mfg logo and age recommendations bottom right corner, 1975. . . . . . . . . . .    **20.00**

**Just like Me, Game of,** McLoughlin Brothers, generic, card game, 4¹/₄ x 5¹/₄", cover shows 2 large monkeys looking at smaller monkey, contains 30 multicolored cards, ©1899. .    **40.00**

## –K–

**K–Tel Superstar Game,** K–Tel International, music, mail order game, lid shows name in circle, guitar and trombone players, and singers, dot background, "The Original Rock N Roll Music Game," contains plastic gold album and real 45 rpm record, 1973 . . . . . . . . . . . . . .       **20.00**

**Ka–Bala,** Transogram, fortune telling, board game, lid shows 2 sets of hands on hexagonal playing surface, 1967 . . . . . . . .       **75.00**

**Kaboom Balloon Busting Game,** Ideal, generic, action game, lid shows hand at top of playing pc blowing up balloon, 1965 . . . .       **15.00**

**Kan–U–Go,** A.A. Burnstine Sales, generic, crossword card game, cover shows crossword puzzle bottom right corner, game name across top and in oval at bottom left corner, 1937 . . . . . . . . . .       **10.00**

**Kate Smith's Own Game America,** Toy Creations, celebrity, board game, cover has picture of Smith with CBS microphone between pictures of White House and Capitol, stars and stripes shield behind Smith, all game proceeds donated to charity, 1940s . . . . . . . . . . .       **55.00**

**"Keeping Up With The Joneses," The Game of,** Phillips Co., social, separate 17½" sq board and 4¾ x 5¼" pcs box, cover shows man wearing top hat holding back of fur coat worn by woman carrying monocle and direction sign to "Sassiety," invented by A.R. Momand, ©1921 . . . . . . . . . . . . . . . . . .       **85.00**

**Kennedy's, The Exciting New Game of the,** Transco, celebrity family/political, board game, cover shows portraits of JFK and 5 other family members carved in in mountain resembling Mt. Rushmore, striped banner upper left corner, contains cards, money, dice and pawns, 1962 . . . . . . . . . . . . .       **60.00**

**Kentucky Derby Racing Game,** Whitman, horse racing, board game, lid shows jockeys riding horses, #4 in center of lid, contains metal horses, 1938 . . .       **20.00**

**Ker Plunk,** Ideal, generic, skill and action game, lid shows

*Ker Plunk*

smiling faces and hand inserting stick into playing pc, "A Tantalizing Game of Nerve and Skills," contains game pc, multicolored sticks, and marbles, 1967 *see illus* . . . . . . . . . . . . . . . .       **15.00**

**Kewpie Doll Game,** Parker Brothers, toy, board game, based on characters created by Rose O'Neill, cover shows doll sitting inside fort with open doors and flying flag, 1963 . . . . . . . . . . .       **30.00**

**Kick Back,** Schaper, generic, skill and action game, cover shows 2 kicking horses, stick with ball on end separates 2 words of game name in lid center, c1965 . . . . . . . . . . . . . . . . . .       **12.00**

**Kimbo,** Parker Brothers, generic, board game, "Game of Fences," multicolored triangles around game name on lid, 1960 . . . . . .       **15.00**

**Kindergarten Building Blocks,** S. L. Hill & Son, No. 13, generic, action game, 8¼ x 5¾", cover shows shrouded figure with cane, steeple in background, leaves and berries border, wooden box with slide

*Kings*

cover, contains 28 colored litho wooden blocks with pictures and letters, c1978 . . . . . . . . . .    **400.00**

**King Kong,** Ideal, movie/monster, board game, lid shows Kong atop building, plane and helicopters in sky, based on remake of original movie, 1976 . . . . . .    **15.00**

**King Kong Game,** Ideal, movie/monster, board game, cover shows Kong hovering above street scene with bus, running people, police station, and mfg logo top right corner, 1963 . . . . . . . . . . . . . . . . .    **95.00**

**King Kong Game,** Milton Bradley, TV/cartoon, board game, cover shows Kong hitting alligator, stars around alligator's head, 4 people on mountain watching, 1966 . . . . . . . . . . . . . . . . . .    **15.00**

**King of the Cheese,** Milton Bradley, generic, board game, cover shows boy and girl seated at table with gameboard, triangular shaped pc of swiss cheese at board center, contains spinner and 4 markers, 1959 . . . . .    **30.00**

**King of the Hill,** Schaper, generic, board game, lid shows hilly playing surface and marbles, "Hazards, Pitfalls, Obstacles, Traps...Galore," 1964 . . . . . . .    **15.00**

**King of the Mountain,** Saalfield, generic, board game, cover shows boy wearing crown, 1957 . . . . . . . . . . . . . . . . . .    **15.00**

**King Oil,** Milton Bradley, business, board game, 3–dimension-al, lid shows triangular inset of man wearing cowboy hat and bowtie in front of oil derricks, 2 hands at playing surface at center right, 1974 . . . . . . . . . .    **18.00**

**King Tut's Game,** Cadaco, educational, board game, lid shows Tut surrounded by Egyptian relics, 1977 . . . . . . . . . . . . . .    **12.00**

**King Tut's Pyramid,** Milton Bradley, generic, puzzle game, lid shows pyramid on triangular playing surface, masked face with small triangle at upper right corner, "For the Puzzle Master," 1962 . . . . . . . . . . . . . . . . . .    **10.00**

**King Zor, The Dinosaur Game,** Ideal, toy, board game, lid shows dinosaur and mfg logo bottom right corner, based on Ideal toy, 1962 . . . . . . . . . . . .    **80.00**

**Kings,** Akro Agates, generic, board game, 11 x $7^1/_8$ x $^7/_8$", triangular shaped board with diamond shaped spaces, king's head above strip with 3 half moon shapes and "Kings" at bottom, crown above game name, 1931 *see illus* . . . . . . . . . . . . . . . . .    **35.00**

**Kismet,** Lakeside, "The Modern Game of Yacht," cover shows 5 dice and dice cup, letters of game name shown in triangles, 1964 . . . . . . . . . . . . . . . . . .    **7.00**

**Kitty Kat Cup Ball,** Rosebud Art Co., generic, action game, 10 x $14^3/_4$ x 2", cover shows 3 kittens around sign with game name and mfg info, "Amusing, Thrilling," c1930s . . . . . . . . . .    **55.00**

**Knapp Electric Questioner,** Knapp Electric, Inc., generic, quiz game, $13^5/_8$ x $9^3/_8$ x $2^1/_8$", cover shows large question mark behind game name, torn paper scrap printed with country flags, c1894–1929 . . . . . . . . . . . . . .    **45.00**

**Knight Rider,** Parker Brothers, TV/adventure, board game, cover shows car and 3 male faces, 1983 . . . . . . . . . . . . . .    **10.00**

**Knock It Off Game,** Marx Toys, generic, action game, cover shows playing surface, "Fast

*Komical Konversation Kards*

Action Wacky Street Game,"
1978 . . . . . . . . . . . . . . . . . .      **10.00**

**Knockout Andy,** Parker Brothers,
generic, skill game, 8³/₈" sq,
cover shows boxing ring with
monkey wearing hat and boxing
gloves hitting elephant dressed
in boxer's shorts, contains red
wooden board with 4 pegs,
8 green wooden bowling pins,
and multicolored metal and
wood spring top, 1926 . . . . . . .      **40.00**

**Kojak, The Stakeout Detective
Game,** Milton Bradley, TV/
detective, board game, cover
with show star Telly Savalas
inset at upper left corner, 2 men
on street, cars in background,
and 2 children playing game
inset at bottom right, 1975 . . . .      **15.00**

**Komical Konversation Cards,**
Parker Brothers, generic, card
game, 5 x 6¹/₂", cover has man
and woman in circles, ship bottom right corner, "A Kuriously
Kontrived Kaptivating Kuriosity,"
contains numerous question
and answer cards, ©1893
*see illus.* . . . . . . . . . . . . . . . . .      **20.00**

**Komical Konversation Kards,**
Selchow & Righter, generic,
card game, 5³/₈ x 4³/₈ x 1", cover
shows 3 children around table
looking at 2 goats coming
through door, mfg info in strip at
bottom, c1890s . . . . . . . . . . .      **22.00**

**Komissar,** Selchow & Righter,
Russia, board game, "The
People's Game," cover shows
game name flanked by stars,
cartoon drawings of man in
"Komissar" uniform and man
holding tape coming from
machine with "$" sign on base,
1966 . . . . . . . . . . . . . . . . . . .      **25.00**

**Kooky Carnival Game,** Milton
Bradley, generic, skill and action
game, "Try Your Skill at
9 different Stunts!," lid shows
square of 2 players and
9 squares of stunts, 1969 . . . . .      **20.00**

• Second cover has carnival scene
showing tent with flags, ferris
wheel, and man wearing straw
hat and striped shirt, 1969 . . .      **20.00**

**Korg: 70,000 B.C. Game, The,**
Milton Bradley, TV program,
board game, cover shows group
of people in stoneage clothes,
1974 . . . . . . . . . . . . . . . . . . .      **12.00**

**Kreskin's ESP,** Milton Bradley, psy-
chic, quiz game, cover shows
Kreskin holding swinging mystery pendulum, "Do You Have
Extra Sensory Perception?," circle at center asks "Will the mystery pendulum answer your
questions about Love? Career?
Finance? Travel?," 1966–67 . . . .      **15.00**

**Kreskin's ESP, Advanced Fine
Edition,** MIlton Bradley, lid
shows 4 ovals resembling eyes
coming from center sphere;
"Yes; No; XX; ?" printed on
"eyeballs," 1967 . . . . . . . . . . .      **20.00**

**Krull,** Parker Brothers, movie/
heroic adventure, board game,
cover shows woman standing
behind man holding 5–pronged
weapon and man in sword fight
with monster, buildings in back-
ground, 1983 . . . . . . . . . . . . .      **10.00**

**Kuti–Kuts (Cutie Cuts): A Comic
Cartoon Game,** Regensteiner
Corp., comic cartoon, puzzle
game, 5⁵/₈ x 9¹/₈ x ³/₄", cover
shows playing pcs and completed combination picture of clown
wearing pointed hat with dots,
2 ducks at his feet, Invented &
Designed by Charles Lederer,

"Entertaining, Instructive, Thousands of Combinations," ©1922 . . . . . . . . . . . . . . . . . 60.00

**–L–**

**Lancer,** Remco, TV/western, board game, cover shows 3 cowboys with lassos, mfg name in oval next to game name, 1968 . . . . . . . . . . . . . . 60.00

**Land of the Giants,** Ideal, TV/monster, cover shows group of small people warding off large animal beside large shoe, "As Seen on ABC Television," 1968 . . . . . . . . . . . . . . . . . . 90.00

**Land of the Lost,** Milton Bradley, TV/monster, board game, cover shows dinosaur and 2 men and girl in circle inset, "From Sid and Marty Kroft's Popular TV Show," 1975 . . . . . . . . . . . . . 40.00

**Landslide,** Parker Brothers, politics, board game, cover has star on either side of game name, top half of circle inset shows game board and pcs, bottom half split into 5 strips with players' faces cards, 1971 . . . . . . . . 15.00

**Larry Harmon's Bozo,** Parker Brothers, circus, board game, cover shows "The World's Most Famous Clown," 1960s . . . . . . . 20.00

**Laser Attack Game,** Milton Bradley, military, board game, cover shows 2 insets of players with board, 1978 . . . . . . . . . . 12.00

**Lassie Game,** Game Gems, TV/book, board game, cover shows mountain behind Lassie, 1965 . . . . . . . . . . . . . . . . . . 25.00

**Last Straw, The,** Schaper, generic, skill and action game, cover shows 3 camels with bucket on humps, first bucket empty, second has hand putting straws inside, and third bucket is overloaded with straws, third camel falling, "The Camel Game," 1966 . . . . . . . . . . . . . . . . . . 10.00

**Laugh–In Squeeze Your Bippy Game,** Hasbro, TV, board game,

*Laverne and Shirley*

cover shows 2 men in tuxedos, woman dressed as maid, woman with headband, woman in bikini, and soldier in bottom right corner, 1968 . . . . . . . . . . . . . 75.00

**Laurel and Hardy,** Transogram, celebrity, board game, cover shows cartoon drawings of famous comedians, 1 with bowtie, 1 with long tie, and 1 carrying umbrella, buildings in background, 1962 . . . . . . . . . . 25.00

**Laverne and Shirley,** Parker Brothers, TV, board game, show stars on cover, "Making Your Dreams Come True Game," 1977 *see illus.* . . . . . . . . . . . . . 15.00

**Lazy Pool,** Dashound, sports/pool, board game, cover shows playing board, dice, and balls including 8 ball within triangular rack, 1965 . . . . . . . . . . . . . . 5.00

**Leap Frog, Game of,** McLoughlin Brothers, generic, board game, $8\frac{1}{2}$ x $10\frac{1}{4}$", cover has 4 rectangular insets, 1 with boys playing leap frog, contains 16 round wooden counters, 8 red and 8 yellow, and cardboard spinner, c1890 . . . . . . . . . . . . . . . . . . 110.00

**Leaping Lena,** Parker Brothers, generic, skill and action game, target ring toss game, $12\frac{3}{4}$ x $7\frac{3}{4}$", cover shows woman in convertible, boy riding on back, policeman with raised hand, "Time To Retire!," contains 1–pc board with attached pegs and easel for standing upright, six rubber rings, 1920s . . . . . . . 95.00

**Leave It To Beaver Ambush Game,** Hasbro, TV/western,

*The Letter Carrier*

board game, cover shows
Beaver wearing cap and 2 cow-
boys with guns waiting to
ambush stagecoach, 1959 . . . .    **40.00**
**Leave It To Beaver Money Maker,**
Hasbro, TV/business, board
game, cover shows Beaver
wearing cap and Beaver looking
at pile of money, 1959 . . . . . . .    **35.00**
**Leave It To Beaver Rocket to the
Moon,** Hasbro, TV/space, board
game, cover shows Beaver
wearing cap, spaceship, and
Beaver and dog with homemade
space vehicle, 1959 . . . . . . . .    **35.00**
**Legend of Camelot,** *see Camelot,
Legend of*
**Legend of Jesse James, The,**
Milton Bradley, western, board
game, cover shows cowboys
holding up train, houses in
background, 1966 . . . . . . . . .    **90.00**
**Let's Drive,** Milton Bradley, trans-
portation/auto driving, cover
shows passengers in car, various
road signs, and highway maze,
"Road Safety Fun Game," 1967    **15.00**
**Let's Face It,** Hasbro, generic,
board game, cover shows smil-
ing and laughing faces, 1955 . .    **50.00**

**Let's Make a Deal,** Milton
Bradley, TV/game show, quiz
game, cover has 3 squares
showing contestant and game
host, 1 square showing a ribbon–tied "surprise package,"
1 square with 3 question marks
for "Mystery Doors," and
1 square inset advertising this
NBC TV Show, 1964 . . . . . . . .    **33.00**
**Let's Play Golf,** Burlu Enterprises,
sports, card game, cover shows
fairway and golfer in full swing,
1968 . . . . . . . . . . . . . . . . . .    **35.00**
**Let's Take A Trip,** Milton Bradley,
transportation/driving, cover
shows car trailer with game
name and aerial view of vehicles on highway, "The Super
Highway Game," 1963 . . . . . .    **20.00**
**Letter Carrier, The,** McLoughlin
Brothers, generic, board game,
$8^{1}/_{2}$ x $14^{1}/_{2}$", cover shows postman carrying bag delivering let-
ter to woman wearing long dress
standing in doorway, contains
spinner, 4 round wooden counters, and 112 small cardboard
"letters," c1890 *see illus* . . . . . .    **200.00**
**Letters, Game of,** J.H. Singer,
educational, card game, 5 x 4",
cover shows seated man wearing crown, 2 fiddlers, bowl with
spoon set on table, "J.H.S.N.Y."
above game name, contains
16 multicolored litho alphabet
and picture cards, c1890 . . . . .    **20.00**
**Letters or Anagrams,** Parker
Brothers, educational, card
game, $5^{1}/_{2}$ x 4", cover shows
2 figures bending over with lettered cards, 1 figure watching
with hands on hips, 1 figure
running carrying card with letter
"E," contains round pink lettered
disks, c1889. . . . . . . . . . . . . .    **20.00**
**Library of Games, (Chess,
Checkers, Chunga, Merelles,
Py–hy–ky, Tigh, Avion, Yumph,
Foregammon, and others),**
American Toy Works, No. 403,
generic, board games, 16 x $12^{1}/_{4}$
x $1^{3}/_{4}$", cover shows 2 knights in
armor riding horses carrying

*Lindy, Improved Edition*

flags containing game names, checkerboard in lid center has circle inset of bearded man and boy seated at game table with table light, contains 2 game boards, chess and checker pcs, and 16 pegs, c1930s . . . . . . .   **25.00**

**Lie Cheat & Steal,** Dynamic Games, A Division of Reiss, politics, board game, cover shows figure before world globe, "The Game of Political Power," 1971   **12.00**

**Lie Cheat & Steal,** Reiss, politics, cover shows game and and playing surface, "The Game of Political Power," flat box version of same game, 1976 . . . . . . . .   **20.00**

**Lie Detector,** Mattel, crime/detective, board game, cover shows suspect faces border and 4 shields in strip, "Official Mattel Lie Detector, Scientific Crime Game," re-released in 1965 with new photographic suspect cards, 1960 . . . . . . . .   **40.00**

**Lieutenant Combat Town Game,** Transogram, military, board game, cover shows shield insignia and "U.S. Marines," lieutenant on left, battle scene on right, 1963 . . . . . . . . . . .   **65.00**

**Life, The Game of,** Milton Bradley, generic, board game, cover shows posts dropping from top with squares holding individual game letters on multicolored backgrounds, contains play money, 1960s . . . . . . . . .   **12.00**

• With "100th Anniversary Game" on cover, 1960 . . . . . . . . . . .   **22.00**

**Lightning Express,** Milton Bradley, railroad, board game, cover shows 2 engines, "A Railroad Game," 1940s . . . . . . . . . . . .   **35.00**

**Li'l Abner Game, The,** Parker Brothers, comic strip character, board game, cover shows Abner and Daisy Mae running along path beneath tree, 1969 . . . . . .   **25.00**

**Li'l Abner His Game,** Milton Bradley, comic strip character, board game, cover shows Abner and Daisy Mae with friends, 1 dressed as Indian, 1969 . . . . .   **25.00**

**Li'l Stinker,** Schaper, generic, tile game, lid shows skunk in center surrounded by 4 tiles, Old Maid type game, contains 41 plastic tiles, 1956 . . . . . . .   **28.00**

**Limbo Legs,** Milton Bradley, dance, skill and action game, cover shows 4 people in circle around playing pc with moving stick,1969 . . . . . . . . . . . . . .   **32.00**

**Lindy,** Parker Brothers, aviation, card game, $2^{3}/_{4}$ x $4^{1}/_{8}$", cover shows plane in cloud, border of small ovals, mfg info across bottom, contains pink backed cards with black and white litho faces, ©1927 . . . . . . . . . . . . . . . . . .   **25.00**

**Lindy, Improved Edition,** Parker Brothers, aviation, card game, $5^{1}/_{2}$ x 4", cover shows plane flying above ocean and 2 ships, mfg info bottom right corner, contains blue and white backed cards with 5 black and white litho planes, ©1927 *see illus*. . .   **25.00**

**Line Drive,** Lord & Freber, sports/baseball, board game, cover shows baseballs, "The Big League Strategy Baseball Game," 1953 . . . . . . . . . . . . .   **80.00**

**Linus the Lionhearted Uproarious Game,** Transogram, TV/cartoon, board game, lid shows smiling lion with outstretched arms in center oval surrounded by 6 other animals, 1965 . . . . . . . .   **70.00**

**Literary Salad,** Parker Brothers, educational card game,

*Little Jack Horner*

16¹/₂ x 5", cover shows bowl and books, copyright and mfg info at lid bottom, contains 48 cards, played like *Authors,* older game in updated box, ©1890 . . . . . . . . . . . . . . . . .   **20.00**

• Second cover shows oval on left and seated graduate reading book, "A Game of Quotations," box contains 36 cards . . . . . . . . . . . . . .   **20.00**

**Literature Game,** L.J. Colby & Co., educational, card game, 3³/₄ x 2¹/₂ x 1³/₈", info on cover includes "500 Questions and Answers on English and American LIterature, 100 Cards," and "Price, 25 cents," copyright info lower left corner, ©1897 by A.W. Mumford . . . . .   **10.00**

**Little Beaver's 3 Game Set,** Built–Rite, western, board game, cover shows Little Beaver on mule, game name on fence board, cactus, and sunset, 1956 . . . . . . . . . . . . . . . . . . .   **55.00**

**Little Black Sambo,** Cadaco, book, board game, cover shows 4 tigers watching Sambo carrying umbrella, 1951 . . . . . . . . . .   **90.00**

**Little Bo–Peep,** Parker Brothers, nursery rhyme, card game, 5¹/₂ x 4", cover shows Little Bo–Peep and meadow scene, contains 28 multicolored litho cards, ©1895 . . . . . . . . . . . . . .   **20.00**

**Little Boy Blue,** Cadaco–Ellis, nursery rhyme, action game, Hide and Go Seek, cover shows boy asleep on haystack, 2 cows, and horn on checkered knapsack, 1955 . . . . . . . . . . . . . . .   **15.00**

**Little Boy Blue,** Milton Bradley, nursery rhyme, board game, 12¹/₂ x 12¹/₄", cover shows Little Boy Blue blowing horn and dog at his feet, c1905–10 . . . . . . . .   **50.00**

**Little Cowboy Game, The,** Parker Brothers, western board game, 10¹/₂" sq, cover shows cowboy with lasso on horse, second horse chasing steer in background, contains 4 round colored wooden counters and spinner, wooden box, ©1895 . . . . .   **95.00**

**Little Hocus Pocus,** unknown manufacturer, magic, card game, 8³/₄ x 4³/₄", lid shows pointing figure and girl wearing cape looking at seated bearded man holding stick wearing, "Merry Game" in oval lower right corner, contains 32 multicolored hand painted cards and 36 markers, wooden box with sliding lid and partitioned bottom, c1840–50 . . . . . . . . . . .   **350.00**

**Little Jack Horner,** Milton Bradley, nursery rhyme, board game, cover shows cat beside seated Jack with feet on pillow holding up thumb of right hand and holding "pie" in left hand, contains 4 round colored wooden markers and spinner, c1910 *see illus* . . . . . . . . . . . . . . . .   **50.00**

**Little Mother Goose,** Parker Brothers, nursery rhyme, card game, 5³/₄ x 4¹/₄", cover shows

*Little Orphan Annie*

*Little Soldier*

Humpty Dumpty riding goose,
c1890 . . . . . . . . . . . . . . . . . .     **30.00**

**Little Noddy's Taxi Game,** Parker
Brothers, book series, board
game, cover shows boy wearing
hat in convertible waving to
woman wearing hat and carrying purse, policeman and buildings in background, 1 of
2 games in series, characters
created by Enid Blyton, 1956 . .     **90.00**

**Little Orphan Annie Game,**
Milton Bradley, No. 4359,
comic character, board game,
comic cover by Harold Gray
shows running Annie and Sandy
with dialog balloons, 1927
*see illus* . . . . . . . . . . . . . . . . .     **130.00**

**Little Pigs, The,** Parker Bros.,
generic, board game, 10 x 7",
cover shows 2 pigs waving to
2 pigs riding in cart pulled by
donkey, c1890 . . . . . . . . . . . . .     **150.00**

**Little Rascals Clubhouse Bingo,
The Original,** Gabriel, movie
characters, board game, cover
shows Little Rascals, dog, and
clubhouse, faces in boxes in
background, mfg name top left
corner, 1958 . . . . . . . . . . . . .     **20.00**

**Little Red Bushy–Tail,** Parker
Brothers, generic, board game,
separate 18¹/₂" sq board and pcs
box, contains 4 wooden counters and numbered cards,
©1921. . . . . . . . . . . . . . . . . .     **50.00**

**Little Soldier, The,** United Games
Co., military, board game,
17¹/₂ x 10¹/₂", cover shows
young saluting soldier wearing
oversized coat, knickers, and
ruffled shirt carrying sword and

standing before tent, mfg ship
logo and "made in Salem,
Mass." in lower left corner, contains spinner and 4 wooden
counters, c1900 *see illus* . . . . .     **50.00**

**Liz Tyler & The Mystery of the
Crown Jewels,** Ideal, mystery,
envelope game, cover shows
woman wearing belted coat
looking at jewels and standing
before man holding blindfold
and man with gun, inset of
2 players bottom left corner,
1963 . . . . . . . . . . . . . . . . . .     **30.00**

**Liz Tyler Hollywood Starlet,** Ideal,
movies, envelope game, cover
shows photographer taking picture of woman in gown being
followed by men in tuxedos,
bystanders in background, "Liz
Tyler" marquee, inset of 2 play-
ers bottom left corner, 1963 . . .     **30.00**

**Lobby,** Milton Bradley, politics,
board game, cover shows
Capitol building, "A Capital
Game," 1949 . . . . . . . . . . . . .     **20.00**

**Logomachy or War of Words,**
F.A. Wright, educational, card
game, 2⁷/₈ x 3⁷/₈", cover shows
group of people watching
boy climb post pointing to
"Premium Game," mfg info at
lid bottom, contains 56 cards,
1875 . . . . . . . . . . . . . . . . . .     **25.00**

**Lolli Plop,** Milton Bradley, generic, skill game, cover shows
2 sticks with enclosed circles
containing marbles, 1962 . . . . .     **10.00**

**London Bridge,** J.C. Singer, generic skill and action game, marble

*Lone Ranger*

roll game, 14³/₄ x 4", cover shows London scene and river, contains diecut cardboard archways, 1899–1900 . . . . . . . . . .    **75.00**

**London Game, The,** Parker Brothers, educational, board game, 25 x 16¹/₂", cover shows London street scene, pillared building, and dome of building above game name, contains 2 dice cups, 4 dice, 4 colored wooden markers, and toy letters, wooden box, ©1898 . . . . .    **800.00**

**Lone Ranger Game, The,** Milton Bradley, TV/cartoon series, board game, cover shows Lone Ranger and Tonto on horses in desert scene, 1966 . . . . . . . . . .    **20.00**

**Lone Ranger Game, The,** Parker Brothers, radio/western, board game, separate 18¹/₂" sq board and 5 x 7¹/₂" pcs box, contains 4 colored metal rearing horses, 2 red plastic markers, and 8 metal markers, ©1938 . . . . . .    **60.00**

**Lone Ranger Game, The,** Parker Brothers, radio/western, board game, cover shows Lone Ranger waving hat on bucking Silver, full size box edition, 1938 *see illus* . . . . . . . . . . . . . . . . .    **55.00**

**Lone Ranger Game, The Legend of the,** Milton Bradley, movie, western, lid shows Lone Ranger on bucking Silver, circle inset of Ranger and Tonto, 1980 . . . . . .    **12.00**

**Long Green, The,** Milton Bradley, horse racing, board game, cover shows jockeys riding horses around center square with game name, "A Big Money Game of Chance," contains play money, dice, riders and horses, and counters, 1936 . . . . . . . .    **20.00**

**Look Out Below,** Ideal, generic, action balancing game, cover shows little boy holding ladder with fireman at the top, also shows people below holding safety net, 1968 . . . . . . . . . . .    **20.00**

**Looney Tunes,** Milton Bradley, cartoon, board game, cover shows racing Bugs Bunny wearing #2, Porky Pig and other comic characters cheering him on, 1968 . . . . . . . . . . . . . . . .    **35.00**

**Lost Gold,** Parker Brothers, adventure/treasure hunt, board game, cover shows boy playing game, man riding horse followed by second horse going through mountain pass, and "Gold Finder," contains special board for burying treasure, treasure maps, gold pcs, and "The Lost Gold of Coyote Canyon" comic book, 1975 . . . . . . . . . . . . . .    **15.00**

**Lost In Space,** Milton Bradley, TV/space, board game, cover shows Robinson family running from one–eyed monster, spaceship, and astronaut 1965 . . . . .    **60.00**

**Lost in Space 3D Action Fun Game,** Remco, TV/space, skill and action game, cover shows 2 boys with 3–dimensional board, inset of 4 adults top right corner, 1966 . . . . . . . . . . . . .    **170.00**

**Lot The Calf,** Brown Games Inc., western/strategy, board game, cover shows man with lasso on horse chasing calf through fence opening, 1964 . . . . . . . . . . . .    **20.00**

**Lotto 6/4 All,** L.L. Ltd., 1989, California Edition, generic, skill and action game, cover shows game name and numbers 6 through 10 on round cylinder, contains number chart, 1989 . .   **5.00**

**Love, The Game of,** Hasbro, generic, board game, Loveable Game series, cover shows hands embracing letters in "Love," 2 legs at bottom of "L," 1960s. .   **23.00**

**Lucan Game,** Milton Bradley, TV, board game, cover shows man with wolf and silhouette of second wolf, 1977 . . . . . . . . . . .   **10.00**

**Lucky Bingo,** Transogram, No. 7012, generic, board game, 13$^{11}$/$_{16}$ x 7$^{1}$/$_{4}$ x 1$^{1}$/$_{8}$", cover shows players seated at table with bingo cards, ©1936 . . . . . . . .   **15.00**

**Lucky '9' Race Game,** Built–Rite, auto racing, board game, cover shows cars on race track, black and white checkered flag, and fans in stands, "Dude Ranch" game on reverse, 1956. . . . . . .   **20.00**

**Lucky Snap Ball,** Milton Bradley, generic, skill game, cover shows 4 figures around gameboard and playing pcs, man and woman holding "score board," 1941 . . . . . . . . . . . . . . . . .   **18.00**

**Lucky Star Gum Ball Game,** Ideal, generic, board game, cover shows gumball machine, multicolored gumball border, 1961 . . . . . . . . . . . . . . . . .   **30.00**

**Lucky Ten The Money Game,** Lucky Ten Co., business, board game, cover shows 3 rectangles, fanned cards, wad of currency, and players at table, 1974 . . . .   **8.00**

**Lucy Show,** Transogram, TV/comedy, board game, cover shows Lucille Ball and 7 cartoon drawings of Lucy in various outfits, mfg logo bottom right corner, faces of 4 show actors top right corner, based on second series, 1962 . . . . . . . . . . . . . . . . .   **80.00**

**Lucy's Tea Party Game,** Milton Bradley, comic strip character,

cover shows Lucy and friends, gameboard on table, contains plastic tea cups, 1971 . . . . . . .   **30.00**

**Ludwig Von Drake Tiddly Winks, Walt Disney's,** Whitman, generic, skill game, cover shows Von Drake wearing flat hat gameboard, vest, and jacket, 3 Disney characters flipping tiddly winks toward hat, 1961. . . .   **8.00**

### –M–

**M\*A\*S\*H Game,** Milton Bradley, TV/military, board game, cover shows Red Cross helicopter, tent flying flag, soldiers, and strip with 4 show star faces, 1981 . . . . . . . . . . . . . . . . . .   **25.00**

**Mad Magazine Card Game,** Parker Brothers, media, card game, cover has game name above playing cards with cartoon drawings, cards numbered 2, 3, and 6 and Joker visible, 1980 . . . . . . . . . . . . . . . . . .   **10.00**

**Mad Magazine Game, The,** Parker Brothers, media, board game, cover has magazine logo and cartoon characters around gameboard, 1 figure wearing cap with "M," 1979 . . . . . . . . .   **10.00**

**Madam Morrows Fortune Telling Cards,** McLoughlin Brothers, fortune telling, card game, 4$^{1}$/$_{2}$ x 6", lid shows seated woman wearing cape holding cards in right hand and pointing with left hand, tripod table to her left, copyright info at lid bottom below "Cards," ©1886 . . . . . . .   **30.00**

**Madame Le Normand's Mystic Cards of Fortune,** McLoughlin Brothers, fortune telling, card game, cover shows cat next to woman with her arms outstretched arms wearing pointed hat, clock tower background, c1882 . . . . . . . . . . . . . . . . .   **40.00**

**Madame Planchette Horoscope Game**, Selchow & Righter, for tune telling, board game, cover shows woman holding cards, inset circle of woman wearing shawl with hand on gameboard, 1967 . . . . . . . . . . . . . . . . . .     **25.00**

**Magic Dots For Little Tots,** Milton Bradley, art, skill and action game, 6 x 9⅝", cover shows child wearing shorts and sailor collar shirt hanging painting with 2 other paintings, dog at his side, contains 10 black and white perforated cards, 2 boxes of cardboard dots for creating colored picture, ©1907 . . . . . .     **30.00**

**Magic! Magic! Magic! Game,** Remco, board game, cover shows 4 players with gameboard, "How'd He Do That?" in dialogue balloon, 1975 . . . .     **20.00**

**Magic Race,** Habob, horse racing, board game, cover shows racing horses, "25 races," "with all the thrills and hazards of an actual horse race," and "Watch 'Em Run," 1940s. . . . . . . . . . . . . .     **70.00**

**Magic Squares and Mosaic Tablets,** Milton Bradley, educational, card game, 7 x 5", cover has game name and mfg and publishing info in oval, contains lettered and numbered cardboard squares, invented by Edward W. Gilman, 1869 . . . . .     **40.00**

**Magnetic Fish Pond,** Milton Bradley, fishing, board game, cover shows game name in circle and goldfish, 1942 . . . . .     **10.00**

**Magnetic Jack Straws,** E.I. Horsman, generic, skill game, 5½ x 3½", cover shows people seated at table with long tablecloth, circle in upper left corner shows hand using tool to pick up stick, contains 35 various shaped metal "straws," metal forceps, pronged magnet, and metal clown and horseman figures, ©1891 . . . . . . . . . . .     **20.00**

**Magnificent Race, The,** Parker Brothers, travel, board game, cover shows ship with steaming smokestack and flying flag, balloon with basket, plane, and open cars, 1975 . . . . . . . . . . .     **15.00**

**Mah–Jongg Game,** unknown manufacturer, generic, tile game, contains ivory and bamboo pcs, 1920s . . . . . . . . .     **55.00**

**Mah–Jongg "Junior,"** Mah–Jongg Sales of America, cover shows inset game name with circles border, "The Game of a Thousand Wonders," wooden set, 1923 . . . . . . . . . . . . . . .     **25.00**

**Mail, Express or Accommodation, Game of,** Milton Bradley, generic, board game, 22 x 14½", updated 1920s' cover of earlier McLoughlin Brothers game shows train with steam engine and railroad signal post, Bradley reissued following Bradley's buyout of Mc Loughlin in 1920, contains 4 round colored wooden markers, spinner, and printed cards, wooden box, ©1895. . . .     **450.00**

**Mail Run,** Quality Games, TV/western, board game, based on "Pony Express" series, cover shows 4 mounted figures, cowboy holding gun, and "wanted" notice, 1960 . . . . . . . . . . . . .     **40.00**

**Major Bowes' Amateur Hour,** Warner Manufacturing Co., No. 1, generic, action game, cover shows game name, "Popular Edition," and mfg name bottom left corner and location bottom right corner, unknown date . . . . . . . . . . . .     **20.00**

**Major League Base Ball Game,** Philadelphia Game Mfg. Co., sports, board game, 19 x 13½", cover has script game name written on angle, contains 20 wooden peg players, 6 wooden score pegs, 2 small red boxes, and 9 line–up card packets, Honus Wagner and Ty Cobb on line–up cards, 1912 . .     **800.00**

**Major Matt Mason Space Exploration,** Mattel, space, board game, cover shows astronaut on moon landscape and "spinning volcano," 1967     **60.00**

**Make A Face,** Milton Bradley, TV/generic, action game, First Edition, cover shows multicolored game name and paper

*The Man From U.N.C.L.E. Game*

*Management*

strips for creating different faces, *Good Housekeeping* and *Parents Magazine* seals of approval, 1962 . . . . . . . . . . .   **20.00**

**"Make–A–Million,"** Parker Brothers, business, card game, cover shows game name in quotes above money bag with "$" sign, mfg info at bottom, 1935 . . . . . . . . . . . . . . . . . .   **10.00**

**Man From U.N.C.L.E. Card Game, The,** Milton Bradley, TV/spy, card game, cover shows Napolean Solo in square inset and running figure carrying briefcase and shooting gun, 1965 . . . . . . . . . . . . . . . . . .   **22.00**

**Man From U.N.C.L.E. Game, The,** Ideal, TV/spy, board game, cover shows man aiming pistol, figure hitting man with briefcase in one hand and gun in other, third figure wearing tie and jacket, and fourth figure in doorway, 1965 *see illus* . . . . . .   **35.00**

**Man From U.N.C.L.E. Shoot Out!,** Milton Bradley, TV/spy, skill and action game, cover shows man shooting gun, second man with light hair wearing sweater and shooting gun, and hand operating game, 1965 . . .   **50.00**

**Man From U.N.C.L.E. Target Game,** Ideal, TV/spy, lid shows 4 action figure strips, gun in separate inset, mfg logo bottom right corner, and man holding gun upper right corner, 1965 . .   **50.00**

**Man From U.N.C.L.E. Thrush 'Ray–Gun Affair,'** Ideal, TV/spy, board game, cover shows man wearing sweater and man in

coat and tie in upper left corner, small man and lined sphere beside game name, oval building with ray gun extension, and mfg logo bottom right corner, "Featuring Mechanical Ray Gun and Dimensional Thrush Hideouts," contains large plastic pcs, 1965 . . . . . . . . . . . . . . .   **75.00**

**Man in The Moon, Game of, The,** McLoughlin Brothers, generic, board game, 14$\frac{1}{8}$ x 15", cover shows checkerboard with man in the moon face and squares with moons, contains 24 round wooden counters, wooden box, ©1901 . . . . . . . . . . . . . . . . . .   **4,000.00**

**Management,** Avalon Hill, business, board game, cover shows side view of man standing at desk and back view of man seated in chair, 1960 *see illus* . .   **30.00**

**Managing Your Money,** Cuna Mutual Insurance Society, business, board game, cover shows game board, "A Credit Union Money and Insurance Game" in dialogue box, 1969 . . . . . . . . .   **10.00**

**Man–Chu,** US Playing Card Co., generic, Mah–Jongg game with cards, cover shows lizard with open mouth, "The Famous Chinese Game, Made in U.S.A." bottom right corner, 1923 . . . . .   **20.00**

**Mandinka,** E.S. Lowe, strategy, board game, cover shows playing surface, 1978 . . . . . . . . . . .   **10.00**

**Mandrake The Magician Game,**
Transogram, magic/comic strip
character, board game, cover
shows Mandrake in cape and
top hat pointing at 2 male figures wearing hats and 1 male
figure with raised arms, includes
"magic eyes" to help player
with next move, 1966 . . . . . . .     **40.00**

**Manhunt,** Milton Bradley, detective, electronic game, cover
shows 2 youngsters with gameboard, electronic computer,
probe, and scanner pcs, police
car, man seated at switchboard,
running figure in spotlight, and
suspect line–up, 1972 . . . . . . .     **10.00**

**Maniac Electronic Game**, Ideal,
generic, action game, Simon
Says type game, cover shows
game name on either side of
electric vibrations emitting from
electronic pc, 1979 . . . . . . . .     **10.00**

**Mansion of Happiness, The,**
Parker Brothers, generic, board
game, 21 x 14", cover shows
mansion in center circle,
"Happiness, First Board Game
in America" upper right corner,
"Authorized Edition" bottom left
corner, contains spinner and
6 colored wooden counters,
wooden box, reissue of 1843
version by W. & S.B. Ives,
©1894. . . . . . . . . . . . . . . . .     **500.00**

**Marble Maze,** Hasbro, generic,
skill game, cover shows circular
playing surface, "It's A Hasbro
Toy" upper left corner, "A
Fascinating Skill Game for All
Ages" below game name, small
sketched figure bottom right
corner, 1966 . . . . . . . . . . . . .     **15.00**

**Marblehead Game,** Ideal, skill
game, cover shows standing
woman, man wearing glasses,
and girl and boy at table with
playing pc, "The exciting game
of a marble landslide," mfg logo
bottom right corner, 1969. . . . .     **10.00**

**Margie The Game of Whoopee!,**
Milton Bradley, TV series, board
game, cover shows Margie,
game name in flag banner, and
4 figures in convertible, 1 wear-

ing striped jacket, other carrying
flag banner, 1961 . . . . . . . . . . .     **35.00**

**Marlin Perkins' Wild Kingdom
Game,** Don Meier Productions,
TV personality, board game,
cover shows Perkins with leopard, inset pictures of animals
including tiger, lion, and ape,
"Where You Save Endangered
Wildlife Throughout the World,"
1977 . . . . . . . . . . . . . . . . . .     **12.00**

**Marlin Perkins' Zoo Parade,**
Cadaco–Ellis, TV personality,
board game, cover shows
Perkins in circle and animals
including elephant, giraffe, lion,
tiger, and moose, 1955 . . . . . . .     **25.00**

**Mary Hartman Mary Hartman,**
Reiss, TV/comedy, board game,
cover shows picture frames on
table, "The Game of Life in
Fernwood," 1976–77 . . . . . . . .     **25.00**

**Mary Poppins Carousel Game,
Walt Disney's,** Parker Brothers,
movie/book, board game, cover
has Poppins riding on small
carousel and holding umbrella,
1964 . . . . . . . . . . . . . . . . . .     **30.00**

**Mary Poppins Game, Walt
Disney's,** Whitman, movie/book,
board game, cover shows street
scene with boy, girl, and
Poppins flying with umbrella,
1964 . . . . . . . . . . . . . . . . . .     **25.00**

**Mask,** Parker Brothers, toy/TV
series, board game, cover shows
trucks, plane, and artillery fire,
"Raid and Rescue Game," 1985     **5.00**

**Masquerade Party,** Bettye–B.,
TV/game show, board game,
cover has game show panel
photo flanked by clown and
masked woman, balloon border
at top, contains 16 cardboard
famous people figures, wooden
stands, clue cards, and costume
photos of Pee Wee Reese, Jack
Dempsey, Leo Durocher, and
other characters, 1955 . . . . . . .     **75.00**

**Mastermind,** Invicta, generic,
guessing and logic game, cover
shows standing woman and
seated man, game name angled
at top, "Break the Hidden
Code," 1972 . . . . . . . . . . . . .     **8.00**

*Match Game*

**Masterpiece,** Parker Brothers, auction, board game, cover shows buyers, auctioneer, and painting on easel, "The Art Auction Game," 1970 . . . . . . .   **15.00**

**Match Game,** Milton Bradley, TV/game show, quiz game, cover shows man and woman before "Super Match Board," panel of 6 people, and game host with 2 contestants seated behind tables with triangle and circle on front, 1974 *see illus* . .   **12.00**

**Match Game, The,** 1st Edition Milton Bradley, TV/game show, quiz game, cover shows dialogue box with "Name a Part of a Chicken" and 5 figures holding cards with words such as Comb, Leg, Beak, and Liver, 1963 . . . . . . . . . . . . . . . . . . .   **20.00**

**"Matchbox" Traffic Game,** Fred Bronner Corp., toy, board game, cover shows cars, gameboard, and Matchbox car box at lower right corner, included 2 Matchbox cars, 1968 . . . . . . . . . . . .   **35.00**

**McDonald's Game, The,** Milton Bradley, advertising, board game, cover shows boy and girl with playing board and pcs, Golden arches in background, 1975 . . . . . . . . . . . . . . . . . . .   **18.00**

**McHale's Navy Game,** Transogram, TV/military, board game, cover shows docked ship, Quonset hut beneath palm trees, and Ernest Borgnine in circle inset, 1962 . . . . . . . . . . .   **40.00**

**Media Careers, WABC–TV's,** TV, ABC, cover shows 7 circle insets with women's faces, "A Game for Aspiring Advertising Executives," 1977 . . . . . . . . . . .   **15.00**

**Meet the Presidents,** Selchow & Righter, politics/educational, board game, cover shows rack of coins with red, white and blue ribbon border, action figures representing various Presidents surround circle with mfg logo, contains presidential picture cards, 1950 . . . . . . . . .   **20.00**

**Mel Allen's Baseball Game,** *see Baseball Game, Mel Allen's*

**Meltdown,** Storeplay, Inc., military, board game, cover shows game name in solid and shaded colors, "The Nuclear Energy Conflict Game," 1980s . . . . . . .   **8.00**

**Melvin Purvis' "G"–Men Detective Game,** Parker Brothers, detective, board game, lid shows circle inset with man's picture, "Former Ace of the Department of Justice," 2 police on motorcycles, and man beside car, 1930s . . . . . . . . . . . . . . .   **45.00**

**Melvin The Moon Man,** Remco, Tumblebum Dice Games series, board game, cover shows waving figure, rocket, and boy holding shaker containing dice, contains 4 large moving pcs, huge playing mat "board," and deck of cards, 1959–60s . . . . . . . . . .   **70.00**

**Men Into Space,** Milton Bradley, TV/space, board game, cover shows man in XMP–13 spaceship, 1960
• First version with blond man in spaceship. . . . . . . . . . . . . . .   **50.00**
• Second version with dark haired man resembling show star Bill Lundigan . . . . . . . . . . . . . . .   **65.00**

**Men of Destiny,** Milton Bradley, politics, cover shows Mt Rushmore and "A Game of our Presidents," 1956 . . . . . . . . . . .   **20.00**

**Mentor,** Hasbro, generic, electronic game, cover shows "Hasbro's Electronic Wizard"

Merry–Go–Round

Miami Vice The Game

face, "Try to Beat the Man of
Bronze," 1961 . . . . . . . . . . . .   **45.00**

**Merit, The Catholic Game,**
Educational Research Corp.,
religion, board game, lid shows
angels flanking game name,
copyright and mfg info, 2robed
men, 1 robed woman, 2 youngsters, "The Approved Game" in
triangle upper left corner, and
"It's Fun to Learn...," 1962 . . . .   **18.00**

**Merry Circus Game, The,** Milton
Bradley, circus, board game,
cover shows smiling clown
wearing small hat and
polka–dot shirt carrying sign
with game name, 1960 . . . . . .   **12.00**

**Merry Game of Old Bachelor,
The,** McLoughlin Brothers,
generic, card game, Old Maid
type game, 5 x 6¹/₂", cover
shows man seated in chair at
table holding cards and playing
game, small lamp on table,
"Forlorn & Lonely" upper right
corner, ©1892 . . . . . . . . . . . .   **35.00**

**Merry–Go–Round,** Milton
Bradley, No. 4688, generic,
board game, 6³/₄ x 5¹/₂ x 1",
cover shows saddled horses
travelling in opposite directions,
c1910 *see illus.* . . . . . . . . . . . .   **25.00**

**Merry–Go–Round Game,**
Whitman, generic, 3–dimensional board game, cover shows
hand turning 3–dimensional
hill, 1965 . . . . . . . . . . . . . . .   **15.00**

**Merry Milkman Exciting Game
and Toy,** Hasbro, generic, board
game, cover shows milkman
carrying milk bottles and dairy
products walking with dog past
3 houses, contains milk trucks
and cardboard houses, 1955. . .   **55.00**

**Merv Griffin's Word For Word
Game,** Mattel, TV/game show,
word game, cover shows Griffin,
woman, girl, and boy with
gameboard, 2 people seated
beside letter "E" in background,
"Beat the Gyro Timer," 1963 . . .   **15.00**

**"Messenger," The,** McLoughlin
Brothers, generic, track board
game, 7¹/₄ x 7¹/₄", cover shows
boy wearing cap running past
bridge, "A Quick Game,"
contains 4 wooden counters
and spinner, c1890. . . . . . . . .   **40.00**

**Meteor Game,** A.C. Gilbert,
generic, skill game, metal board,
7¹/₂ x 5", cover shows 2 girls at
table with playing surface, boy
wearing bowtie looking on,
printed circles border, contains
metal forceps, multicolored clay
marbles, and instruction booklet, mfg by F. Ad. Richter & Co.,
No. 1 game, 1916 . . . . . . . . .   **20.00**

**"Mexican Pete,"** Parker Brothers,
generic, board game, cover
shows 4 men in sombreros at
table, large picture in background of smiling man wearing
sombrero, "(I–Got–It)," 1940s . .   **30.00**

**Miami Vice The Game,**
Pepperlane Industries, TV/crime,
board game, lid shows 2 men,
1 holding pistol, Miami skyline
background, 1984 *see illus*. . . .   **20.00**

*Mickey Mouse Krazy Ikes Club*

**Mickey Mouse Club Game in Disneyland,** Whitman, Disney, board game, cover shows Mickey holding rifle standing before "Mickey Mouse Club House," Pluto and other Disney characters in house, 1956. . . . .   **559.00**

**Mickey Mouse Krazy Ikes Club, Walt Disney's,** Whitman, construction, $15^1/_2$ x $8^1/_4$ x $1^3/_4$", cover shows Mickey, Goofy, and Donald Duck, contains plastic multicolored interlocking pieces, and booklet with illustrations, ©1955, Walt Disney Productions *see illus* . . . . . . .   **45.00**

**Mighty Comics Super Hero Game,** Transogram, comic book characters, board game, cover shows 5 characters, "10 of your favorite hero characters..." in strip at bottom including Fly Man, Fly Girl, and Mr Justice, 1966. . . . . . . . . . . . . . . . . .   **50.00**

**Mighty Hercules,** Hasbro, superhero, board game, cover shows Hercules grasping sword with both hands, 4 figures at right watching, "Thrills and Spills with Hercules on Mount Olympus," 1963 . . . . . . . . . .   **150.00**

**Mighty Mouse Rescue Game,** Harett–Gilmar, cartoon, board game, cover shows Mighty Mouse rescuing figure tied to railroad track and 2 figures tied to post, top hat flying off figure hit by Mighty Mouse, train in background, 1956 . . . . . . . . .   **50.00**

**Mighty Mouse Skill–Roll Game,** Pressman, cartoon, skill and action game, playing surface has scored areas for rolling balls, 1959 . . . . . . . . . . . . . . . . . . .   **60.00**

**Military Chess,** Joseph Cossman & Co., military, board game, cover shows soldier carrying rifle, soldier with bazooka, cannon, and tank, contains military chess pcs and battleground chess board, 1959 . . . . . . . . . . . . . . . . . .   **15.00**

**Mille Bornes,** Edmond Dujardin, travel, card game, "American Model," cover shows card with "1,000," similar to Touring game, 1960 . . . . . . . . . . . . . .   **7.00**

**Mille Bornes,** Parker Brothers, travel, card game, cover shows "Stop" and "Go" traffic signals and speed limit signs, "French Card Game Craze," 1962 . . . . .   **5.00**

**Mille Bornes,** Parker Brothers, travel, card game, lid shows hands of 4 players with playing cards, "French Card Game," 1971 . . . . . . . . . . . . . . . . . .   **3.00**

**Millers Outpost Game, The,** Millers Outpost, advertising, board game, clothing store, cover shows male figures dressed in scout uniforms and a female dressed for hiking, gameboard background, 1976. . . . . .   **15.00**

**Milton The Monster Game,** Milton Bradley, TV/cartoon, board game, cover shows 2 cartoon figures, third figure with skull face and bowtie, and fourth figure with striped tie, player and game object info in triangle at bottom right corner, 1966 . . . . . . . . . . . . . . . . . .   **35.00**

**Mind Over Matter,** Ideal, ESP, board game, "The Great Julian Presents the game of Extra Sensory Perceptions," cover shows man and his hands in colored swirls, 1967. . . . . . . . .   **15.00**

**Mindmaze,** Parker Brothers, generic, board game, cover shows man and woman with upright board and pegs, 1970 . .   **12.00**

**Miss America Pageant Game, The,** Parker Brothers, celebrity event, board game, cover shows 3 girls playing game, crowned Miss

*Monopoly*

America holding bouquet in background, 1974 . . . . . . . . .    **15.00**

**Miss Popularity Game,** Transogram, generic, board game, cover shows crowd and judges cheering girl wearing crown and holding winner's cup, "The Game all Girls Love to Play," 1961 . . . . . . . . . . . .    **30.00**

**Missing Links,** Milton Bradley, TV/game show, cover has 3 rows of linked pictures with game name and "The Game You See on Television" as center links, other links with 2 men, 1 woman, and question mark, 1964 . . . . . . . . . . . . . . . . .    **15.00**

**Mister Ed,** Parker Brothers, TV/comedy, board game, cover shows Mister Ed "The Talking Horse" in horseshoe, 1962 . . . .    **35.00**

**Mixed Pickles,** Adams & Co., generic, card game, 3 x 4½", lid shows jar with game name, "A Merry Game," mfg info and "Boston" on bottom, contains 30 red cards, 30 white cards, and 30 blue cards, 1867 . . . . .    **35.00**

**Mob Strategy,** Hasbro, TV/crime, board game, cover shows 5 men and woman wearing feathered headband around gameboard, NBC logo top right corner, "the take–over game," 1969 . . . . . .    **15.00**

**Monday Morning Quarterback Football Game,** A.B. Zbinden, sport, skill and strategy game, cover shows #60 trying to tackle ball carrier, football play diagram background, 1963 . . . .    **30.00**

**Moneta, Game of,** F.A. Wright, generic, card game, 5½ x 4",

cover shows coins below game name, "or Money Makes Money" in ribbon strip, "By the Author of Logomachy," copyright and publishing info at bottom, contains 50 cards representing US coins, ©1888 . . . . .    **25.00**

**Money Card,** Schaper, advertising/travel, lid shows American Express card, man holding large key standing behind woman wearing slacks, tourist spot buildings in background, map with plane in lower left corner, "An American Express Travel Game," 1972 . . . . . . . . . . . . .    **20.00**

**Money Game of Junior Executive, The,** see *Junior Executive, The Money Game of*

**Money! Money! Money!,** Whitman, business, board game, cover shows man wearing plaid jacket shouting game name through megaphone, currency, and bank building behind "$" figures, 1957 . . . . . . . . . .    **15.00**

**Moneypower,** Sherman Games, business/investments, board game, cover shows multicolored triangular pc in bottom right corner, game name angled from left to right, "The Investment Strategy Game," 1980 . . . . . . . .    **10.00**

**Monkees Game, Hey! Hey! The,** Transogram, TV/music, board game, cover shows Monkees in convertible, "As Seen on NBC Television" lower right corner, 2 versions of game released, 1 with plastic guitar and other with xylophone, 1967 . . . . . . .    **60.00**

**Monkeys and Coconuts,** Schaper, generic, board game, cover shows boy with hands covering eyes, girl with hands over mouth, and center monkey with hands over ears sitting in hut, bird on hut, floral background, 1965 . . . . . . . . . . . . . . . . .    **12.00**

**Monopoly,** Charles Darrow, business/real estate, board game, cover has "Monopoly" on red stripe across center, gameboard ©Chas B Darrow in corner of jail space, instructions on inside

*Monopoly, Popular Edition*

of lid cover, use personal token to play game, wooden buildings, $100 bills gold and $500 bills pink, made 1933–34 prior to Parker purchasing rights to game from Darrow *see illus* ... **3,000.00**

**Monopoly,** Parker Brothers, business/real estate, board game, cover shows railroad cars flanking square with man holding money above "$" sign, mfg info below "$" sign, early versions usually without illus on Community Chest space and Community Chest and Chance cards and include Charles Darrow copyright in Jail space, some have game pcs with moving parts

• 2 patent numbers and 1935 means game dates from 1935, metal pcs . . . . . . . . . . . . . **40.00**
• Any set with 2 patent numbers could date from 1936–43 . . . . . **30.00**
• One patent number could mean set dates after 1943 . . . . . . . . **15.00**

**Monopoly,** Parker Brothers, business/real estate, board game, "Popular Edition," lid has inverted light colored triangle with red border, locomotive and "$" sign in tip, "Parker Brothers Trade–Mark Game for its Real Estate Trading Game" at top,

and "Registered the U.S. Patent Office" below game name, 1950 **20.00**
• Popular Edition, same cover, only game name and "$" sign with locomotive in triangle, "Reg. U.S. Patent Office" below game name, green border, 1930s. . . . . . . . . . . . **30.00**

**Monopoly,** Parker Brothers, business/real estate, board game, Popular Edition, lid shows Rich Uncle Pennybags atop game name running diagonally across cover, "$" sign with locomotive below game name, mfg info near bottom, red border, wooden pawns, 1954 and later . . . . . **15.00**
• Same cover, green border, 1954 *see illus*. . . . . . . . . . . . . . . **15.00**

**Monopoly,** Parker Brothers, business/real estate, board game, White Box Edition No. 9 with Grand Hotels, lid shows gameboard with hotels and man running with money being chased by second man, 1950s . . . . . . . **30.00**
• Same cover but with illustration of playing board differentiating this common edition from others, contains plastic houses, 1940s thru 1960s . . . . . . . . . . **15.00**

**Monopoly,** Parker Brothers, business/real estate, board game, unusual train cover, 1957 . . . . . **15.00**

**Monopoly,** Parker Brothers, business/real estate, board game, common edition, cover shows gameboard, Parker Brothers and General Mills logos, General Mills acquired Parker Brothers in late 1960s . . . . . . . . . . . . . . **8.00**

**Monopoly,** Parker Brothers, business/real estate, board game, Deluxe Edition, styrofoam money holder, cover shows spaces from gameboard including Park Place, Electric Company, Reading, and Chance space, 1960s–70s. . . . . . . . . . **15.00**

**Monopoly,** Parker Brothers, business/real estate, board game, Braille Edition, 1980s . . . . . . . . **35.00**

**Monopoly,** Parker Brothers, business/real estate, board game, Commemorative Edition, 50th anniversary, cover shows game name above gameboard, "Commemorative Edition" written above "1935," metal box with gold tokens and Grand Hotels, 1985 . . . . . . . . . . . . . 50.00

**Monopoly,** Parker Brothers, business/real estate, board game, Deluxe Anniversary Edition, cover has buildings, car, and trees, "Deluxe Anniversary Edition" above game name, contains metal pcs and Grand Hotels, 1985 . . . . . . . . . . . . . 15.00

**Monopoly,** Parker Brothers, 1985, foreign editions, cover shows board written in foreign language
• French Edition, 1985 . . . . . . . . 15.00
• Russian Edition, "Special Limited Edition," 1988 . . . . . . 20.00
• German Edition, 1992 . . . . . . . 10.00
• Spanish Edition, 1978 . . . . . . . 15.00
• Japanese Edition, 1988 . . . . . . . 10.00
• Second Japanese Edition, colorful board, lid shows street scene with man with top hat and mustache holding currency, dice and gameboard spaces angled across right, 1980s . . . . . . . . . . . . . . . . 15.00

**Monopoly,** Waddington, business/real estate, board game, British version, cover shows game name at center below man holding money, "Property Trading Board Game," 1961 . . . 12.00
• Same cover, 1971 . . . . . . . . . . 8.00

**Monopoly,** Waddington, business/real estate, board game, Deluxe British Edition, cover has squares outlined on left, outlined strip with game name, and square inset upper right corner, 1972 . . . . . . . . . . . . . 15.00

**Monopoly Junior,** Parker Brothers, business/real estate, board game, cover shows man with top hat and cane inside second "O" of game name, same man leading group of youngsters across boardwalk, carnival tent, ferris wheel, and balloons in background, 1990 . . . . . . . . . 8.00

**Monopoly Playmaster,** Parker Brothers, electrically operated, placed in middle of gameboard to keep track of game moves, cover shows gameboard with Playmaster in center, inset of players, 1982 . . . . . . . . . . . . . 15.00

**Monorail Game, Disneyland,** *see Disneyland Monorail Game*

**Monster Lab,** Ideal, monster, 3–dimensional board, cover shows boy and girl at either end of laboratory gameboard with masked monster, 1964 . . . . . . . 25.00

**Monster Old Maid,** Milton Bradley, monster, card game, cover shows #1 and #2 monster picture cards and "with Monster Size Cards" in bat, 1964 . . . . . . 35.00

**Monster Squad Game, The,** Milton Bradley, TV/monster, board game, cover shows 3 figures standing in separate archways, 1 wearing cape, 1 in vest, knickers, and boots, and 1 in suit with hands on belt, truck with skull heads on side panel, 1977 . . . . . . . . . . . . . . 20.00

**Moon Blast Off,** Schaper, space, board game, cover shows girl and boy with circular playing surface with rocket in middle, "The Winners Blast Off for Earth Below, the Loser Doesn't Get to Go," 1970 . . . . . . . . . . . . . . . 20.00

**Mork & Mindy Card Game,** Milton Bradley, TV/comedy, card game, cover shows girl and boy surrounded by dialogue boxes, "Speak the Language of Mork From Ork...," 1978 . . . . . . . . . . 10.00

**Mork & Mindy Game,** Parker Brothers, TV/comedy, board game, cover shows girl in plaid jacket pointing at man wearing striped shirt, 1979 . . . . . . . . . 15.00

**Mosquito,** Milton Bradley, generic, skill and action game, cover shows mosquito chasing figure and hand operating gameboard, dotted lines around figure, mosquito, and game name, 1966 . . 20.00

**Mostly Ghostly!,** Cadaco, horror, board game, cover shows

*The Moving Picture Game*

3 skeletons and circle divided into 5 sections each containing skeleton pcs, contains 25 glow in the dark skeleton parts and spinner, 1975. . . . . . . . . . . . .    **20.00**

**Mother Earth's Produce Game,** by Mrs C.B. Sheldon, published by A. Flanagan, generic, card game, 4³/₄ x 3", cover shows game name, inventor's name, and mfg and publisher info in strip at bottom, contains 58 black and tan litho cards, c1880s–1910s . . . . . . . . . . . .    **20.00**

**Mother Hen Target Game,** STS, generic, skill and action game, lid shows boy aiming gun at turkey target, 1970. . . . . . . . .    **25.00**

**Mother's Helper,** Milton Bradley, generic, board game, cover shows girl wearing apron descending stairs while carrying wash basket, mother wearing apron watching, and boy holding broom, "Upstairs... Downstairs...All through the House," 1969 . . . . . . . . . . . .    **20.00**

**Motor Cycle Game,** Milton Bradley, generic, board game, 9" sq, cover shows boy wearing cap riding motorcycle near lake, mfg name and "Springfield, Mass" bottom right corner, contains 4 round colored wooden counters and spinner, ©1905 . .    **60.00**

**Mouse Trap Game,** Ideal, generic, board game, Rube Goldberg, lid shows assembled game with labeled parts and references in bottom left corner, mfg logo bottom right corner, 1963. . . . .    **35.00**

**Mouse Trap Game,** Ideal, generic, board game, cover shows game with marbles and mouse, mfg logo bottom right and upper left corners, "It's fun to build this comical wonder, but woe to the mouse who gets caught under," 1975 . . . . . . . . . . . . . . . . . .    **10.00**

**Mousie–Mousie,** Spears Games, generic, action party game, cover shows dice and 6 multi-colored mice on round surface, "A Fast Party Game, Catch 'Em as They Run," contains 70 counters, 1963 . . . . . . . . . . . .    **10.00**

**Movable Shadowgraphs,** Milton Bradley, generic, skill game, 8¹/₂ x 9¹/₂", cover shows hands creating shadow picture of duck on wall, directions at bottom, contains 5 multicolored litho cards illustrating hand positions for creating shadow pictures, c1905 . . . . . . . . . . . . . . . .    **175.00**

**Movie Land Keeno,** Wilder Mfg. Co., movie, bingo game, 9 x 7¹/₂", cover has cartoon movie stars sitting and standing around table, words in dialogue boxes, game name, trademark info, and "by S. J. Faxe" in spotlight strip, contains 8 large Keeno cards, 48 calling cards, and red chips, ©1929 . . . . . . . .    **95.00**

**Movie Land Lotto,** Milton Bradley, No. 4243, movie, bingo game, 9¹/₂ x 8¹/₄ x 1⁵/₈", cover shows mfg info including "Made in U.S.A." within 2 patterned triangles, ©1920s . . . . . . . . . .    **40.00**

**Moving Picture Game, The,** Milton Bradley, movie, board game, 15 x 9", lid shows people in line to buy tickets, bi–fold billboard in front of ticket booth, contains 4 round colored wood-en markers and spinner, invent-ed by Howard Garis, author of Uncle Wiggily stories and inven-tor of the Uncle Wiggily Game, c1922 *see illus*. . . . . . . . . . . .    **60.00**

**Mr. Brain,** Jacmar, educational, electronic computer game, lid shows computer, 2 children playing game, and multicolored computer cards, "The Electronic Answer Man," 1959 . . . . . . . .    35.00

**Mr. Bug Goes To Town,** Milton Bradley, No. 4310, generic, board game, cover shows cartoon characters surrounding envelope with postmark, stamp, and return address of "Norton South, Bugville, U.S.A.," male figure wearing top hat and tails, girl with floral print skirt, mfg logo bottom right corner, contains 8 wooden pawns, 1955 . .    35.00

**Mr. Doodle's Dog,** Selchow & Righter, generic, track game, cover shows dog in bottom right corner, doghouse in upper left corner, and game name running diagonally from left to right, created by Howard Garis, Uncle Wiggily author, 1950s . . . . . . .    25.00

• Earlier version contains 4 metal bones, metal dog, 4 wooden pawns, and large spinner, c1940 . . . . . . . . . . . . . . . .    35.00

**Mr. Machine Game,** Ideal, toy, board game, cover shows 3 figures wearing top hats saying "Mr. Machine," came with plastic Mr. Machine move indicator, 1961 . . . . . . . . . . . . . . . . . . .    55.00

**Mr. Magoo's Maddening Misadventures,** Transogram, cartoon, board game, cover shows Magoo walking plank atop building, skyscrapers in background, Magoo in car stopped by policeman on motorcycle, and Magoo swinging golf club, "The Nearsighted" above game name, 1970 . . . . . . . . . . . . . .    50.00

**Mr. Novak Game,** Transogram, TV/careers, board game, cover shows students outside high school, game name and show star on blackboard, "Adventures of a Young Teacher in a Metropolitan High School," 1963 . . .    35.00

**Mr. President,** 3M, politics, board game, cover shows candidate at platform with microphones, sign with candidate's picture, and red, white, and blue sign with "USA" in middle, "The Game of Campaign Politics," 1967 . . . . .    18.00

*Mr. Ree*

**Mr. Ree,** Selchow & Righter, detective, separate 18¼" board and pcs box, cover shows moon and dark building through window pane, "The Fireside Detective" below game name, "A Thriller Game" above mfg info in bottom left corner, contains 4 small metal weapon tokens, 76 character cylinders, 7 character cards, and 100 direction cards, c1936–57 *see illus* . . . . .    50.00

• Versions with plaster heads and resin in cylinders . . . . . . . . . .    110.00

• Versions with plaster heads only    85.00

• Versions with metal weapons only. . . . . . . . . . . . . . . . . . .    50.00

**Mr. Ree,** Selchow & Righter, detective, board game, cover shows strip of inset pictures including detective in plaid cape and hat holding magnifying glass and 4 pictures of 2 men and 2 women in different actions, background of moon shining on building with many spires, "The Fireside Detective Game," contains plastic characters, 1957 . . . . . . . . . . . . . . .    20.00

**Mr. T. Game,** Milton Bradley, TV/animated show, board game, cover shows Mr T wearing necklaces and arm bracelet, fist holding "T" of game name, "Team Up with Mr T. In an Exciting Race Against Time," 1983 . . . . .    10.00

*The Muppet Show*

**Mt. Everest,** Gabriel, sport/mountain climbing, 3–dimensional board game, cover shows mountain climbers tied with rope climbing snow capped mountain and 4 children playing game, "Climb the Highest Mountain," 1955 . . . . . . . . . .    **25.00**

**Mulligans,** San Fernando Valley Game Co., sports, skill/chance game, cover shows swinging golfer, movement of golf balls, sand traps, and clubhouse, "Pinehurst Championship Edition, A Game of Skill or Chance...for Golfers and Non–Golfers," various editions produced, 1947 . . . . . . . . . . .    **30.00**

**Multiplication Merrily Matched,** unknown manufacturer, educational, math game, cover shows 2 youngsters in circle at center and flower and leaf border, "A New Game, To Amuse Minor Mathematicians," unknown date    **20.00**

**Mumbly Peg,** The American Toy Airship Co., generic, skill game, $7^{3}/_{8}$ x $7^{1}/_{2}$ x $7''$, cover shows 4 people around table, game name in table center, and small round playing pc in front of each person, "Made in U.S.A. at Mansfield, Ohio by..." and mfg name at bottom, contains target, 21 wooden pegs, 4 round felt pads, 5 rings, and snapper, c1920s . . . . . . . . . . . . . . . .    **20.00**

**Munsters Card Game,** Milton Bradley, TV/monster, board game, cover shows 5 people playing game at table, 3 holding cards, 1 leaning over boy's shoulder, and 1 with hand to

*The Game of Mutuels*

mouth, produced with 2 different covers, 1964 . . . . . . . . . . .    **35.00**

**Muppet Show, The,** Parker Brothers, TV, board game, cover shows Kermit the Frog and other Muppets, 1977 *see illus* . . . . . .    **12.00**

**Murder on the Orient Express,** Ideal, mystery, board game, "A Sherlock Holmes Mystery Game," Famous Mystery Classic Series, based on Sir Arthur Conan Doyle's character, cover shows book with title and bookmark, train, and people around 2 men wearing hats, 1 holding magnifying glass, other holding gun, 1967 . . . . . . . . . . . . . . .    **30.00**

**Murder, She Wrote,** Warren, TV/mystery, board game, cover has show star Angela Lansbury and running figure in front of illuminated house, 1985 . . . . . .    **8.00**

**Musingo,** Mattel, music, board game, cover shows organ grinder with monkey and 3 youngsters playing game, and "A Musical Surprise Game," 1962 . . . . . . . . . . . . . . . . .    **20.00**

**Mutuels, The Game of,** horse race, $23^{1}/_{2}$ x $4^{1}/_{4}$ x $1^{3}/_{4}''$, cover shows "©1938 Mutuels, Inc. Los Angeles Calif." printed on track, contains painted canvas race track, wooden tokens, metal horses, 2 dice, paper money, foul cards, and instruction sheet, *see illus* . . . . . . . . . . . . . . . .    **85.00**

**My Fair Lady,** Standard Toykraft, broadway musical, board game, cover shows man in tuxedo and woman in gown, wrought iron railing and 4 dancing couples in background, 1962 . . . . . . . . . .    **30.00**

**My Favorite Martian,** Transogram, TV/comedy, lid shows man wearing jacket standing with hand on "M" and man with antenna "ears," 1963 . . . . . . . .    **70.00**

*Mystic Skull*

**Mystery Date Game,** Milton Bradley, generic, board game, cover shows 4 people watching woman in long dress opening door marked "?," man in tuxedo behind open door, "Is Your Date Behind This Door?," 1965 . . . . .     **50.00**

**Mystic Eye,** Mr B., fortune telling, board game, cover shows game name, eye, and "She knows all, tells all" in circle, woman's head, arms, and legs extending from circle, word border includes "Lie Detector, Self Analysis, Past, Present, Future, Truth Finder, Lucky Number, Psychometer," and "Lucky Month," 1953 . . . . . . . . . . . .     **35.00**

**Mystic Skull,** Ideal, mystical/voodoo, board game, lid shows cauldron and skull hanging from branch, "The Game of Voodoo...with the mysterious moving skull," mfg logo bottom right corner, 1964 *see illus* . . . .     **40.00**

**Mystic Wanderer, The,** J.H. Singer, mystical/fortune telling board game, Ouija type game, 8¼ x 4¾", lid shows half of sphere containing woman with outstretched arms wearing long dress and cape, winged animal, and small table with smoking sphere, mfg info and "New York, U.S.A." in rect box bottom left, contains 5 multicolored lettered cardboard strips and footed wooden planchette, c1890–95 . . . . . . . . . . . . . . .     **75.00**

**Mythology, The Game of,** Peter G. Thomson, mystic, board game, 3¾ x 5⅛ x 1¼", lid has animal pictures including winged horse in center circle, mfg name and "Cincinnati, O." at bottom, ©1884 . . . . . . . . . . . . . . . . . .     **25.00**

–N–

**Name That Tune Game,** Milton Bradley, TV game show, musical bingo game, cover shows musical note bar with game name, show host George De Witt, musical note with flag at top, and "game" in solid oval on 33⅓ rpm record, 1957 . . . . . . .     **25.00**
- Second edition has show host and figures of man, woman, and child around bingo card with "MUSIC" at top and 5 diagonal holes, came with 33⅓ rpm record, De Witt's voice, 1959 . . . . . . . . . . . . .     **15.00**

**Nancy Drew Mystery Game, The,** Parker Brothers, book, board game, cover shows Nancy in rain storm holding hat and flashlight pointed at house, 1957 . . .     **45.00**
- Second version shows Nancy standing behind tree with flashlight, electrical storm background, 1959 . . . . . . . .     **45.00**

**National–American Baseball Game, The,** Parker Brothers, sports, board game, cover shows batter in triangle at left, mfg info bottom right, no date . . . . . . .     **50.00**

**National Velvet Game,** Transogram, TV/movie/horse racing, board game, cover shows riders on horses, inset of girl with head resting on hand, 1961. . . . . . . .     **35.00**

**Nations, Game of,** Milton Bradley, educational, card game, 6 x 7½", cover shows 3 men placing small flags on globe, contains 36 multicolored litho cards representing nations, ©1908. . . . . . . . . . . . . . . . . .     **20.00**

**Naval Maneuvers,** McLoughlin Brothers, military, board game, 23 x 16", cover shows clouds

*NBC–TV News Game, with Chet Huntley*

closing in on ship at sea, contains 5 metal ships, 5 subs, and spinner, c1920 . . . . . . . . . . . .    **400.00**

**NBA Bas–Ket,** Cadaco, sports, action game, cover shows playing surface for "Real Basketball in Miniature," strips of stars, and NBA team logos, 1983 . . . . . . .    **10.00**

**NBC Game of the Week,** Hasbro, sports, board game, cover shows batter, catcher, and umpire, "The Game Based on Authentic Baseball Statistics from NBC Sports," mfg logo bottom right corner, 1969 . . . . .    **35.00**

**NBC Peacock Game,** Selchow & Righter, TV, board game, cover shows 3 people pointing at NBC's new color "Peacock" on TV set, 1966–67 . . . . . . . . . . .    **25.00**

**NBC Pro Playoff,** Hasbro, sports, board game, NBC Sports in Action series, lid shows #16 ready to throw ball, #73 with hand raised, ref and fans in background, and "NBC" logo top left corner, 1969 . . . . . . . .    **35.00**

**NBC The Home Stretch,** Hasbro, sports, horse racing, NBC Sports in Action series, cover shows jockeys and horses, "NBC" logo and mfg name top left corner, 1970 . . . . . . . . . . . . . . . . . .    **15.00**

**NBC–TV News Game, with Chet Huntley,** Dadan, Inc., educational, broadcasting, board game, cover shows inset of Huntley on phone, "NBC" on microphone, 1962 *see illus* . . .    **25.00**

**Nellie Bly,** J.H. Singer, celebrity, board game, 7¼ x 14¼", cover shows woman in hat and long gown carrying cane, telephone pole in background, contains spinner and wooden markers, c1898 . . . . . . . . . . . . . . . . .    **150.00**

**Nemo,** Creston Industries, fortune telling, board game, cover has face and linked dots in circle surrounded by zodiac signs, "Unlock the Secrets of the Future," 1969 . . . . . . . . . . . . .    **15.00**

**Neutral Game of War, Peace and Indemnity, The,** Biddle Corp., educational/military, card game, 7¼ x 4", cover shows flags of nations in oval and inset of 4 players, "Fascinating; Instructive," contains 104 light green and white backed cards with pictures of swords and cannons, c1910s . . . . . . . . . . .    **25.00**

**Never Say Die,** Parker Brothers, generic, dice game, cover shows game name below mfg logo and above "This Game Has Fast Action," 3 dice over circle bottom right corner, 9 circles down left, 1959 . . . . . . . . . . .    **12.00**

**New Bicycle Game, The,** Parker Brothers, generic, board game, 21 x 12", cover shows man in hat and woman in long dress on bikes in park setting, oval border of trees and bushes, contains spinner, 4 cardboard cyclists on wooden stands, and destination cards, 1894 . . . . . . . . . . . . . .    **525.00**

**New Fox and Geese, The,** McLoughlin Brothers, generic, card game, 6¼ x 4½", cover shows fox watching geese and ducks in water, contains 33 multicolored litho cards, c1888 . . .    **20.00**

**New Frontier,** Colorful Products, politics, board game, cover shows "Seat of Government" rocking chair, stagecoach bottom right corner, "The Game Nobody Can Win," critical of Kennedy administration, 1962 . .    **30.00**

**New Game of Hunting, The,** *see Hunting, The New Game of*

**New Lindy Flying Game, The,** Nucraft Toys, aviation, card game, 2¾ x 4", cover shows

*The Newlywed Game*

*No Time For Sergeants*

plane with wheels extended, line separates "New York to Paris" from mfg name, inventor "Paul K. Gallow, Wakefield, Mass.," contains 79 green backed cards with monoplanes, ©1927 . . . . . . . . . . . . . . . . .   **25.00**

**New National Snake Game,** Charles Magnus, educational, board game, framed, 27³/₄ x 23¹/₂", multicolored litho and hp, board shows track surrounded by pictures including mansion and map, circle inset of man top left corner, c1855 . . . .   **1,500.00**

**New World to World Airship Race, The,** The Chicago Game Co., aviation/sports, cover shows flying airship with spinning propeller, landscape, and face in moon, c1910s . . . . . . .   **390.00**

**New Zoo Revue, The,** Ungame Co., educational, board game, cover shows animal caricatures including frog on skates wearing jacket with "F," 1981 . . . . . . . .   **10.00**

**Newlywed Game, The,** Chuck Barris Productions, TV/game show, board game, cover shows game name imprinted on folded note paper and wedding cake, 1979 . . . . . . . . . . . . . . . . .   **10.00**

**Newlywed Game, The,** Hasbro, TV/game show, board game, original edition, cover shows game name on folded note paper, sketch of figure bottom right corner, 1967 *see illus*   **10.00**

• Third edition, game name imprinted on folded note paper, rectangle with silhou-

ettes of man and woman above "A Lovable Game," 1969 . . . . . . . . . . . . . . . . .   **5.00**

**News Boy, The,** Parker Brothers, generic, board game, 7¹/₂" sq, cover shows newsboy holding paper, newspaper background with 4 people at doorway labeled "The Times," contains spinner and 4 colored wooden counters, ©1895 . . . . . . . . . . .   **40.00**

**No Time For Sergeants,** Ideal, TV/military/movie, cover shows soldiers and jeep, contains spinner, 1964 *see illus* . . . . . . .   **35.00**

**Noah's Ark,** Cadaco, educational, board game, cover shows floating ark, pairs of animals including zebras, rhinos, and chimpanzees on land, "Pre–School Fun," 1961 . . . . . . . . . . . . . .   **15.00**

**North Pole Game, The,** Milton Bradley, travel, board game, 13 x 20", cover shows people in hot air balloon flying over Arctic scene, contains 2 dice cups, 2 dice, and 2 wooden counters, ©1907 . . . . . . . . . . . . . . . . .   **450.00**

**Northwest Passage!,** Impact Communications, educational/ travel, board game, Commemorating Humble's "Maiden Northwest Passage Voyage," lid shows helicopter flying over ship in snow scene, "S.S. Manhattan" in circle inset bottom right corner, 1969 . . . . . . . . . . . . . . . . .   **22.00**

**Notch,** Remco, western, dice game, "Tumble–dum dice game," cover shows cowboy at wooden sign with game name, boy turning 2 dice in tumbler, 1960 . . . . . . . . . . . . . . . . .   **12.00**

*Number Please*

*Oh Blondie!*

**Now You See It,** Milton Bradley,
TV/game show, lid shows game
name highlighted in 3 rows of
letter squares in rectangle at
bottom right corner, game name
also in large multicolored letters
in large frame, 1975 . . . . . . . .    **12.00**

**Number Please,** Parker Brothers,
TV/game show, board game,
cover shows keyboard layout
with game name in second and
fourth rows, first and third rows
have number keys, show host
Bud Collyer at top left corner,
"Bud Collyer Emcees
Television's...," letter "V" in television extends to rectangle in
top right corner with mfg and
ABC–TV program info, game
name, and "A Goodson Todman
Production," 1961 *see illus.* . . . .    **40.00**

**Nurses Game, The,** Ideal,
TV/careers, board game, cover
shows 2 nurses, operation and
patients in background, "Based
on the 'True–To–Life' television
drama on CBS," starring Liz
Thorpe and Gail Lucas, 1963 . .    **20.00**


**–O–**


**O.J. Simpson See–Action Football
Game,** *see See–Action Football
Game, O.J. Simpson*

**Ocean to Ocean Flight Game,**
Wilder Mfg. Co., aviation, board
game, 7½ x 12¼", cover shows
2 men in open plane, second
plane above, triangle shape
upper right corner, c1927 . . . . .    **110.00**

**Off To See The Wizard Game,**
Milton Bradley, cartoon, board
game, cover shows Dorothy,
Toto, and other "Wizard of Oz"
characters walking toward
castle, 1968 . . . . . . . . . . . . . .    **12.00**

**Office Boy, The,** Parker Brothers,
business, board game, 18 x 10",
cover shows 2 circles with office
scenes, game name and mfg
info in slanted diagonal strip,
©1889 . . . . . . . . . . . . . . . . .    **500.00**

**Official Baseball Card Game,**
Milton Bradley, sports, card
game, cover has 3 stars, pictures
of 3 players upper right corner,
bottom strip shows batter,
players sliding into base, and
pitcher, 1970 . . . . . . . . . . . . .    **250.00**

**Official Baseball Game,** Milton
Bradley, sports, board game,
cover has "Endorsed by the
National League Players
Association" below autographed
baseball, pictures of batter,
catcher, and umpire, batter
sliding into base, and faces of
12 players, 1969 . . . . . . . . . .    **100.00**

**Official Radio Baseball Game,**
Toy Creations, sports/radio,
board game, 10½ x 13½ x 1½",
cover shows baseball above
game name, man with microphone, and players in background, contains spinner, team
rosters, team cards, numbered
cards, and pegs, 1939 . . . . . . .    **50.00**

**Oh Blondie!,** Whitman
Publishing, No. 3019, comics,
bingo game, 9¾ x 6 x 1", cover

shows Blondie upper left corner, man and child bottom right, "A game of fun–played like Bingo," 1940 *see illus* . . . . . . . . . . . .   30.00

**Oil,** J. & L. Randall, business/oil drilling, board game, cover has game name below "Merit" and above "the great adventure" and scene with men wearing hard hats, ships, and oil derricks, 1960s . . . . . . . . . . .   25.00

**Old Glory,** Parker Brothers, patriotic, card game, 4 x 5$\frac{1}{2}$", cover shows boy wearing cap holding flag pole and soldier wearing high boots and hat marked "X," copyright and mfg name and location across lid bottom, contains 52 cards and 2 advertising cards with U.S. flag backs and U.S. military hero faces, ©1899. . . . . . . . . . . . . . . . .   40.00

**Old Hogan's Goat,** Whitman Publishing, No. 3938, generic, game platform in box, 11$\frac{1}{2}$ x 8$\frac{1}{2}$ x 1$\frac{5}{16}$", cover shows goat with head against circle, open can bottom right corner, contains 6 colored marbles and die, ©1939. . . . . . . . . . . . . . . . .   20.00

**Old Hunter and His Game, The,** Henry D. Noyes & Co., hunting, card game, 4$\frac{3}{4}$ x 6$\frac{1}{2}$", cover shows hunter carrying day's catch, flowers and animals pictured around board, "Illustrated 52 cards" in triangle bottom right, c1870. . . . . . . . . . . . . .   45.00

**Old King Cole, Game of,** McLoughlin Brothers, nursery rhyme, card game, 3$\frac{1}{2}$ x 4$\frac{3}{4}$", cover shows King Cole surrounded by 3 fiddlers in diamond shaped frame, copyright info bottom left corner, mfg info bottom right corner, ©1888 . . .   35.00

**Old Maid,** Milton Bradley, generic, card game, cover shows seated woman wearing bonnet and knitting, oval frame with silhouette picture on wall, cat with ribbon on second chair, contains 21 multicolored litho cards including "Old Maid," c1905 . .   15.00

**Old Maid,** Milton Bradley, generic, card game, 4$\frac{7}{8}$ x 3$\frac{7}{8}$", left side of cover shows woman wearing bonnet with floral spray behind her head, game directions below game name on right, contains 38 cards and "Old Maid," c1910. . . . . . . . . .   12.00

**Old Maid, Game of,** Selchow & Righter, generic, card game, 4$\frac{5}{8}$ x 3$\frac{5}{8}$", cover shows woman holding bird and sitting in rocking chair next to window, plants on windowsill, teapot and cup on table, printed info in large rect bottom right corner, contains 36 cards including "Old Maid" cards, c1890 . . . . . . . . .   15.00

**Old Maid, Game of,** J.H. Singer, generic, card game, 4$\frac{1}{4}$ x $\frac{3}{4}$", cover shows woman wearing glasses and bonnet with flower on left, directions on right, "Play Cuckoo For Fun" at bottom, contains 18 cards and "Old Maid," c1890. . . . . . . . . . . . .   15.00

**Old Maid and Batchelor, Game of,** Peter G. Thomson, generic, card game, 3$\frac{1}{8}$ x 4$\frac{1}{8}$", cover shows man and woman in circles, mfg name bottom right corner, contains 34 cards and "Old Maid," c1885. . . . . . . . . .   25.00

**Old Mother Goose, Game of,** Chaffee & Selchow, nursery rhyme, board game, 8 x 16", cover shows woman carrying broom riding flying goose, contains 4 wooden counters and spinner, c1890. . . . . . . . .   50.00

**Old Mother Hubbard, Game of,** Milton Bradley, nursery rhyme, board game, 15 x 16", cover shows woman wearing bonnet and print dress and window with curtains and 2 plants on sill, contains 2 dice cups, 2 dice, and 4 round colored wooden counters, c1890 . . . . .   125.00

**Old Woman Who Lived in A Shoe, The,** Parker Brothers, nursery rhyme, board game, 8 x 13", nursery rhyme at bottom left of cover, scene of children in and

*1–900–SEX*

around large high top shoe with buckle, figure wearing pointed hat and cape holding round bowl, contains 16 round colored wooden markers and spinner, c1895 . . . . . . . . . . . . . . . **110.00**

**"Ole" Thousand Faces,** Cardboard Products Co., generic, action game, cover shows 3 adults and child with raised hands looking at faces in box frames, c1925 . . **20.00**

**On the Buses,** Denys Fisher, TV/travel, board game, cover shows bus driver leaning out window, second driver pointing finger and holding clipboard, inset of third driver, and 2 insets of gameboard, "I'll get you Butler," 1973 . . . . . . . . . . . . . **25.00**

**1–900–SEX,** Baron/Scott Enterprises, Inc., generic, 15 x 10³/₄ x 1¹/₂", cover shows 2 women talking on phone, contains gameboard, timer, 1–900–Sex cards, telephone award cards, plastic phone, and die, 1992 *see illus* . . . . . . . . . **15.00**

**Operation,** Milton Bradley, medical, skill game, "Where You're the Doctor," cover shows cartoon patient on operating table, 2 doctors prepared to operate, small table, small girl wearing cap, and small boy carrying bucket, 1965 . . . . . . . . . . . . . **12.00**

**Operation Orbit,** Transogram, TV/space, electro guided game, cover shows electro guided space–age pc with antenna,

velocity and altitude handles, and "Missile Transport" in center, inset of boy operating game pc, 1962 . . . . . . . . . . . . . . . . **110.00**

**Orbit,** Parker Brothers, space, board game, cover shows spaceship with game name, planets in background, 1959 . . . . . . . . . **25.00**

**Organized Crime,** Koplow Games, crime, board game, cover shows game name above 4 printed sections, probably inspired by *The Godfather Part II*, 1974 . . . . . . . . . . . . . . . . **12.00**

**Ouija,** William Fuld, fortune telling, board game, 6¹/₈ x 4¹/₄ x ⁷/₈", cover shows game name flanked by dashes, trademark registration, "Egyptian Luck Board," mfg name, and "Baltimore, Md.—U.S.A., Patented in United States and Canada," Fuld bought rights from Elijah Bond in 1892, then sold them to Parker Brothers, 1920 . . . . . . . . . . . . . . . . . **15.00**

**Ouija,** Parker Brothers, fortune telling, board game, cover shows circle with face upper left corner, "YES" at tip of planchette, gameboard shows alphabet and "Mystifying Oracle" below game name, 1970s . . . . . . . . . . . . . . . . . . **10.00**

**Our Defenders,** Master Toy Co., No. 70, military, board game, cover shows 4 uniformed military men, "The Game of the Day," mfg info bottom left corner, "Made in U.S.A." bottom right corner, combines game play with puzzle, cardboard spinner with wooden handle attached to board, c1944 . . . . . **35.00**

**Our National Ball Game,** McGill & Delany, sports, separate board and pcs box, 17¹/₂" sq board, cover shows baseball diamond and printed directions, contains 2 dice, ©1886 . . . . . . . . . . . . **650.00**

**Outboard Motor Race, The,** Milton Bradley, sports, cover shows 2 racing boats and drivers, #14 boat passing checkered flag, no date . . . . . . . . . . **40.00**

**Outer Limits Game, The,** Milton Bradley, TV/space, board game, lid shows 3 aliens, 1964 . . . . . .   **150.00**

**Outlaws, The,** Transogram, western, board game, cover has 2 insets with men in cowboy hats and Indians watching horses going through pass, "Exciting Western," 1961 . . . . .   **60.00**

**Over the Garden Wall,** Milton Bradley, generic, skill game, lid shows figure chasing boy with hat flying off as he and dog jump over wall, farm buildings in background, 1937 . . . . . . . .   **15.00**

**Owl and The Pussy Cat, The,** E.O. Clark, No. 351, nursery rhyme, board game, Tokalon Series, 19$^1$/$_4$ x 10$^1$/$_2$", cover shows owl and pussy cat in floating boat, contains 4 wooden counters and cardboard spinner, wooden board sides, c1890s . . . . . . . . . . . . . . . .   **300.00**

–P–

**PDQ: TV Game of Secret Letters,** Milton Bradley, TV/game show, quiz, cover shows hand placing game name letters on striped background, letters of "SECRET" on individual strips at lid bottom, 1965 *see illus* . . . . . . .   **15.00**

**PT Boat 109,** Ideal, military, board game, cover shows PT 109 and other ships in water, smoke coming from ship, inspired by JFK's popularity, 1963 . . . . . . . . . . . . . . . . . . .   **30.00**

**Pac–Man Card Game,** Milton Bradley, arcade, card game, cover shows Pac–Man above plus sign, #10 and #5 cards, 1982 . . . . . . . . . . . . . . . . . .   **10.00**

**Pac–Man Game,** Milton Bradley, arcade, marble game, cover shows 3 insets of hand and game surface, and Pac–Man chasing and catching game figures, 1980 . . . . . . . . . . . . .   **12.00**

**Pachinko, American,** Pressman, generic, board game, cover shows players at tilted playing

*PDQ: TV Game of Secret Letters*

surface on round table, mfg name and logo upper right corner, 1970s . . . . . . . . . . . . .   **18.00**

**Palmistry,** unknown manufacturer, fortune telling, card game, 6 x 5", cover shows human hand with palm up and shirt cuff, circle background, contains numbered cardboard squares and 4 diagrams of human hand, c1910 . . . . . . . . . . . . . . . . .   **30.00**

**Pana Kanal Game, The Great,** Chicago Game Co., travel, board game, lid has ship and tugboat framed by striped curtains and side pillars, ©1913 . . .   **145.00**

**Panorama Nursery Alphabet,** unknown manufacturer, educational, scroll type game, 5$^1$/$_2$" sq, cover shows girl wearing bonnet with letter "N," "NELLY, Nutting," c1870 . . . . . . . . . . .   **300.00**

**Par Golf,** W.M. Grimes, sports, action game, cover shows course, putting green, trees, and "PAR" in golf ball on tee, contains metal golf balls, 1959 . . . .   **25.00**

**Par Golf,** National Games, sports, action game, cover shows swinging golfer and crowds watching golfer on putting green, 1960s . . . . . . . . . . . . .   **30.00**

**Par "73,"** Big Top Games, sports, action game, cover shows golf balls on putting green, "A Complete 18 Hole Course in Miniature!," putting green inside cover, 1961 . . . . . . . . . . . . . .   **20.00**

**Parcheesi,** Selchow & Righter, generic, board game, separate board and pcs box with game name only, 1940s . . . . . . . . . .   **30.00**

*Park and Shop*

**Parcheesi,** Selchow & Righter, generic, board game, Popular Edition, separate board and pcs box, folding 18½" sq board shows game name and "A Royal Game of India, Popular Edition," matching 6½ x 3" pcs box, contains 4 dice cups, 8 dice, and 16 colored counters, trademark registered 5/20/1890, patented 3/17/1874, 1946 . . . . . . . . . .    **20.00**

**Parcheesi,** Selchow & Righter, generic, board game, Gold Seal Edition, cover shows "SR" below game name, 1950s . . . . .    **10.00**

**Parcheesi,** Selchow & Righter, generic, board game, Popular Edition, cover shows gameboard, "A Back gammon Game of India," trademark info and mfg logo below game name, 1950s . . . . . . . . . . . . . . . .    **8.00**

**Park and Shop,** Milton Bradley, business, board game, cover shows shoppers' activities at toy store, candy store, and sporting good sale, policeman giving ticket, family of 4 with purchases, originated in Allentown, PA, first version, 1950s . . . . . . . . .    **40.00**

**Park And Shop,** Milton Bradley, business, board game, cover shows street with cars and store fronts, "Super Mart, The Shopping Game," modeled after Allentown, PA, street layout and parking system,1960 *see illus* . .    **25.00**

**Partridge Family Game, The,** Milton Bradley, TV, board game, cover shows 6 family members with musical instruments posed in front of bus, strip of 6 ducks below game name, 1971 . . . . .    **10.00**

**Party Stunts,** Milton Bradley, generic, action game, cover shows 2 spinning wheels wrapped in ribbon, "Do This While You Do This," 1953 . . . . .    **12.00**

**Password,** Milton Bradley, TV/game show, quiz game, cover shows inset of 4 people playing game
• 1st edition, 1962 . . . . . . . . . .    **10.00**
• Collector's Edition, 1963. . . . . .    **15.00**
• 25 other editions . . . . . . . . . .    **8.00**

**Pathfinder,** Milton Bradley, strategy, tile game, cover shows tile layout on playing surface, "Fun and Competition At Its Best," 1954 . . . . . . . . . . . . . . . . . .    **12.00**

**Pathfinder,** Milton Bradley, strategy, board game, cover shows divided board, man, and woman, "Two Player Tracking Game," 1977 . . . . . . . . . . . . .    **10.00**

**Patty Duke Game,** Milton Bradley, TV series/celebrity, board game, cover shows identical cousins Patty and Cathy engaged in various activities including playing records, watching TV, dating, and washing dishes, 1964. . . . . . . . . . .    **30.00**

**Peanuts,** Selchow & Righter, comic strip, board game, cover shows Charlie Brown and friends, "The Game of Charlie Brown and His Pals," circle logo bottom right corner, 1959 . . . . .    **20.00**

**Pebbles Flintstone Game,** Transogram, TV/cartoon, board game, cover shows Dino with diaper, Pebbles playing with blocks spelling "BABY," and Fred and Wilma standing beneath tree, 1962 . . . . . . . . .    **20.00**

**Peeko,** Watkins–Strathmore, educational, word game, cover shows playing surface and figures wearing triangular hats, "Open the Window, Find the Hidden Word," 1964 . . . . . . .    **10.00**

**Peg Top,** Parker Brothers, generic, action game, 12 x 10¾", cover shows boy in center, 2 rows of pegs border 4 sides of lid, "A New Spinning Top Game," unknown date . . . . . . . . . . . . .    **25.00**

**Peggy,** Parker Brothers, generic, board game, 12 x 10³/₄", cover shows woman in center circle labeled "Peggy," 4 ribbon strips extend from circle to swirl decoration in 4 corners, contains 20 colored wooden pegs and wooden spinning top, ©1923 . . **75.00**

**Peg'ity,** Parker Brothers, strategy, board game, 10¹/₄ x 13¹/₂", cover shows 2 men and 2 women around diagonally–placed peg board, "Reg. U.S. Patent Office" below game name, "Who? Wins," contains pegs and gray cardboard board with holes, c1925 . . . . . . . . . . . . . . . . . **35.00**

**Pegity and Other Games,** Parker Brothers, strategy, board game, cover shows man with pipe, boy with striped shirt, and woman with belted dress atop colored pegs, 1953. . . . . . . . . . . . . . . **9.00**

**People Weekly,** Parker Brothers, magazine, trivia quiz game, cover shows familiar magazine name and inset pictures of tennis player, woman wearing cowboy hat, and woman and 2 men, 1984 . . . . . . . . . . . . . **8.00**

**People's Court,** Hoyle Products, TV/justice, cover shows judge with folded hands to left of game name, 1986 . . . . . . . . . **10.00**

**Perfection,** Lakeside, generic, skill game, cover shows 3 youngsters with playing surface and pcs, 3 inset pictures of hand on playing surface, "Fit the Pieces Into Place Before the Timer Pops Them Out," 1973 . . **12.00**

**Perfection,** Lakeside, generic, computer skill game, electronic version, cover shows fingers on wheel and various shaped game pcs, 1979 . . . . . . . . . . . . . . . **10.00**

**Perils of Pauline,** Marx, TV, board game, cover shows woman on railroad track in front of engine, man wearing top hat driving engine, contains large plastic pcs, 1964 . . . . . . . . . . . . . **45.00**

**Perry Mason,** Transogram, TV/detective, board game, cover with show star Raymond Burr,

*Peter Coddle Tells of His Trip to Chicago*

3 policemen chasing man, and 2 police cars, "Case of the Missing Suspect Game," 1959. . **25.00**

**Personality,** Milton Bradley, TV/game show, quiz game, "Based on the NBC TV Show" in upper right corner, cover shows man with letter "H" on sweater, man smoking cigar, woman wearing hat with flowers, bald man wearing glasses, and woman wearing fur stole, all with dream images above their heads, 1968 . . . . . . . . . . . . . **20.00**

**Peter Coddle and His First Trip To New York,** McLoughlin Brothers, travel, card game, cover shows bicycle rider and figure wearing glasses and wide–brimmed hat, contains small pink backed cards with objects printed on faces and story booklet, unknown date . . . . . . . . . . . **25.00**

**Peter Coddle Tells of His Trip To Chicago,** Parker Brothers, travel, card game, 5⁷/₈ x 4³/₈", cover shows boy wearing hat, scarf, and boots pointing with left hand and talking to bearded man wearing coat, cap, and boots, printed section bottom right corner, contains printed cards and reading booklet, c1890 *see illus.* . . . . . . . . . . . **15.00**

**Peter Coddle's Trip,** Milton Bradley, travel, 6¹/₈ x 7¹/₈", cover shows kneeling bearded man wearing hat and holding umbrella, suitcase labeled "P.C.," and flowered border, contains printed slips and booklet "An Account of Peter Coddle's Visit to New York," c1905 . . . . . . . . . . . . . . . . . . **15.00**

**Peter Coddle's Trip to New York,** Parker Brothers, classic/travel, card game, Nickel Edition, 3³/₈ x 4⁵/₈", cover shows boy wearing hat, vest, and jacket and carrying umbrella and suitcase, people and horses in background, mfg name and "Salem Mass. USA" bottom right corner, contains 18 phrase cards and 4–pg 3 x 4" instruction book with story containing blank spaces, c1920s . . . . . . . . **10.00**

**Peter Coddle's Trip To The World's Fair,** Parker Brothers, travel, card game, 6⁵/₈ x 5¹/₈ x 1", cover shows game name, mfg info including "SALEM, MASS., New York, Chicago and London, Made in U.S.A.," 1939 . . . . . . . **12.00**

**Peter Coddles,** Milton Bradley, St Nicholas Series, travel, cover shows man riding in open coach, driver, man with megaphone, woman wearing hat and fur–trimmed coat, and suitcase labeled "Peter Coddles," unknown date . . . . . . . . . . . . **15.00**

**Peter Coddles, The Game of,** Parker Brothers, travel, card game, 4 x 5¹/₂", cover shows boy with hands in pockets standing on street, woman looking in store window, "Smith, Brow..." publishing info at lid bottom, contains printed cards and reading booklet entitled "Peter Codles," c1888 . . . . . . . **20.00**

**Peter Coddles Esq. and His Trip To New York,** J.H. Singer, travel, card game, 4⁵/₈ x 5⁷/₈ x 1", cover shows man in coat with bag under arm and holding travel bag and umbrella, unknown date. . . . . . . . . . . . . . . . . . **20.00**

**Peter Gunn,** Lowell, TV/detective, board game, cover shows man

with gun, 2 men fighting, and 2 men at a table, 1960 . . . . . . . **30.00**

**Peter Pan, Walt Disney's,** Transogram, story/movie, board game, cover shows Pan and 3 children flying over island, produced in both red and blue covers, 1953 . . . . . . . . . . . . . **40.00**

**Peter Rabbit,** Milton Bradley, story, board game, 11¹/₄ x 16¹/₄", cover shows rabbit carrying stick and walking along path, water, and trees, contains 2 round wooden counters and spinner, c1910 . . . . . . . . . . . . . . . . . . **85.00**

**Petticoat Junction,** Standard Toykraft, TV/comedy, board game, cover shows 4 women, seated man, and Hooterville Cannonball train engine, "As Seen On The CBS Television Station," 1964 . . . . . . . . . . . . **45.00**

**Phalanx,** Whitman, military strategy, board game, cover shows battling knights, named after combat formation, 1964 . . . . . . **20.00**

**Phantom, Ruler of the Jungle Game,** Transogram, comic strip, board game, cover shows masked man sitting in chair with skulls on either side and holding dog by leash, contains clay and skull ring, 1965 . . . . . . . . . . . **110.00**

**Phil Silvers, Sgt. Bilko—CBS Television's "You'll Never Get Rich" Game,** Gardner, TV/military comedy series, board game, cover shows Silvers framed by 2 circles, "Can You Beat Bilko?," 1955 . . . . . . . . . . . . . . . . . . **50.00**

**Philco Vance,** Parker Brothers, detective, board game, 19¹/₄ x 9⁷/₈ x 1⁷/₈", lid pictures man wearing jacket with handkerchief in pocket, "S.S. Van Dine's Great Detective Game," contains metal pawns, dice, and picture cards, 1937 . . . . . . . . **65.00**

**Philip Marlowe Game,** Transogram, TV/detective, board game, cover has show star Philip Carey in car with hand on radio, newspaper clipping bottom right corner, 1960 . . . . . . . . . . . . . **40.00**

**Philippines**, J.C. Singer, military/ Spanish–American War, board game, 10¼ x 12½", cover shows soldiers in water and ferns and trees on shore, flag upper left corner, picture of "Dewey," contains spinner and 16 wooden counters, c1898 . . . . . . . . . . . . . . . . .   **95.00**

**Phoebe Snow,** Milton Bradley, travel/railroad, board game, 8¾ x 16⅞", cover shows woman wearing long dress and wide–brimmed hat with out-stretched right arm, train bottom right corner, contains 4 colored wooden counters and spinner, Phoebe Snow character derived from Lackawanna Railroad train in which a woman in white was associated with the clean run-ning of coal–burning engines, 1902 . . . . . . . . . . . . . . . . . .   **220.00**

**Phoebe Snow, Game Of,** McLoughlin Brothers, travel/rail-road, board game, 8½ x 16¼", cover shows woman wearing long coat and feathered hat carrying umbrella and travel case, contains 4 colored wood-en counters and spinner, ©1899 *see illus.* . . . . . . . . . . . . . . . .   **300.00**

**Pigs in the Clover,** Milton Bradley, generic, puzzle game, 8" sq, cover shows 3 upright pigs dressed in jackets and carrying canes, "A Teasing Tantalizing Puzzle," contains 4 steel balls, c1930 . . . . . . . .   **20.00**

**Pinafore Game, The,** Fuller, Upham & Co., nautical, card game, cover shows ship cen-tered between enlarged first and last letters of game name, con-tains 55 cards with silhouetted nautical figures on faces and cat–o'–nine–tails backs, 1879 . .   **40.00**

**Ping Pong,** Parker Brothers, gener-ic, skill and action game, 20 x 7½", cover shows woman wear-ing long polka dot dress holding paddle in right hand, "The Great Tennis Game," contains 2 pad-dles, 6 celluloid balls, 2 clamps, 2 net stanchions, and net, first

*Phoebe Snow*

set manufactured by Parker following purchase of American game rights from Hamley Brothers and J. Jaques & Sons, Ltd. of London, ©1902 . . . . . .   **150.00**

**Ping Pong,** Parker Brothers, gener-ic, skill and action game, 16⅞ x 7⅜", cover shows paddles and balls on either side of game name enclosed in narrow rec-tangle, "Caution" above game name, contains 6 celluloid balls, net, and 4 wooden paddles, Parker's first Ping Pong game after negotiating rights from Britain, balls marked "Match–England," c1904 . . . . . . . . . . .   **120.00**

**Pinhead,** Remco, generic, track game, cover shows boy looking at 2 children hiding under bed, "Game of Hide and Seek," 1959 . . . . . . . . . . . . . . . . . .   **25.00**

**Pink Panther, The,** Cadaco, TV/cartoon, cover shows man holding string attached to hot air balloon, Pink Panther riding in balloon's basket, mfg info bot-tom right corner, 1981 . . . . . . .   **8.00**

**Pink Panther Game,** Warren, TV/cartoon, cover shows Pink

Panther looking at man and 3 animal figures, 1977 . . . . . . .   **20.00**

**Pink Panther Game, The,** Milton Bradley, TV/cartoon, board game, cover shows sea gulls hovering over Pink Panther in life raft, 1970. . . . . . . . . . . .   **25.00**

**Pinky Lee & The Runaway Frankfurters,** Whiting, TV/celebrity/comedy, cover shows Lee wearing checkered hat chasing 2 animated frankfurters, framed in ragged edge circle with dialogue, "Featured Star of NBC" bottom left corner, 1954 . . . . . . . . . . . . . . . . .   **55.00**

**Pinocchio Game, Walt Disney's,** Whitman, Disney, board game, cover shows game name behind Pinocchio's face, Jiminy Cricket hanging from last "o" in game name, 1962 . . . . . . . . . . . . . .   **20.00**

**Pinocchio, Walt Disney Presents,** Parker Brothers, Disney, board game, cover shows walking Pinocchio with apple and book on book strap, Geppetto and Figaro in doorway, Jiminy Cricket and other characters, tent, and ferris wheel, 1971 . . .   **18.00**

**Pinocchio Adventure Game,** Transogram, Disney, board game, cover shows Pinocchio walking on path with Geppetto, houses in background, 1970. . .   **15.00**

**Pinocchio, Pin the Nose on Walt Disney's,** Parker Brothers, Disney, adventure, skill game, cover shows fairy with wand, Jiminy Cricket, and Pinocchio marionette, 1939 . . . . . . . . . .   **95.00**

**Pirate and Traveler,** Milton Bradley, adventure, board game, separate 27 x 16¼" gameboard and 7¼ x 3" pcs box, cover shows pirate carrying sword chasing man, "4563 L2" at bottom left corner, contains metal spinner, 2 counters, and 55 cards, ©1911 . . . . . . . . . .   **60.00**

**Pirate and Traveler,** Milton Bradley, adventure, board game, board shows world map, "A World Geography Game," 1953 . . . . . . . . . . . . . . . . .   **25.00**

**Pirates Island,** Corey Games, adventure, board game, cover shows pirate and 3 helpers uncovering treasure chest, "A Game of Adventure," 1942 . .   **35.00**

**Pirates of the Caribbean,** *see Disneyland Pirates of the Caribbean*

**Pit,** Parker Brothers, generic, card game, red cover with gold print shows game name, "Bull and Bear Edition," patent registration, and mfg info, 1919 . . . . . .   **10.00**

**Pit,** Parker Brothers, generic, card game, cover signed by John Held Jr., "Snappy Exciting, The Jolliest of Card Games" at bottom right corner, 1920s. . . . . . .   **20.00**

**Pit,** Parker Brothers, generic, card game, cover shows game name, "Exciting Fun for Everyone," 1930s . . . . . . . . . . . . . . . . .   **8.00**

**Pit,** Parker Brothers, generic, card game, "The World's Liveliest Trading Game" in dialogue box to right of game name, mfg info below, 1950s . . . . . . . . . . . . . .   **7.00**

**Pit,** Parker Brothers, generic, card game, cover shows 2 wheat stalks against circle background, mfg logo bottom right, 1973 . . .   **5.00**

**Pitchin' Pal,** Cadaco–Ellis, generic, action game, cover shows boy's face and hands, 2 boys playing game, 1953 . . . . . . . . .   **20.00**

**Pivot Golf,** Milton Bradley, sports, action game, playing surface has pivoting golfer on golf course landscape, released 10 years earlier as Golferino by Hubley, 1973 . . . . . . . . . . . . . . . . . . .   **40.00**

**Planet of the Apes,** Milton Bradley, TV/space, board game, lid has 3 figures with ape faces, 2 figures around gameboard, contains cage used to capture diecut human figures, 1974 . . .   **25.00**

**Play and Defend Bridge, Charles Goren's,** Milton Bradley, Fine Edition, generic, card game, cover shows card suits, mfg info top left corner, "Compare Your Game With Goren," 1965 . . . . .   **15.00**

**Play Your Hunch,** Transogram, TV/game show, quiz game,

cover shows the "sturdy, plastic, Automatic Problem Solver, 240 Challenging Problems," electric light bulb with face and bowtie at end of game name, "TV's Popular Guessing Game," 1970 . . . . . . . . . . . . . . . . . . **20.00**

**Playful Trails Game,** Lakeside, TV/animated characters, cover shows Gumby wearing cowboy hat and Pokey, 1968. . . . . . . . . **35.00**

**Playing Department Store, Game of,** McLoughlin Brothers, business, board game, 22¹/₂ x 15", cover shows group of children including girl trying on boot and boy wearing top hat and long coat, contains 54 counters, round cards representing money, and indicator, wooden box, 1898 . . . . . . . . . . . . . . . **1,400.00**

**Ploy,** 3M, strategy, board game, cover shows man with playing pcs, 1970 . . . . . . . . . . . . . . . **10.00**

**Plus One,** Milton Bradley, maze, electronic board game, cover shows hand on playing pc, plus sign cut out on "P" in game name, 1980 . . . . . . . . . . . . . . **10.00**

**Po–Ke–No,** Bee & Bicycle, poker, card game, cover shows ace of spades, 7 of hearts, and 3 small circles, "12 Board Set," 1970s. . **10.00**

**Po–Ke–No,** U.S. Playing Card Co., poker, card game, cover shows ace of spades, 7 of hearts, and 3 small circles, "12 Board Set," 1960s . . . . . . . **12.00**

**Poets With Portraits and Autographs, The Game of,** McLoughlin Brothers, educational, card game, 6 x 8¹/₂", center cover shows bearded man surrounded by frame of flowers and game name, contains 64 cards with black and white illustrations, wooden box, ©1886 . . **35.00**

**Point of Law,** 3M, law, board game, cover shows court scene, man being sworn in, seated woman wearing gloves, judge in front of flag, and partial view of jury, 1972 . . . . . . . . . . . . . . . **10.00**

**Poison Ivy Game,** Ideal, generic, action game, cover shows

youngsters picking leaves from "poison ivy" patch and 2 boys with bandaged fingers running from patch, 1969 . . . . . . . . . . **20.00**

**Polaroid's Party Pack,** Polaroid, advertising, action game, cover shows man at door and people in house shooting pictures with Polaroid Camera, "Games and Fun With A Polaroid Land Camera," 1969 . . . . . . . . . . . . **15.00**

**Police Patrol,** Hasbro, crime, action game and toy, cover shows policeman using phone on lamp post, police car parked on street, grocery, gift shop, hardware, and florist storefronts, striped awning, contains large plastic pcs, 1955–57 . . . . . . . . **60.00**

**Politics, Game of,** Parker Brothers, politics, board game, cover shows Uncle Sam, stars and stripes on letters of "Politics," mfg info bottom right, "Elect Yourself President," 1952 . . . . . **25.00**

**Politics, Oswald B. Lord's Game of,** Parker Brothers, politics, cover shows Uncle Sam looking at elephant and donkey placed on either side of Washington buildings, "Made in U.S.A." bottom left corner, 1930s . . . . . **30.00**

**Polly Pickles: The Great Movie Game: A Burlesque,** Parker Brothers, movie, separate 18⁷/₈ x 19" board and 5¹/₈ x 3³/₈ x 2" pcs box, cover has "Polly Pickles" in rect frame, "Utensils For" at top, mfg info at bottom, contains dice cups, 6 movie dice each with 6 letters, and 4 turned wood playing pcs, ©1921 . . . . . . . . . . . . . . . . . **75.00**

**Pollyanna,** Parker Brothers, generic, board game, separate board and pcs box, picture of girl with headband on pcs box, "Utensils for The Glad Game," 1915–1920s . . . . . . . . . . . . . **30.00**

**Pollyanna,** Parker Brothers, generic, board game, cover shows gameboard and multicolored game name, "With Exciting Turnouts," and "The Glad Game," 1950s . . . . . . . . . . . . **18.00**

*Pop–Eye: Playing Card Game*

**Pollyanna Dixie,** Parker Brothers, generic, board game, cover shows 4 silhouette figures including boy with fishing rod, man with cane, and woman with umbrella, "Pursuit Game," 1952 . . . . . . . . . . . . . . . . . . **20.00**

**Pony Express, Game of,** Polygon Corp, western, board game, cover shows desert scene with Pony Express rider shooting at pursuers, mfg info bottom right corner, 1947 . . . . . . . . . . . . . **20.00**

**Pooch,** Hasbro, generic, board game, cover shows game name above doghouse, dog leaning on doghouse, dogcatcher peeking over doghouse, and bird in birdbath, 1954. . . . . . . . . . . . . **25.00**

**Pool, Game of,** Chaffee & Selchow, sports, action game, 23 x 15", cover shows men and women around pool table, men wearing knicker pants and high socks, 1898 . . . . . . . . . . . . . . **900.00**

**Poor Jenny, The Game of,** Alderman–Fairchild (All–Fair), generic, board game, 11¹/₂ x 11¹/₂", cover shows black Mammy with donkey in front of sign "The Mishaps of a Little Donkey," contains 4 metal donkeys and 4 wooden cubes, ©1927. . . . . . . . . . . . . . . . . . **65.00**

**Pop Yer Top!,** Milton Bradley, generic, board game, cover shows boy with hand on head and girl with outstretched hands

watching playing pc pop its top, 1968 . . . . . . . . . . . . . . . . . . **20.00**

**Popcorn,** Marx Toys, generic, skill game, cover shows players with game pc which has levers to push and colored balls under plastic cover, "Catch Your Color Balls and Win!," 1976 . . . . . . . **20.00**

**Popeye,** Milton Bradley,comic strip/movie, board game, cover shows woman with folded hands next to man wearing sailor hat with hands on hips, bearded man with cap and girl wearing bonnet in circle, buildings in background, 1980 . . . . . **12.00**

**Popeye Card Game,** Ed–U–Cards, comic strip, card game, 5¹/₂ x 5¹/₄", cover shows Popeye rowing boat with Olive Oyl and Swee' Pea holding cards, contains "Exclusive Non–Spill Tray," boxed set, 1961 . . . . . . . **15.00**
• Second version issued as deck of cards . . . . . . . . . . . . . . . . **8.00**

**Popeye Game, Adventures of,** Transogram, comic strip, board game, lid shows Popeye punching Brutus, Wimpy with plate of hamburgers, Olive Oyl tied to tree, and Swee' pea holding open can of spinach, 1957 . . . . **60.00**

**Pop–Eye: Playing Card Game,** Whitman Publishing Co., No. 3070, comic strip, card game, 6¹/₂ x 5¹/₁₆ x 1⁵/₁₆", cover shows Popeye swinging left arm, ©1934 King Features Syndicate *see illus* . . . . . . . . . . . . . . . . . **30.00**

**Poppin' Hoppies,** Ideal, generic, action game, cover shows man wearing top hat with raised left hand upper left corner, multicolored spring loaded game pcs and mfg logo bottom right corner, 1968 . . . . . . . . . . . . . . **25.00**

**Popular Actors, The Game of,** Parker Brothers, theater/vaudeville, card game, 5³/₈ x 6⁵/₈", cover shows 2 actors and actress in circles, contains 36 photo cards of theater and vaudeville stars including Julia Marlowe, Lily Langtry, Joseph Jefferson, and Edwin Booth, ©1893 . . . . . **75.00**

**Popular Jack–Straw,** Parker
Brothers, generic, skill game,
4$^1/_2$ x 6$^1/_4$", cover shows figure
wearing long cape, cap with
feather, and high boots holding
sword, bushel of hay, building
on mountain in background,
contains various shaped
numbered wooden sticks and
2 hooks, c1888 . . . . . . . . . . .   **20.00**

**Portrait Authors,** Noyes & Snow,
educational, card game,
4$^1/_4$ x 6", cover shows man in
bowtie framed by draped curtains, mfg. info lid bottom,
"Successors To West & Lee
Game Co.," contains 62 cards,
1873 . . . . . . . . . . . . . . . . . . .   **15.00**

**Ports and Commerce, The Game
of,** Parker Brothers, business,
card game, 5$^1/_2$ x 4", cover
shows woman holding wreath,
ship on river, and shoreline with
buildings, contains 52 red and
white backed cards with black
and white photos on faces,
©1899. . . . . . . . . . . . . . . . .   **25.00**

**Post Card Game,** unknown manufacturer, postal, card game,
5$^1/_4$ x 7$^1/_4$", cover shows woman
wearing hat holding postcard
and purse, contains 41 cards
including instruction card,
c1905–10 . . . . . . . . . . . . . .   **40.00**

**Post Office,** Hasbro, postal, board
game, cover shows gameboard
on floor, man, woman, 2 boys,
and 2 girls, girl wearing striped
dress, girl with ponytail tickling
foot of boy leaning back on left
arm, 1968 . . . . . . . . . . . . . .   **20.00**

**Post Office Game,** Parker
Brothers, educational, action
game, 9 x 11$^3/_4$", cover shows
woman putting mail in letter
slot, her hand on girl wearing
hat, second girl with ruffled collar, other slot marked "parcels,"
box bottom marked for playing
game, contains postman's mask,
cancel stamp, stationery and
envelopes, sets of Santa Claus
sets, and postcards, c1910 . . . .   **100.00**

**Postman Game, The,** Parker
Brothers, postal, board game,

*Power Punch Batman*

5$^1/_4$" sq, cover shows 2 figures
carrying cases with shoulder
straps, crowds of people, building and part of coach in back-
ground, c1895 . . . . . . . . . . .   **15.00**

**Pot Of Gold, The,** Parker Brothers,
generic, 17 x 11$^1/_2$", cover shows
boy wearing knickers and girl
wearing short skirt running, river
and rainbow in background,
contains 4 wooden counters and
spinner, ©1897 . . . . . . . . . . .   **125.00**

**Power Lords,** Warren, toy/space,
board game, cover shows
extra–terrestrial warriors, woman
wearing cape, and man with
rifle, 1983 . . . . . . . . . . . . . . .   **15.00**

**Power Punch Batman, The Caped
Crusader vs The Penguin,**
Kenner, cartoon, action game,
18$^1/_2$ x 14$^1/_2$ x 5$^1/_2$", contains
jumbo molded plastic Batman
and Penguin figures, large boxing ring with rope, movable
hand controls, distributed exclusively by Kay Bee Toy Stores,
Pittsfield, MA, 1992 *see illus*. . .   **15.00**

**Prediction Rod,** Parker Brothers,
fortune telling, board game,
cover shows hands on table, one
pair of hands holding rod on
gameboard, 1970 . . . . . . . . . .   **15.00**

**Pressman Bingo,** Pressman, generic, bingo game, cover shows
parading figures including 2
bearded men, leader carrying
banner, others carrying flags
with letters "BINGO," and last

*Professional Game of Base Ball*

person carrying banner
"Featuring new metal spinner,"
1960s . . . . . . . . . . . . . . . . .    **10.00**
**Price Is Right, The,** Lowell,
TV/game show, bidding game,
lid shows 4 people seated behind panel with dollar amounts,
price tag with dollar sign and
question mark attached to front
of car, contains large plastic
1950s–era prizes, 1958 . . . . . .    **35.00**
**Prince Valiant,** Transogram,
comic strip/movie, board game,
cover shows Prince riding horse
followed by woman on horse,
castle in background, comic
strip artwork, game tied in with
20th Century Fox movie starring
James Mason, 1955 . . . . . . . .    **35.00**
**Pro Bowling,** Milton Bradley,
sports, action game, cover
shows bowlers, ball hitting pins,
1962 . . . . . . . . . . . . . . . . . .    **30.00**
**Pro Draft,** Parker Brothers, sports,
card game, cover shows cards
in holders and hand holding
card out to boy holding card in
left hand, football helmet upper
left corner, 1974 . . . . . . . . . .    **20.00**
**Pro Football,** Milton Bradley,
sports, board game, cover
shows player running with ball,
#30 and others in play, 1964 . .    **20.00**
**Pro League Basketball,** Gotham,
sports, action game, playing surface has 2 baskets and movable
players, 1958 . . . . . . . . . . . . .    **40.00**

**Pro Soccer,** Milton Bradley,
sports, board game, cover shows
2 teams playing soccer, "The
Official Game," soccer league
symbols down right side,
contains dice, 1968 . . . . . . . .    **15.00**
**Probe,** Parker Brothers, generic,
word game, cover shows players
around gameboard, 2 men with
ties, "Game of Words," 1964 . .    **8.00**
**Probe,** Parker Brothers, generic,
word game, cover shows
3 insets of players at top, center
square shows woman with hand
to head, and gameboard with
playing pcs at bottom, 1974 . . .    **5.00**
**Professional Game of Base Ball,
The,** Parker Brothers, sports,
board game, 8¼" sq, cover
shows batter and catcher in
circle, faces in top corners,
baseballs in bottom corners,
contains 8 round colored
wooden counters and 2 dice,
c1889 *see illus*. . . . . . . . . . . .    **75.00**
**Project CIA,** Waddington, espi-
onage, board game, "A Spy
Training Game," cover shows
aerial view of partitioned office
building, brick walls, and man
walking dog, 1973 . . . . . . . . . .    **10.00**
**Prospecting,** Selchow & Righter,
adventure, board game, cover
shows man sitting by stream sift-
ing water for gold, rainbow in
background, "The Gold Rush
Game," 1953 . . . . . . . . . . . . .    **25.00**
**Pull The Rug Out,** Schaper, gener-
ic, spinner/action game, cover
shows 4 youngsters playing
game, clenched fist upper left
near game name, 1968. . . . . . .    **20.00**
**Pursuit,** Aurora, military/aviation,
strategy game, board game,
World War I Flying Ace game,
Don Adams on cover, lid shows
upright playing surface, woman
watching 2 men in flying gear at
gameboard, and 4 inset pictures
at bottom, 1973 . . . . . . . . . . .    **18.00**
**Puss in The Corner, The Game of,**
McLoughlin Brothers, generic,
card game, 3½ x 4⅞", cover
shows cat under chair in triangular frame, contains 32 cards

*Pyramids*

*Quick Shoot Game*

with cat, mouse, and rat illus,
©1888. . . . . . . . . . . . . . . . .   **40.00**
**Pussy and The Three Mice, Game
of,** McLoughlin Brothers, gener-
ic, board game, $10^{1}/_{2}$ x $10^{3}/_{4}$",
cover shows clothed cat stand-
ing behind tree watching 3 mice
at bench, 2 mice dressed as
men wearing top hats and 1 as
woman wearing hat and dress,
upside down umbrella in front
of bench, contains large wood-
en counters representing cat,
3 smaller wooden counters representing mice, and double
arrow spinner, ©1890. . . . . . .   **220.00**
**Put And Take,** Schaper, generic,
board game, cover shows spinning top with numbers and container with chips, "An Exciting
Game For All," 1965 . . . . . . . .   **5.00**
**Puzzle–Peg,** Lubbers & Bell Mfg.
Co., generic, board game,
$6^{3}/_{4}$ x $6^{11}/_{16}$ x $1^{3}/_{16}$", cover shows
owl holding stick in hole on cir-
cular gameboard with red and
white blocks, "Can You Solve
It," contains 32 green wooden
pegs, c1920. . . . . . . . . . . . . .   **15.00**
**Puzzling Pyramid, The,** Schaper,
generic, magnetic skill game,
cover shows pyramids, camels,
and playing surface, contains
magnetic wand and metal ball
to be maneuvered through maze
up side of Pyramid to hole in
top, 1959 . . . . . . . . . . . . . . .   **15.00**

**Pyramids,** Knapp Electric, Inc.,
Division of P.R. Mallory, educational, problem solving game,
6 x 6 x 1", cover shows 2 pages
of open book, "A Problem from
the Ancients, A Master Thinker
Creation," c1930s *see illus*. . . .   **15.00**

### –Q–

**Quarterback,** Transogram, sports,
computerized action game,
cover shows man and boy with
playing surface, 18 NFL quarter-
backs faces at top, football on
"QU" of game name, contains
plastic stadium, 1970 . . . . . . . .   **25.00**
**Quien Sabe,** Parker Brothers,
western, card game, $5^{1}/_{4}$ x $3^{1}/_{2}$",
cover shows cowboy on bucking
horse, game name, and "Keyen
Sarvy, Who Knows, Cowboy
Game," contains 120 numbered
green and white cards with
Spanish cowboys, ©1906 . . . . .   **20.00**
**Quick Draw McGraw, Private Eye
Game,** Milton Bradley, cartoon
characters, board game, cover
shows friends following
McGraw holding flashlight,
1960–61 . . . . . . . . . . . . . . . .   **25.00**
**Quick Shoot Game,** Ideal, gener-
ic, action marble game, cover
show 2 girls and 2 boys holding
playing surface levers and shoot-
ing marbles, 1970 *see illus* . . . .   **15.00**

*Quiz of the Wiz*

**Quick Wit,** Parker Brothers, generic, card game, cover shows man wearing jacket and tie seated at table, one hand on head, other tapping table, cards on table, 1938 . . . . . . . . . . . .     **15.00**

**Quickflip Volleyball Game,** Ideal, sports, board game, lid shows boy and girl with playing surface, men in uniform shirts with volleyball in play, 1973 . . . . . .     **15.00**

**Quinto,** 3M, educational, number game, cover shows men wearing togas and headbands, tails with Roman numerals, 1964. . .     **10.00**

**Quiz Kids Electric Quizzer,** Rapaport Bros., Inc., No. 1000, educational/radio, quiz game, 12¼ x 9⅜ x 2³/₁₆", cover shows seated children wearing graduates' hats with name cards on desk fronts, circle inset of boy and girl with playing surface, "Approved and Endorsed by the Quiz Kids," c1940 . . . . . . . . .     **40.00**

**Quiz Kids Own Game Box,** Parker Brothers, educational/radio, quiz game, 17⅛ x 9 x 1½", cover shows figure quizzing children with raised hands seated at long table, child wearing graduate's hat and open book with "QK," ©1940 . . . . . .     **20.00**

**Quiz of the Wiz, The,** H.J. Phillips Co. Inc., quiz, educational, 5¾ x 3⅛", lid shows seated man holding paper, dialogue box directed at man with disheveled hair representing Edison, cover signed "J.N. Ding," mfg and copyright info center bottom, ©1921 *see illus* . . . . . . . . . . .     **20.00**

**Quiz Panel,** Cadaco–Ellis, educational, game, cover shows 3 faces in small strip, 4th face and hand coming through circles, hand pointing at "200 Questions," 1954 . . . . . . .     **15.00**

**Quizziac, The Golden,** Golden Capitol, eductional, automatic machine game, cover shows disks and automatic answer machine "with the Magnetic Brain, Prepared by Editors of Golden Encyclopedia," contains question disks, authority book, and score sheets, 1960 . . . . . . .     **20.00**

**Qwik Quiz Game,** Transogram, educational, board game, cover shows hand using tool on playing surface and "48 Different Category Cards for beginner, intermediate and expert," 1958 . . . . . . . . . . . . .     **25.00**

**–R–**

**Race For The North Pole,** Milton Bradley, polar exploration, board game, cover shows game name above circles, scrolled background, directions across bottom, contains spinner and 2 round wooden counters, c1902 . . . . . . . . . . . . . . . . . .     **8.00**

**Race–O–Rama,** Builtrite, automobile racing, race game, cover shows car #51, #6, and #33, "4 Exciting Race Games, Road Race, Demolition, Drag Race, 500 Mile Race," 1960s . . . . . . .     **20.00**

**Race Trap,** Multiple Toymakers, automobile racing, action game, cover shows starting gate, figure in open car, and multicolored game name, "The Wildest Race Game Ever," 1960s . . . . . . . . . .     **35.00**

**Races,** Milton Bradley, sports, board game, 4⅞ x 3¾", cover shows boy wearing cap and striped shirt with band over shoulder and chest next to box with game directions, contains paper race course, teetotum, and 2 cardboard horses on

*Radio Game*

*Raiders of the Lost Ark*

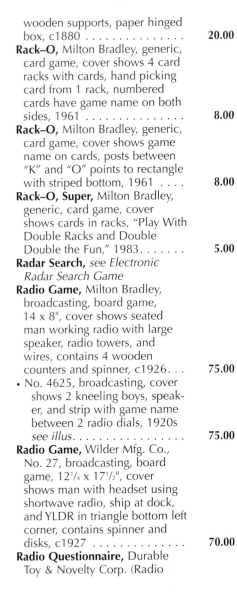

wooden supports, paper hinged
box, c1880 . . . . . . . . . . . . . .     **20.00**
**Rack–O,** Milton Bradley, generic,
card game, cover shows 4 card
racks with cards, hand picking
card from 1 rack, numbered
cards have game name on both
sides, 1961 . . . . . . . . . . . . . .     **8.00**
**Rack–O,** Milton Bradley, generic,
card game, cover shows game
name on cards, posts between
"K" and "O" points to rectangle
with striped bottom, 1961 . . . .     **8.00**
**Rack–O, Super,** Milton Bradley,
generic, card game, cover
shows cards in racks, "Play With
Double Racks and Double
Double the Fun," 1983 . . . . . . .     **5.00**
**Radar Search,** *see Electronic
Radar Search Game*
**Radio Game,** Milton Bradley,
broadcasting, board game,
14 x 8", cover shows seated
man working radio with large
speaker, radio towers, and
wires, contains 4 wooden
counters and spinner, c1926. . .     **75.00**
• No. 4625, broadcasting, cover
shows 2 kneeling boys, speaker, and strip with game name
between 2 radio dials, 1920s
*see illus.* . . . . . . . . . . . . . . .     **75.00**
**Radio Game,** Wilder Mfg. Co.,
No. 27, broadcasting, board
game, 12¼ x 17½", cover
shows man with headset using
shortwave radio, ship at dock,
and YLDR in triangle bottom left
corner, contains spinner and
disks, c1927 . . . . . . . . . . . . .     **70.00**
**Radio Questionnaire,** Durable
Toy & Novelty Corp. (Radio

Questionnaire Corp., education-
al/radio, battery operated game,
9½" sq, cover shows players in
center circle, 10 strips of questions emanating from circle
toward lid sides, "Flashes the
Answer to Thousands of
Questions," contains 6 quiz
cards, metal indicator and light
bulb attached to box bottom,
©1928. . . . . . . . . . . . . . . . .     **40.00**
**Raggedy Ann,** Milton Bradley, toy,
board game, cover shows waving Raggedy Ann and Andy riding on wooden horse, castle in
background, "A Little Folks
Game," 1954 . . . . . . . . . . . . .     **25.00**
**Raggedy Ann's Magic Pebble
Game,** Milton Bradley,
No. 4865, toy, board game,
15½ x 8¹¹⁄₁₆ x 1¾", 16½ x 13"
game board, cover shows
Raggedy Ann holding magic
pebble and sitting beneath trees,
Andy lying on stomach with
face propped in hands, contains
8 colored bases, cardboard
figures, and die, inside box
labeled "Game of Raggedy Ann,
Raggedy Andy and the Wishing
Pebble," ©1940 and 1941 by
Johnny Gruelle Co.. . . . . . . . . .     **60.00**
**Raiders Of The Lost Ark,** Kenner,
No. 40590, movie, board game,
18¼ x 9½ x 1⅜", contains game
board, plastic multicolored
tokens, die, game cards, instruc-
tion sheet, 1981 *see illus* . . . . .     **18.00**
**Ralph Edwards' This Is Your Life,**
unknown manufacturer, celebri-
ty/TV, board game, cover shows
Edwards at left bottom, book
with game name as title, people

*Ren & Stimpy Show Log Cereal Game*

gathered around woman seated on sofa, "Seen Coast to Coast on NBC Television," 1950s . . . . **30.00**

**Ranger Commandos,** Parker Brothers, military, board game, cover shows soldiers landing on beach, 1942 . . . . . . . . . . . . . **35.00**

**Rat Patrol Desert Combat Game, The,** Transogram, TV/military strategy, board game, cover shows desert scene with soldier shooting weapon from jeep, based on TV's Allied Unit in North Africa in World War II, includes plastic overlay to plot next attack, 1966–67 . . . . . . . **40.00**

**Rat Patrol Spin To Win Game,** Pressman, TV/military strategy, spin cycle toy, cover shows driver and soldier shooting weapon from jeep, tree in background, "The Official TV 'Rat Patrol' Spin Cycle Toy," 1967 . . **40.00**

**Rattle Battle,** Parker Brothers, generic, marble game, cover shows 2 players with upright playing surface, 1970 . . . . . . . **15.00**

**Real Ghostbusters Game, The,** Milton Bradley, TV/cartoon, cover shows ghost with large teeth and tongue outstretched fingers, car full of people chasing and shooting at ghost, "A 3–D Game of Tricks and Traps," clown in circle bottom right corner, 1984 . . . . . . . . . **10.00**

**Rebel, The,** Ideal, western, board game, 19½ x 9¾ x 1¾", contains game board, molded plastic cowboy and Indian figures, spinner, and instruction sheet, 1961 . . . . . . . . . . . . . . . . . . **20.00**

**Rebound,** Ideal, generic, action game, cover shows playing surface, mfg name on diagonal at left, 1980, original version dated 1971 . . . . . . . . . . . . . . . . . **10.00**

**Recall,** Milton Bradley, generic, memory game, cover shows boy, man, woman, and girl with playing pcs, "A fast moving challenging Game of Observation," 1967 . . . . . . . . . . . . . . **20.00**

**Red Riding Hood, Game of,** Parker Brothers, story, board game, 9½ x 6½", cover shows Riding Hood carrying lunch box and walking with wolf, house in background, mfg and copyright info bottom right corner, contains 2 colored wooden counters and spinner, ©1895 . . . . . . . . . **120.00**

**Red Riding Hood and the Wolf,** McLoughlin Brothers, story, board game, cover shows wolf looking at Red Riding Hood seated in grass next to tree, unknown date . . . . . . . . . . . . **50.00**

**Red Rover,** Cadaco, generic, board game, cover shows dog running toward group of children, girl with cane, boy waving, boy in hiking outfit, bear hiding under bush, and forest scene, 1963 . . . . . . . . . . . . . **15.00**

**Red Skelton's "I Dood It!,"** Zondine Game Co., celebrity, board game, cover shows Skelton with hand caught in box, dialogue box with game name, 1947 . . . . . . . . . . . . . . **70.00**

**Regatta,** 3M, sports, board game, cover shows people aboard tilting sailboat, other boats in background, 1967 . . . . . . . . . **20.00**

**Ren & Stimpy Show Log Cereal Game,** Parker Brothers, cartoon, 11¼ x 14½ x 4", cover shows Ren & Stimpy eating bowl of cereal, contains 4 two–sided TV episode story mats, 1 "history

*Rin–Tin–Tin*

eraser" mat, 25 puzzle pcs,
10 log pcs, and prize sticker,
"All Natural Splinter Free–High
Fiber, Just Ask Kids," ©1992,
Nickelodeon *see illus*. . . . . . . .    **15.00**

**Restless Gun,** Milton Bradley,
western, board game, cover
shows 3 cowboys with guns,
1 riding horse, and log building,
game re–released 1 year later as
"Shotgun Slade," 1959 . . . . . . .    **40.00**

**Return To Oz Game,** Golden,
Walt Disney film/book, cover
shows Dorothy on Lion, Tin
Man, Scarecrow, and others,
player age info bottom left
corner, 1985 . . . . . . . . . . . . .    **10.00**

**Revlon's $64,000 Question Junior
Quiz,** Lowell, TV/game show,
quiz, lid shows person in booth,
"Categories & Questions For
Children of All Ages," 1955 . . .    **25.00**

**Revlon's $64,000 Question Quiz
Game,** Lowell, TV/game show,
cover shows part of game name
in center oval, person in booth,
show host bottom right corner,
and checkerboard background,
1955 . . . . . . . . . . . . . . . . . . .    **25.00**

**Rex Morgan, M.D.,** Ideal, med-
ical/ comic strip character,
board game, "A 'Sunday
Funnies' Game," cover shows
"Sunday Funnies" behind man's
face, "Race To Emergencies with
America's Favorite Doctor,"
1972 . . . . . . . . . . . . . . . . . .    **25.00**

**Rich Uncle Stock Market Game,**
Parker Brothers, business/Wall
Street, board game, cover shows
man with mustache and top hat
seated in chair near window
looking out on high–rise build-

ings, old ticker tape machine
near game name, 1955 . . . . . . .    **25.00**

**Rich Uncle Stock Market Game,**
Parker Brothers, business/Wall
Street, board game, cover shows
man with phone seated at desk,
3 bags with "$" sign below win-
dow looking out on high–rise
buildings, 1959 . . . . . . . . . . .    **20.00**

**Richie Rich,** Milton Bradley,
comic book character, board
game, cover shows Richie and
friends holding boxes with jewels, girl with bow in hair, "The
Poor Little Rich Boy," 1982 . . . .    **10.00**

**Rifleman Game, The,** Milton
Bradley, TV/western, board
game, cover shows young cowboy behind show star Chuck
Connors holding rifle, hand
reaching for gun in holster at
right, 1959 . . . . . . . . . . . . . . .    **35.00**

**Ring My Nose,** Milton Bradley,
generic, skill/target game,
8¼ x 12¼", cover shows clown
with smiling face, ruffled collar,
and small pointed hat with
flower, contains 8 cardboard
rings and metal screw for
clown's nose, c1926–28 . . . . . .    **45.00**

**Rin–Tin–Tin,** Transogram, book/
movie, board game, cover
shows Rin–Tin–Tin running
ahead of mounted soldiers carrying guns and flag, cactus, and
mountains, 1955 *see illus* . . . . .    **40.00**

**Rio, The Game of,** Parker
Brothers, travel, board game, lid
shows beach scene with beach
umbrellas, swimmers, mountains
in background, 1956 . . . . . . . .    **25.00**

**Ripcord,** Lowell, aviation, action
game, cover shows sky diver,
airplane wheel, circle inset of
2 players, and boy blowing
through tube at small figure
wearing parachute, "An Action
Packed Skydiving Game,"
includes "Giant Sized Playboard
and Real Parachute," 1962 . . . .    **55.00**

**Rip–Van Win–kle,** Parker Brothers,
story, board game, 15 x 9",
cover shows center oval with
Van Winkle carrying 2 sticks,
small figures, and house, top

*Robinson Crusoe*

oval frame with bow and barrel
flanked by men wearing pointed
hats, 5 balls on ground, contains 4 colored wooden coun-
ters and spinner, c1890 . . . . . .    **125.00**
**Risk!,** Parker Brothers, military,
card game, Original Edition,
"Continental Game," cover
shows game name above globe,
large exclamation point, and
fanned cards at bottom left,
wooden pcs, 1959 . . . . . . . . .    **20.00**
• Later versions with plastic pcs. .    **10.00**
**Risk,** Parker Brothers, military,
card game, cover shows circle
with pie–shaped pcs, arrow
pointing at game name, horse
and rider with flag, players, and
part of map, 1968 . . . . . . . . .    **10.00**
**Rival Doctors, The,** McLoughlin
Brothers, medical, board game,
10½ x 10¼", lid shows 2 men
with top hats around men sitting
in bed, table with bottles at end
of bed, "A Comic Game" left
side, contains 4 wooden coun-
ters and spinner, 1893 . . . . . . .    **110.00**
**Rival Policeman,** McLoughlin
Brothers, crime, board game,
21 x 12¼", cover shows
2 policemen chasing man carrying roll of material under arm
and sack on back, "A New
Comic Game," copyright and
mfg info bottom left corner,
contains 2 wooden dice cups,
4 dice, 4 lead policemen, and

13 wooden counters represent-
ing crooks, wooden box,
©1896 . . . . . . . . . . . . . . . . . .    **1,400.00**
**River Boat Game, Disneyland,**
*see Disneyland, Riverboat Game*
**Road Runner Game,** Milton
Bradley, cartoon, board game,
cover shows desert scene, Road
Runner, Wile E. Coyote, Tweety
Bird, Sylvester, game "object"
bottom right corner, 1968 . . . . .    **25.00**
**Road Runner Game, The,**
Whitman, cartoon, board game,
cover shows Road Runner, Wile
E. Coyote, "Beep–Beep! Outrace
Wile E. Coyote," 1969 . . . . . . .    **25.00**
**Robin Hood (and His Merry Men
of Sherwood Forest),** Harett–
Gilmar, book, board game, lid
shows Robin Hood shooting
arrow in forest, "A Game of
Adventure," includes gold coins,
1955 . . . . . . . . . . . . . . . . . . .    **40.00**
**Robin Hood, The Adventures of,**
Bettye B, TV series/book, board
game, 3–dimensional, cover
shows Robin Hood standing
with feet apart holding arrow in
right hand, other hand on hip,
"wanted, capture, reward," and
"beware" strips across bottom,
"Official Game" top right
corner, series starred Richard
Greene, contains unique
"gravity spinner," 1956 . . . . . . .    **60.00**
**Robin Hood Game, Walt Disney
Productions,** Disney/ movie/
book, board game, cover shows
forest scene, figure carrying
arrow, figure carrying money
bags, robed figure with crown,
and others, 1973 . . . . . . . . . .    **15.00**
**Robinson Crusoe,** McLoughlin
Brothers, book, board game,
7½" sq, cover shows back view
of Crusoe climbing mountains,
animal on left side above
"Game," mfg info bottom left
corner, printed instructions bottom right corner, contains wood-
en counters and spinner, c1890
*see illus* . . . . . . . . . . . . . . . .    **35.00**
**Robinson Crusoe, Game of,**
Parker Brothers, book, card
game, 3⅞ x 5½", cover shows

*Robo Rally*

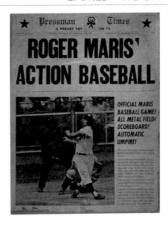

*Roger Maris' Action Baseball*

back view of Crusoe looking out over water framed by circle of clover designs and palm trees, copyright and mfg info along bottom, contains 33 multicolored litho cards, ©1895 ...... **25.00**

**Robo Rally,** Garfield Games, space, 12³/₄ x 12³/₄ x 2", contains 8 pewter robot figures, 6 color boards, cards, and operating manual, ©1994, Wizards of the Coast, Inc. *see illus.* .... **15.00**

**Robot Sam The Answer Man,** Jacmar, educational, electronic, 8¹/₈ x 10¹/₄ x 2", contains elecric panel, and 6 two sided cards, "156 Questions About The World Answered By The Electrical Robot Man," no date ..... **35.00**

**Rock 'Em Sock 'Em Robots,** Marx, sports/boxing, skill game, cover shows 2 boxing robots, "Knock His Block Off...," inset pictures at bottom show "action, the left jab, the knockout, skill," 1966 .................... **125.00**

**Rodeo, The Wild West Game,** Whitman, western, board game, cover shows 2 tracks and rodeo scenes, contains spinner, play money, and illustrated rodeo story, 1957. ............... **30.00**

**Roger Maris' Action Baseball,** Pressman, sports, action, 15¹/₄ x 20 x 1", newspaper style cover shows game name in headline, contains instruction sheet, metal

baseball field game board with wooden sides, wooden bat, and marbles, 1962 ............ **50.00**

**Rolawheel (Three in One),** Rosebud Art Co., No. 36, generic, board game, 9³/₄ x 6⁵/₈ x 11³/₁₆", cover shows seated man wearing vest, standing woman, girl with hair bow, and seated man and woman with gameboard on table, "Everybody's Game," contains board with attached wheel, 1926 ........ **20.00**

**Rollamatic Bridge, Charles Goren's,** Milton Bradley, generic, automatic card game, cover shows circle with 2 arrows pointing at Rolomatic Bridge Machine, "Set II For Experienced Players," 1969 ............ **15.00**

**Roman X,** Selchow & Righter, educational, board game, "The Game of Caesars," cover shows strip of 7 cards with Roman numerals and men in Roman clothing, figure holding shield and sword at left, 1964 ....... **15.00**

**Romper Room Magic Teacher,** Bar–Zim, educational, card game, cover shows Jack–in–the–Box and bee buzzing at card with "A" and apple, contains plastic answer board and picture flash cards, 1960s ..... **20.00**

**Rook,** Parker Brothers, generic, card game, printed cover shows

*'Round the World With Nellie Bly*

game name beside bird, "The
Famous Home Game," reg info
and "Combination Game"
below game name, "The Game
of Games" bottom right corner,
1920s . . . . . . . . . . . . . . . . .    **8.00**
**Rook,** Parker Bothers, generic,
card game, cover divided into
4 sections, game name, mfg
info, blank space, bird bottom
right corner, 1936 . . . . . . . . . .    **8.00**
**Rook,** Rook Card Co, Dixie–Rook
Edition, generic, card game,
picture of animal beside game
name, 1924 . . . . . . . . . . . . . .    **10.00**
**Ropes and Ladders, Game of,**
Parker Brothers, generic, board
game, cover shows 2 figures
dressed as pirates, 1 climbing
rope ladder, 1954 . . . . . . . . .    **45.00**
**Rose Ball,** E.S. Lowe, sports,
board game, cover shows players in action, #81, #66, and
#89 visible, "All The Thrilling
Plays of Big–Time Football,"
contains 3–dimensional plastic
playing field and official timer,
1966 . . . . . . . . . . . . . . . . . .    **15.00**
**Rough Riders, Game of,** Clark &
Snowden, Tokalon Series,
No. 353, military/Spanish
American War, board game,
10$^{1}$/$_{4}$ x 19$^{1}$/$_{4}$", cover shows man
seated on horse wearing wide
brimmed hat and waving lasso,
c1900 . . . . . . . . . . . . . . . . .    **120.00**

**Round Game of Tiddledy Winks,**
McLoughlin Brothers, generic,
skill game, 4$^{5}$/$_{8}$ x 3$^{1}$/$_{2}$", cover
shows Tiddledy Winks as heads
on figures moving toward round
container with game name on
side, contains wooden cup,
4 large, round, colored, bone
Tiddledies, and 24 smaller,
round, colored, bone winks,
1890 . . . . . . . . . . . . . . . . . .    **20.00**
**'Round the World With Nellie
Bly,** McLoughlin Brothers, travel,
board game, 16 x 19$^{1}$/$_{2}$", cover
shows Bly carrying travel bag
and walking on highway with
telephone lines in background,
contains 4 wooden dice cups,
4 large turned pawns, and
2 bone dice, largest of the
Nellie Bly games, © J. A.
Drozier, 1890 . . . . . . . . . . . . .    **500.00**
• Same cover, 8$^{3}$/$_{4}$ x 16$^{1}$/$_{4}$ x 1$^{1}$/$_{4}$",
1890, © J.A. Drozier . . . . . . .    **325.00**
**'Round the World With Nellie
Bly, Game of,** McLoughlin
Brothers, Standard Series, travel,
board game, 12$^{1}$/$_{4}$ x 12$^{1}$/$_{4}$", cover
shows woman in long dress car-
rying travel bag, list of world
cities down both sides, contains
4 wooden counters and spinner,
wooden box, ©1890 by J.A.
Drozier, © inside is 1904 *see
illus* . . . . . . . . . . . . . . . . . .    **200.00**
**Round Up, The,** unknown manu-
facturer, western, skill game,
4$^{3}$/$_{4}$ x 3$^{3}$/$_{4}$", cover shows man on
horse, herd of steer, c1900 . . . .    **15.00**
**Route 66 Travel Game,**
Transogram, TV/travel, board
game, cover shows game name
in route sign, convertible with
2 male passengers, and faces of
show stars Martin Miner and
George Maharis on strip near
telephone poles, "Travel the
Highway to Adventure with Tod
and Buzz," road map back-
ground, mfg logo top left and
bottom right corners, 1962 . . . .    **85.00**
**Royal Game of Kings and
Queens, The,** McLoughlin
Brothers, No. 429, generic,
board game, 20 x 11$^{1}$/$_{2}$", cover

shows bowing man and members of royalty gathered around standing king and queen seated on throne, mfg info bottom right corner, contains knights and pawns, ©1890 and 1892 . . . . .    **125.00**

**Rrib–Bit**, Genesis Enterprises, generic, board game, cover shows plastic frog chess pcs and spired buildings in background, 1973 . . . . . . . . . . . . . . . . . .    **15.00**

**Rubik's Race**, Ideal, toy, board game, cover shows divided board with multicolored squares, inset strip with game players' hands, 1982 . . . . . . . .    **10.00**

**Ruff and Reddy Circus Game**, Transogram, TV/cartoon/circus, board game, cover shows Ruff, Reddy, and friends in circus setting, 1962 . . . . . . . . . . . . .    **30.00**

**Rummy**, unknown manufacturer, generic, card game, 5³/₈ x 7⁵/₈", "Rummy in America and As Cooncan in England, with Rules for Moosehead, Numero, Foozle, Sachem and other Absorbing Games" printed on lid, scroll design in corners, c1910 . . . . . . . . . . . . . . . . .    **15.00**

**Rummy Royal**, Whitman, generic, card game, also known as Michigan Rummy, cover shows jack of hearts, 2 of spades, king and queen of hearts, poker chips, and part of "kitty," contains playing cards and poker chips, 1959 . . . . . . . . . . . . . .    **10.00**

### –S–

**S.O.S.**, Durable Toy and Novelty, generic, bagatelle, 23 x 14", metal game, S.O.S. stands for "Stay Off Street, Stay On Sidewalk," metal playing pc has pictures of traffic cop with raised hands, street scene traffic, c1947 . . . . . . . . . . . . . . . . .    **55.00**

**S–S–S–Scat**, Cadaco, generic, action game, cover shows cat chasing mouse, 1967 . . . . . . . .    **10.00**

**S.W.A.T. Game, The**, Milton Bradley, TV/crime, board game,

*The S.W.A.T. Game*

cover shows S.W.A.T. team members with guns outside building, 2 inset pictures at right, 1976 *see illus* . . . . . . . . .    **15.00**

**Safari**, Selchow & Righter, jungle adventure, board game, cover shows running lion and 3 men with rifles, mfg info top right corner, "The Great New Hunting Game," 1950 . . . . . . . . . . . . .    **30.00**

**$ale of the Century**, Milton Bradley, TV/game show, "The Game of Incredible Bargains," cover shows man at podium and 3 people on panel, smaller inset pictures along bottom, 2 editions released, 1969 . . . . .    **15.00**

**Salute**, Selchow & Righter, military, board game, cover shows man and woman saluting Uncle Sam holding stars and stripes decorated playing pc, background scattered with stars, contains wooden pcs, 1940s. . .    **30.00**

**Sambo, The Game of**, Parker Brothers, story, skill/target game, 5¹/₈ x 10³/₈", cover shows black man with hands on hips wearing checkered pants and cap, contains 2 wooden supports, black man figure, pipe, and 4 colored cardboard rings, c1920. . . . . .    **450.00**

**Samsonite Pro Football Game**, Samsonite, sports, board game, cover shows football players in tackle play, 1969 . . . . . . . . . .    **15.00**

**Sandlot Slugger**, Milton Bradley, sports/baseball, action game, mechanical, cover shows 12" h "Slugging Sam the Mechanical Batter," 1968 . . . . . . . . . . . . .    **25.00**

*Say When!!*

*Scooby–Doo...Where Are You? Game*

**Santa Claus Game,** Milton Bradley, holiday, board game, 12 x 8½", cover shows Santa wearing hat trimmed with leaves, mfg info bottom right corner, c1920–24 . . . . . . . . . .  **240.00**

**Say When!!,** Parker Brothers, TV/game show, cover shows coins, currency and cards with various pictures including television, lamp, coffeepot, dollar sign, and question mark, 1961 *see illus* . . . . . . . . . . . . . . . .  **20.00**

**Scavenger Hunt,** Milton Bradley, No. 4239, generic, cover shows woman wearing long gown, men in tuxedos and top hats, and man lighting cigarette, contains cardboard object tokens and cards with collecting list, 1933 . . . . . . . . . . . . . . . . . .  **20.00**

**Scooby–Doo and Scrappy–Doo Game,** Milton Bradley, TV/cartoon characters/mystery, board game, cover shows 2 ghosts and bat at open doorway, dog wearing crown and holding coins and gem, "Join the Doggy Duo on a Wild Romp in a Haunted Castle," 1983 . . . . . . . . . . . . .  **10.00**

**Scooby–Doo...Where Are You? Game,** Milton Bradley, TV/cartoon character, board game, cover shows man in open doorway, 2 women and man inside, woman with high socks falling backwards, cartoon character holding man, and vehicle seen in window, 1973 *see illus*. . . . .  **20.00**

**Scoop,** Waddington, media, board game, British version, cover shows man in hat with phone, man in press room on phone, and newsboy with "extra" sign, "Game by the Makers of Monopoly," 1955 . . .  **30.00**

**Scoop, The Game,** Parker Brothers, media, board game, "Publish your Own Newspaper" across lid bottom, cover shows helicopter, man on phone, newsboy, and others, 1956 . . . .  **30.00**

**Score Four,** Funtastic, strategy, board game, cover shows dice cups, beads spilling from cup, and playing surface with stacked beads, "a fascinating new 3 dimensional family game," 1968–75 . . . . . . . . . . . . . . .  **10.00**

**Scouting, Game of,** Milton Bradley, #4648, generic, board game, 5½ x 7½", cover shows boy scout wearing wide brimmed hat in circle, 2 figures wearing Indian headdresses at border bottom, and 2 eagle figures at border top, produced under license of Boy Scouts of America, contains 52 cards with merit badges, patrol signs, scout laws, oaths, mottos, honors, badges, medals, etc. 1930s . . . .  **200.00**

**Scouting Game, Untitled,** McLoughlin Brothers, generic, board game, 16 x 9", cover shows outdoor scene, Scout leader at table, Scouts standing in formation, flag, and tent, contains 22 multicolored litho scouts in wooden supports, "Headquarters" tent, and 13–star flag, 1914 . . . . . . . . . . . . . . .  **325.00**

**Scrabble,** Selchow & Righter, generic, word game, plain cover has circle with printing upper

left corner, contains wooden
tiles, 1953 . . . . . . . . . . . . . . .   **10.00**

**Scrabble, Deluxe,** Selchow &
Righter, generic, word game,
cover shows table with open
playing board, 4 player positions with tiles on racks, tiles
spilling from bag, includes
revolving board, plastic tiles,
and racks, 1953 . . . . . . . . . . .   **15.00**

**Scrabble For Juniors**, Selchow &
Righter, generic, word game,
cover shows tiles forming words
on playing surface, tiles in front
of 4 youngsters playing game,
girl reaching to put tile on
board, "edition three" . . . . . . .   **5.00**

**"Screwball" A Mad Mad Game,**
Transogram, media, board
game, revised cover shows
figure wearing triangular shaped
hat labeled "Screwball" standing in front of microphone with
"WILD," figures in background
include woman with long hair
and long dress, lawsuit threat by
Mad Magazine over original
cover caused Transogram to
alter cover slightly . . . . . . . . .   **50.00**
• Value for cover without micro-
phone . . . . . . . . . . . . . . . .   **60.00**

**Scribbage,** E.S. Lowe, generic,
word game, cover shows hand
spilling lettered dice, timer, and
dice formed into words,1963 . .   **8.00**

**Scribbage, Twin,** E.S. Lowe,
generic, word game, cover
shows 4 lettered cubes and
shaker cups, timer in bottom
right corner, "8 New Ways to
Play, 2 Complete Sets," mfg logo
upper left corner, 1965 . . . . . . .   **8.00**

**Scr–unch,** Mattel, generic, action
game, cover shows boy and girl
with hands on playing pc,
"A Snaggle Game," 1967 . . . . .   **40.00**

**Scruples, A Question of,** High
Game Enterprises, generic,
board game, Original Edition,
cover shows 7 game names atop
each other, 1984 . . . . . . . . . .   **10.00**

**Sea Battle,** Kaywood Corp., military, cover shows sailor peering
through binoculars at sea battle

scene, "An Exciting Realistic
Naval Battle Game," 1950s . . . .   **25.00**

**Sea Battle,** Lido Toy Co., military,
board game, cover shows tilting
"Enemy Battleship" at sea,
planes, figures above anchor,
contains plastic ships, 1940s . . .   **25.00**

**Sea Hunt Underwater Adventure
Game,** Lowell, TV/adventure,
board game, cover with show
star Lloyd Bridges and divers,
1960 . . . . . . . . . . . . . . . . .   **40.00**

**Sealab 2020 Game,** Milton
Bradley, TV/space, cover shows
group of people in laboratory
wearing futuristic uniforms, lab
machines and fish in back-
ground, 1973 . . . . . . . . . . . . .   **15.00**

**Seance,** Milton Bradley, mystical,
board game, "The Voice From
the Great Beyond," cover shows
room setting with table, chairs,
picture on wall above fireplace,
draped windows, grandfather's
clock, and knight in armor,
1972 . . . . . . . . . . . . . . . . .   **30.00**

**Secrecy,** Universal Games,
spy/espionage, board game,
cover shows man peering
around building at approaching
man with briefcase, "An
International Game of World
Conquest," 1965 . . . . . . . . . .   **25.00**

**Secret of NIMH Game,** Whitman,
animated movie, board game,
cover shows large black bird
with spread wings above 3
figures, tree and building at
right, 1982 . . . . . . . . . . . . . .   **8.00**

**See–Action Football Game, O.J.
Simpson's,** Kenner, sports, board
game, cover shows Simpson
autograph, picture and 3 players, inset of game players with
upright game surface, "Give–A–
Show Technology," 1974 . . . . . .   **40.00**

**See New York 'Round the Town
Game,** Transogram, travel, board
game, cover shows Manhattan
Island, boat, plane, Statue of
Liberty, and skyscrapers, 1964   **20.00**

**Senior Prom Game, The,**
Built–Rite, generic, board game,
lid shows Prom Queen with

*Sergeant Preston Game*

*The Shadow*

crown, wand, and cape and
dancing couples, 1966. . . . . . .      **15.00**
**Sergeant Preston Game,** Milton
Bradley, military/ranger, board
game, lid shows Preston holding
gun and dog, 1956 *see illus* . . .      **25.00**
**Set Back, The Beverly Hillbillies
Card Game,** *see Beverly
Hillbillies Set Back Card Game*
**Seven Keys,** Ideal, TV/game show,
board game, cover shows
6 squares with pictures above
car, shield shape, playing surface with row of keys on side
edge, row of red dots with mfg
logo at right, 1961 . . . . . . . . .      **20.00**
**Seven Seas,** Cadaco, business/
trade, board game, cover shows
ship surrounded by smaller
boats, mountain background,
"The Game of Trade" in rectan-
gle at bottom right, 1960 . . . . .      **25.00**
**Seven–Up Game,** Transogram,
generic, board game, cover
shows hands grasping baseball
bat and game board, 1961 . . . .      **15.00**
**77 Sunset Strip,** Lowell, TV/detec-
tive, board game, cover shows
3 show stars in circle insets, mfg
info top left corner, "A 'Private
Eye' Game of Mystery and
Suspense," 1959 . . . . . . . . . .      **35.00**
**"76, Game of,"** or **The Lion &
Eagle,** Noyes & Snow, generic,
card game, 5⁷/₈ x 4¹/₄", cover-
shows eagle, lion, and Capitol,
contains 50 cards, c1870s . . . .      **85.00**
**Shadow, The,** Milton Bradley,
movie, radio, "The Ultimate
Between Good And Evil,"
19 x 9¹/₂ x 2", includes
3–dimensional gameboard,
2 blank dice, 1 black and

1 white die, plastic buttons,
label sheets, plastic pawn stand,
parts sheets, and instructions,
1994 *see illus.* . . . . . . . . . . . .      **15.00**
**Shadowlord!,** Parker Brothers,
dungeons/dragons, board game,
cover shows men and women
wearing headdresses in dungeon, man with beard at
forefront, man holding knife,
woman holding rolled paper,
1983 . . . . . . . . . . . . . . . . . .      **10.00**
**Sha–ee, Game of Destiny,** Ideal,
fortune telling, board game,
cover shows sphinx–like figure,
1963 . . . . . . . . . . . . . . . . . .      **45.00**
**Shake Bingo,** Schaper, generic,
action bingo game with dice,
cover shows pc on spaces of
playing board, "America's Fastest
Action Game," 1960s . . . . . . . .      **12.00**
**Sharp's Shooter,** Sharp, generic,
bagatelle, 10¹/₄ x 20¹/₂", red and
black heart motif painted on
wooden pc, unknown date . . . .      **75.00**
**Shenanigans Carnival of Fun
Game,** Milton Bradley, carni-
val/circus, board game, cover
shows 2 boys and girl at playing
surface, boy pressing buzzer and
shooting pc into pie, 1964 . . . .      **20.00**
**Sherlock Holmes, The Game of,**
Parker Brothers, detective, card
game, 5¹/₂ x 4", red box with
gold lettering, cover shows
game name, "Laughter and
Excitement," mfg info, and
"Salem, MASS U.S.A," contains
56 cards, 1904 . . . . . . . . . . . .      **50.00**
• Later edition with carriage sil-
houette illustration on box lid      **65.00**
**Shindig,** Remco, TV/music show,
board game, "Teen Game,"

cover shows 4 insets of people, "ABC" over second "i" in game name, mfg logo top left corner, "Test Your Knowledge About Top Teen Entertainers," 1965 . . . . . .   **35.00**

**Shoot the Hat, Game of,** McLoughlin Brothers, generic, card game, Punch and Judy Series, 4$^1$/$_4$ x 3$^1$/$_4$", cover shows Indian with bow and arrow, man wearing sombrero pierced by arrow, contains 21 multicolored litho cards with blue backs, ©1892 . . . . . . . . . . .   **35.00**

**Shopping, The Game of,** Parker Brothers, shopping, card game, 3$^3$/$_4$ x 5$^1$/$_2$", cover shows man behind counter showing clothing to woman wearing long dress, girl wearing hat holding hand of second woman wearing long dress, merchandise on shelves, contains merchandise cards and small price cards, 1888 . . . . . . . . . . . . . . . . .   **35.00**

**Shopping Center Game,** Whitman, shopping, board game, cover shows boy in striped shirt carrying shopping bag with hand outstretched to girl wearing hat carrying bag with flower, stores in background, 1957 . . . . . . . . . . . . .   **18.00**

**Shotgun Slade Game,** Milton Bradley, TV/western, board game, cover shows cowboy lying on stomach, holding rifle, woman and horse behind, starred Scott Brady, 1960 . . . . .   **25.00**

**Show–Biz,** Lowell, movies, board game, cover shows theatre marquee with game name and "The Game of the Stars," people at ticket booth and around theatre, 2 "All Star Cast" billboards with stars' pictures including Jack Benny, Milton Berle, George Burns, Bing Crosby, and Sammy Davis, Jr., 1956 . . . . . . . . . . .   **40.00**

**Showdown Poker,** E.S. Lowe, generic, dice/poker game, cover shows playing surface with dice and cubes, "combines fast action cube play with stimulating poker strategy," contains

"sturdy 3–dimensional grid and new quick–set timer," 1971 . . . .   **12.00**

**Shuffle King, The,** Marx, generic, action game, cover shows 3 people with playing surface, "4 Shuffle Board Games!," picture of "steel center rolling pcs," mfg info bottom right corner, 1960s . . . . . . . . . . . . . . . .   **25.00**

**Shuffle–Board, The New Game of,** Samuel Gabriel Sons & Co., #T21, sports, skill and action game, 15 x 8$^3$/$_4$", cover shows men and women playing game on deck of ship at sea, second ship in background, contains 6 wooden rings, c1920 . . . . . .   **85.00**

**Siege, Game of,** Milton Bradley, military, skill, 14$^1$/$_4$ x 10$^1$/$_4$", cover shows soldier on horse, right hand raised, man on ground with rifle, contains metal and wood pistol, 10 wooden "shots," 14 cardboard soldiers on wooden supports, c1918 . . .   **140.00**

**Siege Game,** Milton Bradley, military, board game, cover shows knights on horses in battle in front of fort flying flags, contains plastic knights, 1966 . . . . . . . .   **25.00**

**Siege of Havana, The,** Parker Brothers, military, board game, 22$^1$/$_2$ x 16$^1$/$_4$", cover shows ships engaged in battle, contains 4 colored metal battleships, dice cup, 3 dice, spinner, and colored wooden "shot" and shells, wooden box, ©1898 . . . . . . . .   **525.00**

**Sigmund and the Sea Monsters Game,** Milton Bradley, TV/monster, board game, cover shows kneeling boy with sea monster, inset picture bottom right corner, based on children's show, 1975 . . . . . . . . . . . . . . . . .   **15.00**

**Signs, Game of,** Milton Bradley, mystical, card game, 5 x 6", lid shows cat with paw on salt shaker, cup and saucer, turkey in circle, and "Signs" on diagonal slant, contains 32 multicolored litho cards pertaining to omens and superstitions, c1890 . . . . . .   **20.00**

**Silly Safari,** Topper, generic, board game, 3–dimensional, lid shows

The Six Million Dollar Man

The Sinking of the Titanic

animals including giraffe, monkey, and alligator, inset picture of 3 players top left corner, contains plastic animals, 1966 . . . . **50.00**

**Silly Sidney,** Transogram, TV/cartoon, Hector Heathcote show, board game, cover shows question mark in dialogue box coming from animated elephant with flower at its trunk, "the absent–minded elephant game," mfg info top left corner, 1963 . . **35.00**

**Simple Simon Balloon Game,** Hasbro, nursery rhyme, action game and toy, cover shows Simon wearing top hat and looking at Pieman's pies, Pieman wearing short pants, 3 balloons, 1966 . . . . . . . . . . **15.00**

**Sinbad,** Cadaco, movie, board game, cover shows Sinbad and friends on large rocks pointing to ship at sea, large bird right side, film strip down left side, 1978 . . . . . . . . . . . . . . . . . . **25.00**

**Sinking of the Titanic, The,** Ideal, adventure, board game, 20 x 12 x 1½", cover shows ship sinking, people in row boat, includes movable game board, cards, tokens, plastic playing pieces, dice, metal binder screw with post, and instructions, 1976 *see illus* . . . . . . . . . . . . **30.00**

**Sir Lancelot, Adventures of,** *see Adventures of Sir Lancelot*

**Situation 7,** Parker Brothers, space, puzzle game, cover shows 4 people with game at table, 1969 . . . . . . . . . . . . . . **15.00**

**Six Million Dollar Man, The,** Parker Brothers, TV/space, board game, cover with show star Lee Majors and 4 inset action shots including 1 with astronaut, 1975 *see illus* . . . . . . . . . . . . . . . . . **10.00**

**Skatterbug, Game of,** Parker Brothers, generic, spinning game, cover shows hand placing disks on spinner, 4 people around playing surface, mfg info bottom left corner, 1951 . . . . . . **30.00**

**Skee Ball,** Eldon, generic, action game, playing surface has plunger that pushes balls up ramp toward target rings, includes automatic scoring and ball return, 1963 . . . . . . . . . . **30.00**

**Ski Gammon,** American Publishing Co., sports, board game, cover shows playing surface resembling ski slopes, 1962 . . . **12.00**

**Ski–Hi: New York to Paris,** Cutler & Saleeby Co., Inc., aviation, board game, cover shows 4 planes flying over water, view of buildings bottom left corner, c1900–20s . . . . . . . . . . . . . . . **85.00**

**Skip–A–Cross,** Cadaco–Ellis, generic, word game, cover shows letter tiles on board forming words "Repeater, Apron," and "Center," "The Word Tally Game, Licensed by the Makers of Scrabble," 1954 . . . . . . . . . . **20.00**

**Skipper Game,** *see Barbie's Little Sister Skipper Game*

**Skirmish, American Heritage,** Milton Bradley, military/ American Revolution, board game, cover shows battle scene against 5–star flag, 1975 . . . . . . **20.00**

*Slap Jack*

**Skirmish at Harper's Ferry,**
McLoughlin Brothers, military,
board game, 16$\frac{1}{8}$ x 15", lid has
Civil War scene of soldiers with
wheeled cannon, 1891 . . . . . . .  **500.00**

**Skit Scat,** Mcloughlin Brothers,
generic, card game, 6$\frac{1}{4}$ x 4$\frac{5}{8}$",
cover shows cat looking at fish
bowl, scroll design on left and
right, contains 24 numbered
multicolored litho cards
showing cat in different
positions around fish bowl,
©1905. . . . . . . . . . . . . . . . .  **25.00**

**Skittle–Bowl,** Aurora, sports/bowl-
ing, action game, cover shows
pole with string and falling pins,
inset of man and boy with
playing surface, 1969 . . . . . . .  **25.00**

**Skittle Pool,** Aurora, sports/pool,
action game, cover shows man
and playing surface with cue
balls, contains cue balls and
"magic cue" on skittle stand,
1972 . . . . . . . . . . . . . . . . . .  **30.00**

**Skittle Score–Ball, All American,**
Aurora, generic, action game,
cover shows boy in striped shirt
and girl, playing pc with balls,
and stars at boy's hand and top
of playing pc, 1972 . . . . . . . .  **15.00**

**Skudo,** Parker Brothers, generic,
board game, cover shows game
name above playing surface,
"The Turn–Table Game," mfg
name bottom right corner, 1949  **15.00**

**Skunk,** Schaper, generic, dice
game, cover shows skunk sitting
on game name, 4 game players,
girl with raised arm, and dice
and cards on table, "A Funny
Party Game," 1968 . . . . . . . . .  **10.00**

**Sky's The Limit, The,** Kohner, TV/
game show, stunt game, 18$\frac{1}{2}$ x
13$\frac{3}{4}$", lid shows Gene Rayburn,
game name on star in circle,
"Competitive Family Fun
Game," contains objects to be
attached to string or dowel,
spinner, balloons, 1955 . . . . . .  **25.00**

**Slap Jack,** Russell Press, Inc.,
No. 54, generic, card game,
2$\frac{5}{8}$ x 3$\frac{1}{2}$ x $\frac{3}{8}$", cover shows face
wearing crown and ruffled collar
in circle, "Pep and Fun For
Everyone," 1935 *see illus* . . . . .  **20.00**

**Slap Stick,** Milton Bradley, generic, action game, cover shows
game pcs flying around 4 people kneeling at playing surface
on floor, man and woman
holding pie in her right hand
watching, 1966–67 . . . . . . . . .  **20.00**

**Slap Trap Game,** Ideal, generic,
action game, cover shows
4 smiling players, boy lifting top
from game pc, spinning top, and
flying game pcs, 1967 . . . . . . .  **20.00**

**Sleeping Beauty, Walt Disney
Presents,** Parker Brothers,
Disney/movie, board game,
cover shows 5 inset pictures
from story including girl in long
dress, man with cape, 2 musicians wearing shirts with striped
sleeves, and 3 royal figures, mfg
info bottom left, 1958 . . . . . . .  **25.00**

**Smack–A–Roo,** Mattel, generic,
action game, cover shows
woman and boy with game-
board, "Play Baseball, Bowling,
Smack–It and Many Other
Wonderful Games," 1964 . . . . .  **20.00**

**Smitty Game,** Milton Bradley,
No. 4254, comics, board game,
16$\frac{1}{2}$ x 8$\frac{1}{2}$ x $\frac{3}{4}$", cover shows
Smitty blowing horn in backseat
of convertible, driver with
dialogue box, drawn by Bernd,
licensed by Famous Artist
Syndicate, c1930s . . . . . . . . . .  **110.00**

*Snap!*

**Smokey Bear Game,** Milton
Bradley, advertising character,
board game, cover shows park
scene with Smokey and animals
near lake, 1973 . . . . . . . . . . .    **30.00**
**Smurf Game, The,** Milton Bradley,
TV/cartoon, 3–dimensiona
game, cover shows Smurfs,
house, and trees, 2 smurfs carry-
ing wrapped present, 1981 . . . .    **15.00**
**Snagglepuss Fun At The Picnic
Game, Yogi Bear Presents,**
Transogram, TV/cartoon, board
game, cover shows Yogi putting
mustard on friend's hot dog,
another character dressed in
chef's outfit holding frying pan
and fork, 1961 . . . . . . . . . . . .    **40.00**
**Snake Eyes,** Selchow & Righter,
ethnic/Black collectibles, card
game, 11 x 7¹/₂", cover shows
2 dice, black man wearing straw
hat and black woman wearing
polka dot scarf looking over
game name, contains 120 numbered cards with "craps" expres-
sions, dice cup, 2 wooden dice,
and 62 chips, c1930s–57 . . . . .    **55.00**
• Versions after 1957 . . . . . . . .    **25.00**
**Snake Game,** McLoughlin
Brothers, generic, board game,
1³/₅" sq, cover shows snake
wrapped around tree aiming
at 2 upright frog–like figures

holding sticks, instructions bottom left corner, contains
4 wooden counters and spinner,
c1888 . . . . . . . . . . . . . . . . .    **30.00**
**Snake's Alive!, The Game of,**
Ideal, generic, action game,
cover shows snake popping
out of container held by 4 people, "Featuring the Mystery
Basket and the Popping Snake,"
1966 . . . . . . . . . . . . . . . . . .    **20.00**
**Snap,** Milton Bradley, generic,
card game, 5 x 7³/₈", cover
shows 2 swans in pond, contains 32 multicolored litho
cards, ©1905 . . . . . . . . . . . . .    **15.00**
**Snap,** Milton Bradley, generic,
card game, 6³/₄ x 5¹/₂", cover
shows 2 children, "Snap! Went
the Trigger," contains 32 multicolored litho cards, ©1905 *see
illus* . . . . . . . . . . . . . . . . . . .    **15.00**
**Snap, The Game of,** Parker
Brothers, generic, card game,
cover shows alligator with open
mouth and 2 black children
holding hands and running in
bottom right corner above mfg
info, c1885 . . . . . . . . . . . . . .    **45.00**
**Snap Judgement,** Milton Bradley,
generic, word association
game, cover shows "snapping"
fingers and 4 laughing faces,
1968 . . . . . . . . . . . . . . . . . .    **10.00**
**Snap Judgment,** Simon &
Schuster, celebrity, memory
game, 6¹/₄ x 9¹/₄", cover shows
numbered photos of famous
people with "A," by Herbert E.
Marks and Jerome S. Meyer,
pictures of Smith Brothers as
"Simon" and "Schuster,"
copyright info, contains eight
17¹/₄ x 26¹/₄" game sheets with
famous buildings, men, women
and child star photos, answer
card, and note pad, "the Photo–
Recognizing Game," 1933 . . . .    **35.00**
**Snip, Snap, Snorum, Game of,**
McLoughlin Brothers, generic,
card game, Banner Series,
3⁷/₈ x 4⁷/₈", cover shows "Snip,
Snap, Snorum" in open birds'
beaks, mfg name bottom right
corner, c1898. . . . . . . . . . . .    **25.00**

*The Soldier On Fort*

**Snoopy and the Red Baron,** Milton Bradley, cartoon/comic strip character, action game, playing pc shows Peanuts Gang watching Red Baron shoot colored marbles at Snoopy, 1970     **25.00**

**Snoopy Come Home Game,** Milton Bradley, cartoon/movie, board game, cover shows Snoopy carrying stick with polka dot knapsack, 1973. . . . .     **15.00**

**Snoopy's Doghouse Game,** Milton Bradley, cartoon/comic strip character, board game, cover shows Snoopy and plastic game houses placed around gameboard, 1977. . . . . . . . . . .     **12.00**

**Snow White and The Seven Dwarfs, The Game of,** Milton Bradley, story, board game, cover shows Snow White pointing with right hand, dwarfs lined up beneath tree, mfg info bottom right corner, contains 2 dice, 8 colored wooden counters, 7 dwarf counters, 1 Queen, 1 Hunstman, 1 Poisoned Apple, 28 small multicolored wooden sticks, and 4 kiss pcs, ©1937 Walt Disney Enterprises . . . . . .     **120.00**

**Snuffy Smith's Hootin Holler Bug Derby,** Jaymar, comic strip character, action game, "Exciting Bug Race," cover shows figure in checkered shirt waving racing flag, 2 figures in pointed hats, and bugs crawling on floor, from game series, another box version available, 1950s . . . . . . . . . . .     **25.00**

**Society Today,** Dynamic Design Ind., generic, board game, cover shows men and women of various size, age and race, 1971. . .     **12.00**

**Solarquest,** Golden, space, board game, cover shows planets and spaceship against starry background, "The Space–Age Real Estate Game," 1986 . . . . . . . .     **8.00**

**Soldier On Fort, The,** Joseph Borzellino & Son, military, separate board and 3³/₄ x 6¹/₄ " pcs box, cover shows fort flying flag, patent and mfg info with Atlantic City, NJ address on lid bottom, contains 14 wooden pcs, based on tactics at Fort of Verdun in World War I, ©1931 *see illus* . . . . . . . . . . . . . . . .     **25.00**

**Soldier Ten Pins,** McLoughlin Brothers, military, skill game, 8³/₄ x 7¹/₄", cover shows 2 soldiers and cannon, contains 12 multicolored litho soldiers with wooden supports, wooden cannon, and wooden cannon "bullets," c1890 . . . . . . . . . . .     **120.00**

**Soldiers Five With Pistol,** Milton Bradley, military, skill game, 10⁵/₈ x 8¹/₄", cover shows 2 soldiers at wheel–drawn cannon and mounted soldier, contains 10 multicolored litho cardboard soldiers on wooden supports, metal and wood gun, and several wooden bullets, c1915 . . . . .     **125.00**

**Soli-Peg,** Rosebud Art Co., generic, board game, 10³/₁₆ x 6¹/₄ x ⁷/₈", cover shows 2 women, 2 men, and boy at table with playing surface, train and ship at table corners, "For Travelers on Land, For Travelers on Sea," c1930s. . . . . . . . . . . . . . . . .     **20.00**

**Solotaire,** Milton Bradley, generic, card game, cover with Lucille Ball, hand holding 2 of diamonds, and gameboard with cards, 1973 . . . . . . . . . . . . . .     **8.00**

*The Soupy Sales Game*

*Space: 1999*

**Sonar Sub Hunt,** Mattel, military, board game, "A Naval Battle Game," cover shows boy at gameboard, periscope, sub, and mines, 1961 . . . . . . . . . . . . .   **45.00**

**Sons Of Hercules Game, The,** Milton Bradley, movie, board game, cover shows man in shorts with wrists tied by chains and inset pictures with knight on horse and chariot, 1966. . . .   **30.00**

**Sooperbowl Pro–Football Game,** Sportswise Inc., sports, board game, cover shows #80 and others trying to tackle #33 carrying football, 1967 . . . . . . .   **10.00**

**Sorry!,** Parker Brothers, generic, board game, "The Great Game," cover shows game name on diagonal, mfg info bottom right corner, "Parker Brothers Trade–Mark Name for Its Slide Pursuit Game," 1950 . . . . . . . .   **20.00**

• Same design, separate board and pcs box, 1950s . . . . . . . .   **15.00**

**Sorry!,** Parker Brothers, generic, board game, right side of cover shows mfg info below game- board and playing pcs, "Parker Brothers Slide Pursuit Game," 1958 . . . . . . . . . . . . . . . . .   **12.00**

**Sorry!,** Parker Brothers, generic, board game, left side of cover shows hand holding card and hand holding playing pc on open gameboard, game name at right, mfg info bottom right corner, 1964 . . . . . . . . . . . . .   **8.00**

**Soupy Sales Game, The,** Ideal, celebrity/TV/comedy, board game, cover shows Sales in hat and large checkered bowtie, "Soupy Sez," 1965 *see illus* . . .   **75.00**

**Soupy Sez Go–Go–Go!,** Milton Bradley, TV/comedy, board game, cover shows running Soupy Sales wearing top hat and checkered bowtie and carrying checkered flag, row of 4 cars, "Wow! What a Game!," 1961 . .   **65.00**

**Space Alert Game,** *see Black Hole Space Alert Game, The*

**Space Chase,** United Nations Constructors Inc., space, board game, cover shows planet earth, spaceship headed toward moon, game name bottom right corner, 1967 . . . . . . . . . . . . . . . . . .   **25.00**

**Space Checkers,** Pacific Game Co., generic, 3–dimensional board game, cover shows swirled lines ending at checker- board surface, 1971 . . . . . . . . .   **15.00**

**Space Game,** Parker Brothers, space, board game, cover shows spaceship traveling from earth to moon, second spaceship return- ing to earth, "A Race for Treasure," mfg info bottom right corner, 1953 . . . . . . . . . . . . .   **45.00**

**Space: 1999,** Milton Bradley, TV/space, board game, cover shows spaceship and 4 action insets across bottom, "Adapted From the Television Series," 1976 *see illus*. . . . . . . . . . . . .   **15.00**

**Space Pilot,** Cadaco–Ellis, space, board game, cover shows back view of 5 people looking at rockets, spaceships, and space buildings, 1951 . . . . . . . . . . . .   **30.00**

**Space Race Game,** Built–Rite, space, track game, cover shows

3 spaceships, 3 planets, and
partial view of earth bottom
right corner, 1960s . . . . . . . . .      **15.00**
**Spare–Time Bowling,** Lakeside,
sports/bowling, dice game,
cover shows hand shaking dice
from cup, 4 people playing
game, bowling pins pictured on
dice, 1974 . . . . . . . . . . . . . . .      **12.00**
**Spear–Em,** W.G. Young & Co.,
military, skill/target game,
12 x 6$^1/_2$", cover shows girl
throwing spear at target placed
on roof of dog house, 2 boys in
cavalry uniforms, dog, and
child's wagon, contains 2 wood-
en spears, 6 cardboard cavalry
figures, each horseman representing different country, Willis
Young, inventor, 1916 . . . . . . .      **25.00**
**Special Agent,** Parker Brothers,
detective, board game, cover
shows figure in jacket with
hands behind back standing at
lamp, arrow reads "Bus Stop,"
1966 . . . . . . . . . . . . . . . . . . .      **10.00**
**Special Detective/Speedway,**
Saalfield, detective/racing,
"2 Games in One," cover shows
racing cars at top and evening
scene with man wearing raincoat and holding gun at bottom,
game names divide pictures,
1959 . . . . . . . . . . . . . . . . . . .      **25.00**
**Speculation,** Speculation, busi-
ness, "Stock Market Game"
above game name at lid bottom,
1969 . . . . . . . . . . . . . . . . . . .      **20.00**
**Spedem Auto Race,** Alderman–
Fairchild ( All–Fair), auto racing,
board game, separate 17 x 17$^1/_2$"
board and 4$^1/_2$ x 3$^3/_4$" pcs box,
race track board with game
name in corners and cars, buildings, and people at center, contains dice cup, 6 wooden dice,
6 different colored metal cars
labeled "Saxon, Dodge,
Maxwell, Paige, Ford" and
"Buick," patented April 20,
1922 . . . . . . . . . . . . . . . . . . .      **95.00**
**Spedem Junior Auto Race Game,**
Alderman–Fairchild ( All–Fair),
No. 407, auto racing, board
game, 11$^1/_2$" sq, cover shows

racing car and grandstand, "An
All–Fair Game" at bottom
center, contains 4 metal cars
and cardboard race track with
3$^1/_2$" spinner in center and
spaces labeled "Ford, Buick,
Stutz," and "Dodge," ©1928 . . .      **110.00**
**Speed Boat Race,** Milton Bradley,
No. 4506, sports, track game,
14$^1/_4$ x 8$^1/_4$ x 1$^3/_{16}$", cover shows
3 speed boats in water,
c1930s . . . . . . . . . . . . . . . . .      **45.00**
**Speed Buggy Game,** Milton
Bradley, TV/cartoon, cover
shows 2 men and woman
around small convertible,
1973 . . . . . . . . . . . . . . . . . . .      **15.00**
**Speed Circuit,** 3M, auto racing,
board game, cover shows
#2 and #7 race cars, buildings
and sun in background,
"Watkins Glen," 1971 . . . . . . . .      **15.00**
**Speedorama,** Jaymar Mfg. Co.,
sports/horse racing, cover shows
race horses, speedboat, track
lines around ocean scene,
mountains, buildings, lighthouse, and plane, contains
gameboards, unknown date . . .      **35.00**
**Speedway,** Ideal, auto racing,
action game, cover shows 2 cars
above boy wearing helmet and
glasses, girl with bow in hair,
and playing pc, "Big Bopper
Game," 1961 . . . . . . . . . . . . .      **40.00**
**Spella,** Noyes, Snow & Co., educational, word game, 5$^5/_8$ x 3$^3/_8$",
cover shows 3 seated figures,
1 wearing striped socks, animal
on stool, and flowers on table,
"Words Within Words," 1874 . .      **30.00**
**Spelling Bee, Paul Wing's,** Milton
Bradley, educational, 11$^3/_4$ x 7$^1/_2$
x 1$^1/_4$", cover shows man with
mustache wearing glasses standing by NBC microphone,
includes red cloth drawstring
bag, round wooden numbered
discs, red and green wooden
discs, playing cards, and
instructions, ©1938 . . . . . . . .      **35.00**
**Spider and Fly Game,** Milton
Bradley, #4734, generic, board
game, 9" sq, cover shows cartoon drawing of spider wearing

jacket and top hat and small fly wearing hat, contains 2 wooden top spinners, c1925 . . . . . . . . **50.00**

**Spider and the Fly,** Whitman, generic, skill game, cover shows spider and bug caught in web, mfg info top left corner, "Exciting Fun," 1962 . . . . . . . **12.00**

**Spider–Man,** Milton Bradley, comic book character, cover shows Spider–man in fight, 2 dialogue boxes, "Marvel Super Heroes," 1967 . . . . . . . **48.00**

**Spider's Web,** McLoughlin Brothers, generic, cover shows spider and bug caught in web with numbered sections, plane, trees, and stream in background, 1898 . . . . . . . . . . . . **85.00**

**Spin It,** Milton Bradley, generic, skill game, 11 x 7½", cover shows girl with bow in hair seated at table, second girl standing at table, "Made in U.S.A." and "No. 4198" bottom left corner, contains 2 wooden tops and red and gray target board with instructions on bottom, c1926. . . . . . . . . . . . **30.00**

**Spin the Bottle Game,** Hasbro, generic, stunt/action game, cover show 6 people playing game, girl with striped shirt, man with glasses, game surface on floor, 1968 . . . . . . . . . . . **10.00**

**Spin–O,** Corey Games, generic, action game, cover shows 2 figures at bottom tossing balls at bottle on square platform, "Top Scoring Game," 1942 . . . . . . . **25.00**

**Spinette,** Milton Bradley, generic, skill game, cover shows circle around spinning top, "Made in U.S.A." and "No. 4305" at bottom left corner, contains spinner, 10 beads, and orange target board with numbered holes, c1924 . . . . . . . . . . . . . **15.00**

**Spingo and Whirlette,** Transogram, No. 1090, generic, action games, cover shows game name in circle around 5 players, "Let's Go!" in dialogue box, "Gold Medal" bottom left corner, 1930s . . . . . **45.00**

**Split Level Aggravation,** *see Aggravation, Split Level*

**Splurge,** Createk, gambling, board game, cover shows Las Vegas hotel and casino names and gameboard, "The games that made Las Vegas Famous," 1968 **10.00**

**Spoof,** Milton Bradley, generic, card game, 7½ x 5½", cover shows running deer, figure wearing hat and carrying stick, "The Cheer–Up Game," contains 52 cards with orange and white backs and orange and black litho Indian designs and 8 wooden knobbed sticks, ©1918. . . . . . . . . . . . . . . . . . **20.00**

**Sports,** Milton Bradley, sports, board game, 15 x 9", cover shows woman on first "S" in game name, golf clubs, football, and boaters, contains 2 round colored wooden counters and spinner, c1910 . . . . . . . . . . . . . **75.00**

**Sports Arena,** Milton Bradley, sports, action game, cover shows playing surface "with Dual Control," 1962. . . . . . . . . **40.00**

**Spot A Car Bingo,** Hasbro, travel, bingo game, cover shows family in car, boy holding bingo card out window, "Hassenfeld Bros., Inc., Pawtucket, R.I., U.S.A." across lid bottom, 1950s . . . . . . **20.00**

**Spot, Game of,** Milton Bradley, generic, board game, 12½" sq, cover shows bulldog standing beside dog house, contains 4 round colored wooden counters and spinner, c1925 . . . **40.00**

**Spots,** Milton Bradley, generic, memory game, cover shows 5 faces above game letters placed in circles, old car, 1959 **25.00**

**Spring Chicken,** Mattel, generic, action game, cover shows chicken head on spring attached to base, boy and girl playing game, "Mattel Game" bottom left corner, 1968 . . . . . . . . . . . . . **20.00**

**Sprint,** Mattel, drag race, large plastic track game, cover shows 2 boys with playing surface, "Hot New Drag Race Game," mfg info in circle at right, 1965 **30.00**

*Star Trek The Next Generation
Interactive VCR Board Game*

**Spy, International Game of,**
All–Fair, espionage, board
game, cover shows man with
mustache, hat, and tie at left,
figures in suits and capes in
background, "Learn to Play in
Five Minutes," 1940s . . . . . . .   35.00

**Spy Detector Game,** Mattel,
espionage, board game, cover
shows "Amazing Mattel Spy
Detector," man wearing hat
holding gun and briefcase next
to pictures of people, 1963. . . .   30.00

**Spy's–A–Poppin,** Transogram,
No. 3931, espionage, target
game, staircase, boy shooting
suction pc, flying "lady captive,"
and printing on large box cover,
1965 . . . . . . . . . . . . . . . . . .   45.00

**Square Mile,** Milton Bradley,
business/real estate, board
game, "Land Development
Game," train crossing cover
with buildings, trees, mountains,
and men on high beam and
earth digging equipment, 1962   25.00

**Stage,** C.M. Clark Publishing Co.,
Inc., theatre/movies, card game,
7½ x 2¾", cover shows game
name between 2 circles with
faces of man and woman,
contains advertising card and
66 picture cards with famous
opera stars and entertainers of
the time including Tony Pastor,
Edwin Booth, Lillian Russell,
and Eva Tanguay, ©1904 . . . . .   65.00

**Stagecoach,** Schaper, western,
board/track game, cover shows
cowboy shooting while driver
tries to control speeding
stagecoach, *Parents* magazine

approval seal above "Roaring
With Western Adventure," 1958   30.00

**Stagecoach West Adventure
Game,** Transogram, TV/western,
cover shows stagecoach and
show stars Richard Eyer, Wayne
Rogers, and Robert Bray,
"Exciting Adventures of the Early
Western Stage Drivers," issued
year earlier as "Johnny Ringo,"
1961 . . . . . . . . . . . . . . . . . . .   65.00

**Star Basketball,** Star Paper Box
Co., sports, bagatelle/skill game,
19 x 19½", cover shows 4 players reaching for basketball, "An
Interesting Game of Skill,"
contains 5 black balls and metal
bagatelle board with net
"basket" in center, c1926 . . . . .   95.00

**Star Reporter,** Parker Brothers,
media, board game, left side
cover shows man in raincoat
and hat, newsboy at bottom
right corner, 3 stars at top,
"News Game," same as "Boake
Carter's Star Reporter Game,"
1950s–60. . . . . . . . . . . . . . . .   40.00

**Star Trek,** Hasbro, TV/space, marble maze game, circular maze
with picture of 2 show stars and
game name in arrow, "It's A
Hasbro Toy" top left, 1967 . . . .   75.00

**Star Trek Game,** Ideal, TV/space,
board game, cover shows 2 men
and woman in space ship with
crash on screen viewer, 1967 . .   60.00

**Star Trek The Next Generation
Interactive VCR Board Game,**
Decipher Inc., TV/space, 17¾ x
8¾ x 3", board game, "A
Klingon Challenge," cover
shows Enterprise and Klingon,
includes 60 minute videotape,
game board, colored plastic
stands, cardboard crew
members, cards, clear plastic
cylinders, tokens, cardboard
phasers, tricorders, and isolinear
chips, spinner, die, and sticker
sheet, ©Paramount Pictures,
1993 *see illus.* . . . . . . . . . . . .   20.00

**Star Wars,** Parker Brothers, movie,
space, cover shows man in helmet, plane, and space vehicle,
1982 . . . . . . . . . . . . . . . . . .   25.00

**Star Wars Battle at Sarlacc's Pit Game,** Parker Brothers, movie, board game, cover shows figures at ship railing watching fighting man with sword, man with ray gun, and others, "Features 3–D Sail Barge and Star Wars Figures," based on *Return of the Jedi,* 1983 . . . . . .    **12.00**

**Star Wars Destroy Death Star Game,** see *Destroy Death Star Game, Star Wars*

**Star Wars Escape From Death Star Game,** see *Escape From Death Star Game, Star Wars*

**Star Wars Hoth Ice Planet Adventure Game,** see *Hoth Ice Planet Adventure Game, Star Wars*

**Star Wars Wicket the Ewok,** see *Wicket the Ewok, Star Wars*

**Star Wars Yoda the Jedi Master Game,** see *Yoda The Jedi Master Game, Star Wars*

**Stars and Stripes or Red, White and Blue, Game of,** McLoughlin Brothers, generic, board game, 16$^1$/$_2$ x 18", cover shows hand holding pole with American flag, eagle above "Stars," contains 2 dice cups, 2 dice, 44 small silver stars, 1 large star, and 4 lead soldiers carrying American flag, wooden box, ©1900. . . . . . . . . . . . . . . . .    **2,500.00**

**Starsky & Hutch,** Milton Bradley, TV/detective, board game, cover shows action film strip shots, car with 2 passengers, 1977 . . .    **10.00**

**State Capitals, Game of,** Parker Brothers, educational, board game, cover shows U.S. map against buildings background, "How Many State Capitals Can You Name?," 1952 . . . . . . . . . .    **15.00**

**States, Game of, The,** Milton Bradley, educational, board game, cover shows people involved in activities representing different states, "With Alaska and the Hawaiian Islands," lid divided into 3 diagonal and vertical sections, contains plastic cars, 1954. . . . . . . . . . .    **15.00**

• Cover divided into 3 horizontal sections, 1960 . . . . . . . . . . .    **10.00**
*See also Game of The States*

**Steady Eddie,** Milton Bradley, generic, balancing game, cover shows hand snapping at pc balanced on seal's nose, 1962. .    **12.00**

**Steeple Chase,** J.H. Singer, horse racing, board game, 5$^1$/$_4$" sq, 2 racehorses and 2 jockeys in cover center, instructions printed bottom right corner, contains 6 round wooden counters and spinner, c1890 . . . . . . . . . . .    **95.00**

**Steeple Chase, Game of,** McLoughlin Brothers, sports, board game, 8$^1$/$_4$ x 14$^1$/$_4$", cover shows man wearing cap and shirt with striped sleeves riding race horse, contains 4 round colored wooden markers and spinner, c1910 . . . . . . . . . . . .    **40.00**

**Steeple Chase, Game of,** Parker Brothers, horse racing, board game, Popular Edition, 14$^7$/$_8$ x 8$^7$/$_8$", cover shows men on horses jumping fence, "Popular Edition" bottom left corner, contains 4 round colored markers and spinner, 1895 . . . . . . . .    **65.00**

**Stencils,** Milton Bradley, generic, action game, 4$^3$/$_4$ x 6$^3$/$_4$", cover shows seated girl with paper and writing tool, sheets of paper on table, contains tan stencils and tracing paper, c1900 . . . . .    **15.00**

**Step Lively Shuffleboard,** Marx, generic, board game, cover shows 3 youngsters with playing board on table, "Featuring the Scooter Shooters" bottom right corner, 1972 . . . . . . . . . . . . .    **15.00**

**Steve Canyon,** Lowell, comic strip character/military, board game, cover shows pilot and jet planes, "Exciting Air Force Game," strip of shield insignias down right side, contains cockpit control panels for 4 pilots, 1959 . . . . . .    **35.00**

**Steve Scott Space Scout,** Transogram, space, board game, cover shows boy in space suit, rocket, planet, and moon surface, "A Game of Adventure in

Outer Space," game named after Transogram president's grandson, 1952 . . . . . . . . . . . . . . .    **50.00**

**Sting Game, The,** Ideal, movie, board game, cover shows horses below 2 men wearing hats, 1 man smoking cigar, vintage car, open treasure chest beneath palm tree, plane in cloud next to man's hat, and piles of coins above mfg info, 1976. . . . . . . .    **15.00**

**Stingray,** Transogram, generic, maze game, cover shows underwater diver with gun attacking monster, "The Underwater Maze Game," 1966. . . . . . . . . . . . .    **40.00**

**Stock Market Game,** Whitman, business, investing, board game, cover shows multicolored strips behind game name, mfg info bottom left corner, "The Aristocrat of Money Games," 1963 . . . . . . . . . . . . . . . . . .    **10.00**

**Stocks and Bonds,** 3M, investing, business, board game, cover shows group of men against numbered background, 1964 . .    **10.00**

**Stoney Burke,** Transogram, western, board game, cover shows cowboy with steer and cowboy in circle, "Rodeo Circuit Game," 1963 . . . . . . . . . . . . . . . . . .    **35.00**

**Stop and Go,** Shell Oil, advertising, board game, 10 x 10³/₄" paper track, cover shows playing surface, pcs, and printed instructions, 5¹/₂ x 10³/₄" strip attached to board has 40 cutout gasoline tickets, 4 shell counters, spinner, separate red and green sheet with 4 cutout cards, c1930s . . . . . . . . . . . . . . . .    **40.00**

**Stop, Look and Listen, Game of,** Milton Bradley, generic, board game, 14¹/₈ x 8¹/₈", cover shows people at street corner, vehicles and drivers, and stoplight, contains 4 round colored wooden counters and spinner, c1926. . .    **35.00**

**Stop Thief,** Parker Brothers, crime, board game, "Featuring the Electronic Crime Scanner," cover shows hand holding scanner, "Cops and Robbers," 1979    **10.00**

**Story of the U.S. Air Force Game, The,** Transogram, military, board game, cover shows pilot next to modern aircraft, second pilot in earlier uniform next to older aircraft, Landmark Game Series, Published by Random House, 1961 . . . . . . . . . . . . . . . . . .    **40.00**

**Story Stage,** VIP Corp., TV/theater, action game, "starring Jackie Gleason and his TV Troupe," cover shows Gleason's face and 4 of his TV characters, stage curtains border cover, contains stage curtain, players' scripts, studio tickets, and 2 stage sets, 1955 . . . . . . . . . . . . . . . . . .    **40.00**

**Straight Arrow,** Selchow & Righter, radio program/western, board game, cover shows man on horse holding bow and arrow and wearing Indian headband, mfg logo top right corner, "The Rip–Snortin' Cowboy and Indian Game!," 1950 . . . . . . . .    **40.00**

**Straight Away,** Selchow & Righter, TV/auto racing, board game, cover shows 4 race cars and man standing next to driver seated in car, 1961 . . . . . . . .    **50.00**

**Strat: The Great War Game,** Strat Game Co., Inc., military, cover shows areas of England and Germany top 2 corners, "English Channel" and "Kiel Canal" printed above checkerboard surface, ©1915 . . . . . . . . . . .    **45.00**

**Strategic Command Game,** Transogram, military, 3–dimensional board game, cover shows plane, ship, tank, and 4 people around upright playing board, 1962 . . . . . . . . . . . . . . . . . .    **35.00**

**Stratego,** Milton Bradley, strategy, board game, Original Edition, cover shows men on horses, "Old World Game," letters of game name in individual blocks, contains wooden pcs, 1961 . . .    **20.00**

**Stratego,** Milton Bradley, strategy, board game, cover shows 4 players at table, printed info next to picture, letters of game name in individual blocks, 1962    **15.00**

*Game of Strategy*

*Sugar Ray Leonard
Electronic Talking Boxing*

**Strategy,** Corey Games, military, board game, cover shows large figure wearing headband and gloves and carrying globe hovering above figures with military weapons, "The Game of Armies," 1938 . . . . . . . . . . .    **40.00**

**Strategy,** Corey Games, military, board game, cover shows 2 knights in battle and parade of figures in medieval dress going toward fortress with moat and flags, 1945. . . . . . . . . . . . . . .    **30.00**

**Strategy, Game of,** McLoughlin Brothers, military strategy, board game 19³/₄ x 10¹/₂", cover shows cavalry soldiers on horses, leader lifting sword in right hand, contains 16 white and black checkers and spinner with 2 arrows, ©1891 *see illus*. . . . .    **250.00**

**Stratosphere,** Parker Brothers, space, board game, 15 x 11¹/₂", cover shows elongated playing pc connected to pin, mfg info bottom right corner, c1930. . . .    **60.00**

**Street Car Game, The,** Parker Brothers, travel, board game, cover shows No. 694 trolley with animal passengers, contains 8 round colored wooden markers and spinner, c1892 . . .    **400.00**

**Strike It Rich,** Lowell, TV, quiz game, cover shows Warren Hull, "On TV Coast–To–Coast," "L" in bottom left corner, 1955    **40.00**

**Stubborn Pig, Game of, The,** Milton Bradley, generic, board game, 15 x 9", cover shows man with pig on leash, house and tree in background, mfg info middle lid bottom, contains

4 colored wooden counters and spinner, c1910 . . . . . . . . . . . .    **50.00**

**Stump the Stars,** Ideal, TV/game show, charades game, cover shows man standing in front of group of people, based on CBS game show "Charades," 1962 . .    **20.00**

**Stymie Card Game,** Milton Bradley, TV/comedy, card game, cover shows Samantha, Endora and Darrin from the Bewitched TV series, 1964 . . . . . . . . . . . .    **20.00**

**Sub Attack Game,** Milton Bradley, military, board game, cover shows sea battle scene, 1965 . .    **25.00**

**Sub Search Game,** Milton Bradley, military, 3 level 3–dimensional game, cover shows boy and girl with playing surface and figures at sub's periscope, 1973 . . . . . . . . . . . .    **25.00**

**Submarine Chaser,** Milton Bradley, military, skill game, cover shows ship and submarine, contains wooden pcs, 1939 . . .    **35.00**

**Sugar Bowl,** Transogram, generic, board game, cover shows 2 girls and boy at soda fountain, soda jerk mixing drinks, gameboard on table, "A 'Gold Medal' Game" upper left corner, c1950    **35.00**

**Sugar Ray Leonard Electronic Talking Boxing,** Tiger Electronics, Inc., sports, electronic, 18 x 10¹/₂ x 4", cover shows Sugar Ray wearing boxing gloves, includes molded plastic game piece with LCD display screen and instruction booklet, 1989 *see illus*. . . . . . . . . . . . . . .    **20.00**

*Sunset Limited*

**Summit,** Milton Bradley, military strategy, board game, lid shows oval above game name, "Global Strategy" game, 1960–61 . . . . .  **30.00**

**Sunken Treasure,** Milton Bradley, adventure, board game, cover shows fish and octopus near hand putting pc on playing surface, "Buzz," 3 inset pictures of game play at bottom left, 1976  **15.00**

**Sunken Treasure Game,** Parker Brothers, adventure, board/track game, cover shows ship at sea, men on deck helping diver, 1948 . . . . . . . . . . . . . . . .  **20.00**

**Sunset Limited,** Milton Bradley, railroad, board game, 11 x 7 x ³/₄", cover shows children waving as train passes by, includes game board, and 4 wooden discs *see illus*. . . . . . . . . . . . .  **45.00**

**Super Market,** Selchow & Righter, shopping, board game, "The Red Light Green Light Shopping Game," cover shows stoplight and people in front of Super Market, trees and buildings in background, mfg logo at center above building, 1953 . . . . . . . .  **20.00**

**Super Spy,** Milton Bradley, spy/espionage, board game, cover shows man in hat, woman in coat with raised collar, and rear view of man walking toward car, metal disk under board activates alarm, "The Electric Alarm Game," 1971 . . .  **20.00**

**Super Sunday Football,** Hasbro, sports, strategy game, includes projector, screen, 16 mm

offense and defense filmstrips, and offense and defense play books, 1973 . . . . . . . . . . . . . .  **30.00**

**Super Target Dart Game,** Superior/T. Cohn, generic, target game, target board shows flying space ships and planes and valued scoring areas, "300" top right corner, 1950s . . . . . . . . . .  **45.00**

**Superboy,** Hasbro, comic strip, board game, cover shows figure with cape and "S" on shirt, dog with cape, flying space ships, and planet, 1965 . . . . . . . . . .  **55.00**

**Supercar to the Rescue Game,** Milton Bradley, cartoon, board game, cover shows figure in flying "supercar," based on Gerry Anderson series, 1962 . . .  **50.00**

**Superman, Calling,** *see Calling Superman*

**Superman and Superboy,** Milton Bradley, comic strip, board games, "2 Super Games in One," cover shows action shots of both superheros, man with gun, and monster being hit, "Bam" in dialogue box, 1967 . .  **50.00**

**Superman Card Game,** Ideal, comic strip, card game, cover shows armored truck robbery scene with Superman, police car, policemen, and robbers, 1966 . . . . . . . . . . . . . . . . . .  **55.00**

**Superman Quoit & Horseshoe Set,** Super Swim, Inc., comic strip/sports, quoit set, cover shows Superman, 1950s . . . . . .  **100.00**

**Superstition,** Milton Bradley, mystical, board game, cover shows gameboard, house, moon, trees, cemetery, and 3 inset pictures right side, 1977 . . . . . . . . . . .  **15.00**

**Surfside 6,** Lowell, TV/crime, board game, cover with 3 show stars' faces in circles, floating barge, and palm trees, 1962 . . .  **45.00**

**Susceptibles, The,** McLoughlin Brothers, strategy, board game, 15 x 16", cover shows man in straw hat walking in park with woman wearing hat and long dress, cover design in triangle, "A Parlor Amusement," contains 1 wooden leader, 4 compan-

*'Swayze'*

ions, 5 colored wooden aids,
8 checker susceptibles, and
6 additional colored compan-
ions, wooden box, ©1891 .... **600.00**

**Swack! Game,** Ideal, generic,
action game, cover shows children looking at pcs of cheese on
trap playing pc, 1968 ........ **30.00**

**Swahili Game,** Milton Bradley,
strategy, board game, cover
shows small figures on circular
platform facing large statuesque
figure, 1968 .............. **15.00**

**Swamp Fox, Walt Disney's,** Parker
Brothers, TV/Disney, board
game, cover shows Revolutionary War hero in vest and feathered hat near swamp, from
"Disneyland" television show,
1960 ................... **45.00**

**Swap,** Ideal, business, trading,
board game, cover shows
4 scenes of people trading
items, "The Wheeler–Dealer
Game, Out–Swap Everyone,"
1965 ................... **15.00**

**'Swayze,'** Milton Bradley, TV/
celebrity/broadcasting, cover
shows John Cameron Swayze
and world globe, 1954 *see illus* **25.00**

**Sweeps,** All–Fair, finance, board
game, cover shows hand
holding money, "The Popular
'Money' Game," contains paper
money, counters, dice, and
tokens, 1940s ............ **25.00**

**Sweepstakes,** WM, horse racing,
electromatic board game, cover
shows 4 race horses on track,
1970s ................... **30.00**

**Swingin' Sam,** Peerless Playthings
Co., educational, word game,
cover shows 2 boys with
"hanging" figure and spinner,
1960s ................... **10.00**

**Swivel,** Milton Bradley, generic,
action game, cover shows
4 people holding threads connected to center pc, playing
surface on floor, "Partners Swing
and Sway to Make The Striker
Swivel; Knock Down Oppo-
nent's Pins," 1972 .......... **20.00**

**Sword in the Stone, Walt
Disney's,** Parker Brothers,
Disney/movie, board game,
cover shows boy with out-
stretched hands, man wearing
cape and pointed hat and dog
leaving house walking toward
sparkling figure rising from
bowl, 1963 .............. **20.00**

**Swords and Shields,** Milton
Bradley, military, board game,
cover shows sword and knight's
helmet next to checkered playing surface with playing pcs,
1970 ................... **20.00**

–T–

**T.H.E. Cat Game,** Ideal, TV/crime,
board game, cover shows man
with rope atop building looking
at people in window of next
building, 1967 ............ **40.00**

**Table Croquet,** Milton Bradley,
sports, skill game, 12½ x 6½",
cover shows men, women, and
children around large table with
playing pcs, seated woman, fireplace in background, contains
2 wooden goal posts, 4 table
clamps, cloth tape, 4 wooden
mallets, 4 wooden balls, and
11 wickets, wooden box with
slide top, c1890 ........... **75.00**

**Taffy's Baubles & Bangles Game,**
Transogram, generic, board
game, cover shows girl wearing
bracelets posed with finger on
earring and holding necklaces,
1966 ................... **12.00**

*Talking Monday Night Football*

**Taffy's Party Game,** Transogram, generic, board game, cover shows girl seated at table, boy holding record with hand on phonograph, and dancing people, 1966 . . . . . . . . . . . . .  **12.00**

**Taffy's Shopping Spree,** Transogram, shopping, board game, cover shows girl holding purse and striped hat box, 1966  **12.00**

**Take It Or Leave It,** Zondine, radio game, quiz game, cover shows bespectacled man at microphone in bottom right corner, "Play Your Favorite Radio Quiz at Home" at top, "Try for the $64 Question" upper left corner, 1942 . . . . . . .  **40.00**

**Take–Off,** Russel Mfg. Co., No. 529, aviation, card game, 6¼ x 5", cover shows prop plane flying over mountains, oval with figure and mfg name bottom left corner, game name on mountains, ©1930 . . . . . . .  **20.00**

**Tales of the Texas Rangers, Jack Pearson's,** All–Fair, TV/western, board game, cover shows cowboy with gun, wanted notice, and 2 figures on horses in background, series starred Willard Parker and Harry Lauter, 1956  **45.00**

**Talk to Cecil,** Mattel, generic, board game, cover shows Cecil's face and multicolored game name, contains Cecil–shaped puzzle track, 1961 . . . . . . . . . . . . . . . .  **40.00**

**Talking Football,** Mattel, sports, board game, cover shows players in action, fans in stands, and

man and boy playing game, includes small records describing action, 1971 . . . . . . . . . . .  **25.00**

**Talking Monday Night Football,** Mattel, sports, board game, cover shows player #32 tackling ball carrier, coach in background, inset of man and boy playing game, "The Call The Play, Hear It Happen Game," 1977 *see illus.* . . . . . . . . . . . .  **18.00**

**Tammy Card Game,** Whitman, TV, card game, cover shows girl wearing headband, mfg logo at top below "Tammy," "Rule Card Included," 1964 . . . . . . . . . . .  **10.00**

**Tammy Game, The,** Ideal, TV, board game, cover shows 4 hearts above girl talking on telephone, "Sweet Sixteen... The Ideal Teenage Girl," 1963 . .  **30.00**

**Tank Battle Game,** Milton Bradley, military strategy, board game, cover shows tank, 3 inset pictures bottom right, contains miniature tanks, 1975 . . . . . . . .  **18.00**

**Tarzan to the Rescue Game,** Milton Bradley, literary hero, board game, cover shows lion approaching man near tree, Tarzan in tree, 1977 . . . . . . . .  **15.00**

**Taxi,** Selchow & Righter, automobile, board game, cover shows police chasing taxi, mfg logo bottom right corner, "The 'Drive As You Please' Traffic Game," revamped "Cabby," 1960 . . . . .  **15.00**

**Taxology,** Gloria Game Co., money, cover shows man wearing hat and barrel holding stick, Taxpayers' "Guide To Survival," 1957. . . . . . . . . . . .  **15.00**

**Tee Party,** Milton Bradley, golf, board game, cover shows golf bags with clubs and group of people playing game, "#19" at top, mfg logo top left corner, 1968 . . . . . . . . . . . . . . . . . .  **25.00**

**Teed Off,** Pacific Game Co., sports, dice game, cover shows dice spilling from open golf ball, golfer atop ball, phrases on dice include "Over Green, On the Green, Out of Bounds," and "1 Putt," 1972. . . . . . . . . . . . . . .  **15.00**

*Telegraph Messenger*

*The $10,000 Pyramid Game*

**Telegraph Boy, Game of The,**
McLoughlin Brothers, Horatio
Alger theme, board game, 17⅛
x 9½", 3 section cover shows
ticker tape machine, messenger
boy running from office, and
messenger boy with man seated
at desk, contains 4 lead messenger boys and metal arrow,
wooden box, ©1888 . . . . . . .   320.00

**Telegraph Boy, Game of The,**
McLoughlin Brothers, Horatio
Alger theme, board game,
18¾ x 17", cover shows dog
next to messenger boy on bicycle, buildings, horse and carriage in background, contains
4 lead messenger boys and
spinner arrow, ©1888. . . . . . .   2,000.00

**Telegraph Messenger,** J.H. Singer,
generic, board game, 7¼" sq,
cover shows messenger boy in
foreground, people and buildings in background, contains
2 counters and card with
spinner, c1890 *see illus* . . . . . .   40.00

**Tell Bell, The,** Knapp Electric,
Inc., Division of P.R. Mallory,
educational, 13⅞ x 9½ x2⅛",
"Spelling, Geography, Fractions"
across top of cover, children
looking at man wearing pointed
hat at open door, bell in
window, 1928 . . . . . . . . . . . .   30.00

**Ten Commandments Bible Game,**
Cadaco, religious, board game,
cover shows oval inset of players, mfg info at left, flower

borders at top, bottom, and
between "Bible" and "Game,"
1964 . . . . . . . . . . . . . . . . . .   15.00

**Ten Little Niggers, The Game of,**
Parker Brothers, ethnic/Black
collectibles, card game,
5¾ x 4¼", cover shows black
man and woman holding fan,
"One got Married" bottom left
corner, mfg info bottom right
corner, c1895. . . . . . . . . . . .   400.00

**$10,000 Pyramid Game, The,**
Milton Bradley, TV/game show,
cover shows 2 people seated at
table, 1 person standing, game
name surrounded by colored
lights, "Based on the TV Game
Show" bottom right corner,
1974 *see illus.* . . . . . . . . . . . .   12.00

**Tennessee Tuxedo Game, The
Zany Zoo Adventures of,**
Transogram, TV/cartoon, board
game, cover shows cartoon
characters carrying net and pc of
cheese and chasing 2 mice, mfg
logo upper left corner, 1963 . . .   70.00

**Terminator 2 Judgement Day,**
Milton Bradley, movie/crime,
board game, cover shows
Schwarzenegger wearing sun
glasses, 3 inset pictures below
game name, 1990s . . . . . . . . .   10.00

**Terrytoons Hide & Seek Game,**
Transogram, TV/cartoon, board
game, cartoon characters on
diving board, boy wearing
beanie with outstretched hands
beneath tree, "Lively Novel

*Tete–A–Tete and Lucko*

Action...Rescue Dinky Duck
From Sourpuss," 1960 . . . . . . .   **45.00**
**Tete–A–Tete and Lucko,** unknown
manufacturer, strategy, board
game, separate 5³/₄ x 6³/₄" board
and 7¹/₄ x 6¹/₈ x 1⁵/₈" pcs box,
cover shows children near fence
at bottom right corner, house
upper right corner, pigs and
fence at left, contains 2 dice,
wooden cup, and 20 playing
pcs, ©1890 *see illus*. . . . . . . .   **50.00**
**Texas Checkers,** Azco, generic,
board game, giant checkers
game, re–usable carrying case,
1960s . . . . . . . . . . . . . . . . .   **10.00**
**Texas Millionaire, Neiman–
Marcus',** Texantics Unlimited,
finance/business, board game,
cover shows man with hand on
large money bag marked "$,"
"The Game with a Million
Laughs and 266 Million Bucks!"
in star, 1953 . . . . . . . . . . . . .   **30.00**
**That's Me,** Parker Brothers,
generic, action game, 18¹/₄ x
9¹/₂ x 2¹/₈", cover shows circle
behind each word of game
name, c1836 . . . . . . . . . . . . .   **15.00**
**The States, Game of,** Milton
Bradley, educational, board
game, cover shows people
involved in activities indicative
of different states, "With Alaska
and the Hawaiian Islands,"
contains plastic cars

• Cover divided into 3 diagonal
and vertical sections, 1954 . . .   **12.00**
• Cover divided into 3 horizontal
sections, 1960 . . . . . . . . . . .   **10.00**
*See also Game of The States*
**They're At The Post,** Maas
Marketing, horse racing, board
game, cover shows front view of
racing horses, includes records
that play races with different
results, 1976 . . . . . . . . . . . . .   **30.00**
**"They're Off!" Horse Race Game,**
Parker Brothers, horse racing,
board game, cover shows
4 checkered squares behind
racing horses, 1950s . . . . . . . .   **30.00**
**Thing Ding,** Schaper, generic,
action game, cover shows
3 youngsters with pcs and
"Thing Ding" machine used to
build mechanical people or
animals, 1960s . . . . . . . . . . . .   **35.00**
**Things and Places,** Pressman,
educational, memory game,
cover shows seated boy and girl
with chins resting in hands,
"Thinker" statue upper left
corner, game name in oval, oval
pictures strip borders at top and
bottom, 1960 . . . . . . . . . . . . .   **25.00**
**Think–A–Tron,** Hasbro, educa-
tional computer game, cover
shows "machine that thinks like
a man," arrows with directions
for feeding machine and location of answers, re–released in
1968 as "Mark 106 Computer,"
1961 . . . . . . . . . . . . . . . . . . .   **75.00**
**Thinking Man's Golf,** 3M, sports,
board game, cover shows golf
course layout, game name upper
left corner, 1969 . . . . . . . . . . .   **20.00**
**This is Your Life,** *see Ralph
Edwards' This Is Your Life*
**Three Bears, The,** Noble and
Noble Publishers, Inc., story,
board game, 8¹/₄ x 6¹/₈ x ³/₄",
cover shows 3 bears walking
away from house, Goldilocks
with 3 chairs and 3 bowls,
"Games My Children Love Best
of All," 1922 *see illus* . . . . . . .   **45.00**
**Three Blind Mice, Game of,**
Milton Bradley, nursery rhyme,
board game, 9 x 15", cover

*The Three Bears*

*Throwing The Bull*

shows 3 dressed mice, 1 carrying knapsack with hat flying, 1 with cane, and 1 dressed as woman wearing apron, house and trees in background, contains 6 round colored wooden counters, c1925 . . . . .    **45.00**

**Three Chipmunks Big Record,** Hasbro, music, board game, cover shows chipmunks around "Big Record," 1960 . . . . . . . .    **35.00**

**Three Chipmunks Cross Country Game,** Hasbro, travel, board game, cover shows chipmunks around U.S. map, 1960 . . . . . .    **35.00**

**Three Little Kittens, The,** Milton Bradley, nursery rhyme, board game, 7½" sq, cover shows 3 little kittens crying around Mother kitten wearing glasses seated in striped chair, c1910 . .    **35.00**

**Three Men in a Tub,** Milton Bradley, nursery rhyme, skill game, 11¾ x 8¾", cover shows 3 men in floating tub, island with trees, flying bird, contains 3 multicolored cardboard figures, wash tub, 2 wooden supports, and 3 colored wooden balls, c1935–36 . . . . . . . . . . .    **35.00**

**3 Men on a Horse,** Milton Bradley, No. 4637, movie/game of chance, board game, 19¾ x 10¾ x 1½", cover shows 3 men on rocking horse, mfg name below horse, "From Warner Bros. 'Laff Hit!' " 1936 . . . . . . .    **45.00**

**Three Musketeers,** Milton Bradley, literary characters/strategy, board game, cover shows 3 figures holding swords in right hands with outstretched left arms and legs, 1950 . . . . . . . . . . . . . .    **40.00**

**3 Point Landing,** Advance Games, Co., aviation, board game, cover shows plane with circles on wings and plane body, partial view of Earth, mfg info bottom left, 1940s . . . . . . . . . . . . . .    **25.00**

**Three Stooges Fun House Game,** Lowell, celebrity, cover shows 1 Stooge in mouth of whale, 1 on rolling barrel, and 1 sliding into molasses, 1959 . . . . . . . . .    **75.00**

**Through the Locks to the Golden Gate,** Milton Bradley, travel, board game, 9 x 15", cover shows strip with boats above circles with tunnel scene and spired buildings, girl and boy wearing hats, contains 2 round colored wooden pcs and spinner, c1905 . . . . . . . . . . . .    **85.00**

**Throwing The Bull,** unknown manufacturer, 9 x 7¾ x 1", western, cover shows 2 cowboys, 1 with lasso riding horse, other holding bull by horns, includes cardboard bull, wooden stand, and rings, no date *see illus* . . . .    **30.00**

**Thrush 'Ray Gun Affair' Game, The,** *see Man From Uncle Thrush 'Ray Gun Affair' Game*

*Tic–Tac Dough TV Quiz Game*

*Tiddledy Winks*

**Thunderball,** *see James Bond 007 Thunderball Game*

**Thunderbirds,** Parker Brothers, TV/puppets/space, board game, cover shows swirled circle at end of game name above 4 inset pictures, contains cards, wooden disks, and metal spaceships, 1967 . . . . . . . . . .  **50.00**

**Tic–Tac Dough TV Quiz Game,** Transogram, TV/game show, quiz game, cover with show host Jack Barry, game board with "X" and "O" squares, man and woman contestants behind panel, TV camera at right, includes "Exclusive Automatic Category Selector," 1956 *see illus*. . . . . . . . . . . . . . . .  **25.00**

**Ticker,** Glow Products Co., Wall Street/stock market/finance, board game, 16 x 2½", cover shows 2 animals in circles at either end of strip containing game name and "The Wall Street Game," buildings skyline, and old tickertape machine, mfg info top center, contains cloth board, 2 dice, dice cup, 14 stock certificates, 7 composition markers, 16 cards, and 104 clay chips, cylinder wrapped in game cloth inside game box contains black box for playing pcs, 1929 . . . . . . . .  **75.00**

**Ticker Tape,** Cadaco, stock market/finance, board game, cover shows old fashioned tickertape

machine next to game name, mfg info left side, 1963. . . . . . .  **20.00**

**Tickle Bee,** Schaper, generic, skill/maze game, cover shows multicolored bee wearing shoes between words of game name, contains magnetic wand and magnetic bee, 1959 . . . . . . . . .  **20.00**

**Tiddledy Ring Game,** Milton Bradley, generic, skill game, 21¾ x 4½", cover shows clown and 3 pigs jumping through rings, contains 4 bone rings and 4 bone winks, ©1905 . . . . . . . .  **55.00**

**Tiddledy Winks,** I.B. & W. Co., generic, skill game, 8⅜ x 4⅛ x 1⅞", cover shows 3 people in circle between words in game name, c1880s . . . . . . . . . . . .  **35.00**

**Tiddledy Winks,** I.B. & W. Co., generic, skill game, 5½ x 4 x 1¾", cover shows game name on diagonal, man in circle below "Winks," various size circles border, mfg info bottom right corner, "The New Merry Round Game," wooden box with sliding lid, c1880s . . . . . .  **30.00**

**Tiddledy Winks,** Milton Bradley, generic, skill game, 6¼" sq, cover has scrolled design behind game name, mfg info bottom right corner, c1905 . . . . . . . . .  **15.00**

**Tiddledy Winks,** Milton Bradley, generic, skill game, 7 x 7 x 1½", cover shows animals dressed in winter clothes ice skating and

2 animals in box labeled "soap" being pulled by third animal, c1920s *see illus* . . . . . . . . . . . **15.00**

**Tiddledy Winks, Complete,** Parker Brothers, generic, skill game, cover shows 3 rows of circles, "i" letters in game name are bowling pins, 5 ways to play including "Basketball, Target, Tiddledy Winks, Twenty," and "Bowling," 1962 . . . . . . . . . . **10.00**

**Tiddly Winks,** Whitman, generic, board game, cover shows playing surface, boy on hands and knees, and game name on diagonal, 1950s . . . . . . . . . . . **5.00**

**Tiddly Winks, Walt Disney's,** Whitman, Disney, board game, cover shows Mickey Mouse, Donald Duck, Goofy, and Pluto in 4 corners, 1963 . . . . . . . . . **10.00**

**Tie 'N Tangle,** Hasbro, generic, action game, cover shows 2 women, man, and boy standing on circles while tied up in string, Twister–type game, 1967 **20.00**

**Tiger Island, The Game of,** Ideal, generic, marble game, cover shows figures around lion holding club, 1966 . . . . . . . . . . . **40.00**

**Tilt Score,** Schaper, generic, tilting marble maze game, cover shows tilting playing surface with game instructions, mfg info in oval at bottom right corner, oval with ragged edges bottom left corner, 1964 . . . . . . . . . . **12.00**

**Tiltin' Milton,** Ideal, generic, balancing game, cover shows boy and girl putting items on man in hammock, 1968 . . . . . . **25.00**

**Time Bomb,** Milton Bradley, generic, action game, cover shows game name on bomb, "Tic, Tic," 1964 . . . . . . . . . . . **35.00**

**Time Tunnel Game, The,** Ideal, TV, cover shows planes, figures in tunnel, and faces of 2 men above ship, mfg logo bottom right corner, 1966 . . . . . . . . . **90.00**

**Time Tunnel Spin–To–Win, The,** Pressman, TV, cover shows 2 men with raised arms in swirling tunnel, 1967 . . . . . . . . **75.00**

**Tin Can Alley,** Ideal, advertisement, electronic game, Chuck Connors on cover with boy holding rifle aimed at Dr. Pepper cans, 4 inset pictures at bottom, mfg info bottom right corner, 1976 . . . . . . . . . . . . . . . . . . **45.00**

**Tip–It,** Ideal, generic, balancing game, cover shows 4 people with playing pcs, "The Wackiest Balancing Game Ever!," re-released in 1990, 1965 . . . . . **20.00**

**Tip Top Fish Pond,** Milton Bradley, No. 4159, generic, skill game, 10 x 9 x 1³/₈", cover shows boy with fishing rod seated in row boat, mfg info bottom left corner, contains 6 fish and 2 poles with strings and hooks, c1930s. . . . . . . . . . . . . . . **20.00**

**Tit Tat Toe, Game Of,** Parker Brothers, generic, marble skill game, cover shows hand on wooden playing surface, "3 in a Row," 1930s . . . . . . . . . . . . **15.00**

**To Tell The Truth,** Lowell, TV/game show, cover shows 3 seated panelists wearing striped ties and 1 standing panelist, large arm with game info, "An Exciting Game of Fact, Fun... and Mystery," 1957 . . . . . . . . . **30.00**

**To The North Pole By Airship, Game of,** McLoughlin Brothers, travel, board game, 19¹/₂ x 10¹/₄", cover shows dog, bears, men in hooded outfits, passengers in airship basket, and American flag, contains spinner and 4 colored wooden counters, 1897 . . . . . . . . . . . . . . . . . . **850.00**

**Tobaganing At Christmas, Game of,** McLoughlin Brothers, holiday, board game, 19¹/₂ x 17", cover shows children riding toboggans and playing in the snow, contains 4 lead tokens of reindeer pulling Santa in sleigh and spinner, wooden box, ©1899 . . . . . . . . . . . . . . . . . **1,800.00**

**Today with Dave Garroway,** Athletic Products, Inc., TV, 3–dimensional game unfolds to miniature television studio, cover shows Garroway holding

*Toonerville Trolley Game*

open game box, "Just Like Producing the Real NBC–TV Show," 1950s . . . . . . . . . . . . .    **50.00**

**Toll Gate, A Game of,** McLoughlin Brothers, generic, board game, 15½ x 13½", cover shows children riding in horse–drawn cart trying to go over arm of gate, dog barking at horses, woman wearing hat with out-stretched arms, "Toll Gate" sign, mfg info bottom right corner, contains 2 dice, 2 dice cups, and 16 wooden counters, wooden box, c1890 . . . . . . . .    **450.00**

**Tom and Jerry Game,** Milton Bradley, TV/cartoon characters, board game, cover shows Tom chasing Jerry carrying cheese, carrots, and bottle, open refrigerator and checkerboard design in background, diagonal strip in right hand corner, 1968 . . . . . .    **20.00**

• Same cover without diagonal strip, 1977 . . . . . . . . . . . . . .    **15.00**

**Tom Sawyer, The Game of,** Milton Bradley, movie/book, board game, 19 x 10", cover shows 2 boys, 1 painting fence, inset picture of Tommy Kelly as Tom Sawyer, contains 8 colored wooden counters, 2 dice, 14 yellow round disks, and 48 cards, c1937 . . . . . . . . . . .    **75.00**

**Tom Sawyer and Huck Finn, Adventures of,** see *Adventures of Tom Sawyer and Huck Finn*

**Tomorrowland Rocket to the Moon Game, Walt Disney's,** Parker Brothers, Disney/space, board game, cover shows people walking toward rocket, man with megaphone announcing

"Next Rocket Flight in 5 Minutes," 1956 . . . . . . . . . . . .    **40.00**

**Toonerville Trolley Game,** Milton Bradley, No. 4838, cartoon characters, board game, 17 x 8¾ x 1½", cover shows trolley with waving figure and driver with pipe, fat woman with umbrella running toward trolley, other figures, stop sign, and sun, unknown date *see illus* . . . . . . .    **120.00**

**Toonin Radio Game,** Alderman–Fairchild (All–Fair), radio/broad-casting, board game, separate 17¼ x 17⅝" board and pcs box, cover shows circle with game name between 2 radio towers, mfg logo below circle, mfg info between seated boy and girl, contains 6 metal speakers, tokens, 6 wood cubes, and dice cup, c1910s . . . . . . . . . . . . . .    **95.00**

**Toot,** Parker Brothers, automobile, card game, 5½ x 4", cover shows driver and back seat pas-sengers in convertible, "A Bright Novel Card Game" above mfg info, contains 76 red and white backed cards with vintage auto-faces, ©1905 . . . . . . . . . . . . .    **25.00**

**Tootsie Roll Train Game,** Hasbro, railroad/advertising, board game, cover shows Tootsie Roll candy train and engineer with striped cap, "Have Fun Being the Engineer, Win Tootsie Rolls," 1964 . . . . . . . . . . . . . . . . . . . .    **25.00**

**Top Scholar,** Cadaco–Ellis, educa-tional, cover shows faces of male and female graduates' faces above world globe, Statue of Liberty, Eiffel Tower, Sphinx, and other famous landmarks in background, "World–Wide Knowledge Game," 1957 . . . . .    **12.00**

**Topsy Turvey, The Game of,** McLoughlin Brothers, generic, board game, 15 x 14½", cover shows pig in collar and other animals in and around boxes, contains 8 wooden men, 17 round wooden counters and spinner, wooden box, ©1899 . .    **500.00**

**Toss Across Game,** Ideal, generic, action/skill game, tic tac toe,

*Toss–O*

*Tour Golf*

cover shows 3 people watching boy tossing bean bag onto game surface with "X" and "O" squares, contains bean bags, 1969 . . . . . . . . . . . . . . . . . .   **15.00**

**Toss–O,** Lubbers & Bell Mfg. Co., generic, action game, 6³/₄ x 6³/₄ x 1¹/₈", cover shows round pc falling into circle with holes, mfg info including "Clinton, Iowa, U.S.A." across bottom, 1924 *see illus* . . . . . . . . . . . .   **7.50**

**Totopoly,** Waddington, horse racing, board game, cover shows jockeys on race horses, "The Great Race Game," 1949 . . . . .   **30.00**

**Touch,** Parker Brothers, fortune telling, cover shows hand marked with sections and symbols, "Game of Palmistry," 1970 . . . .   **10.00**

**Touché Turtle,** Transogram, TV/cartoon, board game, cover shows upright turtle wearing hat, "Our Hero To the Rescue" bottom left, "Touché Away!" on sign carried by second character, 1962 . . . . . . . . . . . . . . . .   **60.00**

**Tour Golf,** Bill Lavigno and Hardy Johnson, golf, 14¹/₂ x 22¹/₂ x 1¹/₂", cover shows golf course, red flag with game name in center, includes game board, plastic golf tees, dice, score cards, and instructions, ©1977–78–79 *see illus*. . . . . . .   **15.00**

**Touring,** Wallie Dorr Co., travel, card game, 5¹/₄ x 3¹/₄", cover

shows boy and dog leading horse pulling vintage car at bottom, newer convertible on street in front of house at top, boy on bicycle, and mfg info bottom right, contains 100 red and white backed cards with old touring car picture, 1926 . .   **25.00**

**Touring,** Parker Brothers, travel, card game, Improved Edition, 5¹/₄ x 4", cover shows passengers in auto with open sides and spare wheel on side, registration and mfg info and "Improved Edition" below game name at bottom, contains red and white backed cards with touring car picture, ©1926. . . . . . . . . . . .   **25.00**

**Touring,** Parker Brothers, travel, card game, cover shows street scene with houses and trees, "The Famous Automobile Card Game," 1955 . . . . . . . . . . . . . .   **5.00**

**Touring,** Parker Brothers, travel, card game cover shows landscape with water inlet and fence around land, game name on diagonal, 1958. . . . . . . . . . . .   **8.00**

**Touring,** Parker Brothers, travel, card game, cover shows passengers in old fashioned open car, 1965 . . . . . . . . . . . . . . . . . . . .   **5.00**

**Tourist, The, A Railroad Game,** Milton Bradley, railroad, board game, 15 x 9", cover shows passengers looking out train window, telephone poles alongside tracks, mfg info in scroll design at bottom right, contains 4 round wooden colored counters and spinner, c1900 . . . . . . . . . . . . . . . . .  **125.00**

**Tournament Golf,** Rigely Banada, sports, board game, cover shows golf course with flag on green, flags in center of game name "O's," "Green Valley Country Club" upper right corner, endorsed by PGA, 1969. . .  **15.00**

**Town Hall,** Milton Bradley, No. 4602, generic, board game, 12$^1$/$_4$ x 8$^1$/$_2$ x 2", cover shows path through houses and town hall in circle, contains cardboard tokens that fit together to form path, 1939. . . . . . . . . . . .  **20.00**

**Toy Town,** Milton Bradley, generic, action game, cover shows boy and girl at table with gameboard, boy's hand on playing surface, "with remote control," 1962 . . . . . . . . . . . . . . . . .  **50.00**

**Toy Town Bank,** Milton Bradley, educational, action game, 16 x 10$^1$/$_2$", cover shows woman at "receiving and paying" teller window next to game name, contains litho teller window with 3 supports, toy money, account books, checks, and deposit slips, ©1910 . . . . . . .  **175.00**

**Toy Town Conductors Game,** Milton Bradley, railroad, action game, 13$^3$/$_4$ x 8$^3$/$_4$", cover shows standing conductor, seated train passengers, and bell hanging on ring at right corner, contains conductor mask, multicolored litho folding ticket office, punch, wooden whistle, tickets, telegrams, and passenger checks, ©1910. . . . . . . . . . . .  **200.00**

**Toy Town Telegraph Office,** Parker Brothers, educational, action game, 9$^3$/$_8$ x 13$^7$/$_8$", cover shows 2 uniformed men, 1 walking into office, and 2 men seated at table, contains 2 Western Union masks, 2 office windows with

4 wooden supports, 2 wooden telegraph keys, ink pad, packet of toy money, pads of cablegrams, telegrams, and night letters, and Western Union envelopes, c1910 . . . . . . . . . .  **320.00**

**Track & Trap,** Whitman, hunting, board game, cover shows men on elephants chasing tiger, "The Tiger Hunt Game," mfg info in oval at bottom left, 1969. . . . . .  **15.00**

**Track Meet,** Sports Illustrated, sports, board game, cover shows row of running athletes, game name bottom right corner, and mfg name upper right corner, 1972 . . . . . . . . . . . . . . . . .  **12.00**

**Trade Winds,** Parker Brothers, pirate adventure, board game, cover shows pirate, pirate ships, and island with palm trees, "Caribbean Sea Game," 1960 . .  **25.00**

**Traffic,** E.S. Lowe, automobile, board game, cover shows cars on highway and street map below game name, "A Game of Real Driving Experiences," 1968 . . . . . . . . . . . . . . . . .  **15.00**

**Traffic Hazards,** Trojan Games, automobile, board game, 21$^1$/$_4$ x 13$^1$/$_4$ x 1", cover shows mfg name down both sides, "Realistic—Fascinating— Instructive" in gameboard center, c1930s . . . . . . . . . . . .  **45.00**

**Trail Blazer Game, The Fess Parker,** see *Fess Parker Trail Blazer Game*

**Trailer Trails With "Terry The Terrible Speed Cop,"** Offset–Gravure Corp., automobile, skill and chance game, 9$^1$/$_4$ x 14$^1$/$_2$", cover shows cop on motorbike, car pulling trailer, woman holding pie out window, woman standing in doorway, and man seated at table outside second trailer, "The Laugh Cruise From Coast To Coast," 1937 . . . . . . . . . . . . . . . .  **20.00**

**Train for Boston,** Parker Brothers, railroad, board game, 16$^1$/$_2$ x 14$^1$/$_2$" cover shows scroll design around train at station and man with luggage, "Boston"

*Travel America*

above mfg info bottom right
corner, ©1900 . . . . . . . . . . . . **1,200.00**
**Transaction,** John R. Tusson, stock
market/finance, board game,
cover shows "The Authentic
Stock Market Game" above
square inset with man's face and
printed game info, 1962 . . . . . . **12.00**
**Transatlantic Flight, Game of The,**
Milton Bradley, aviation/travel,
board game, 21½ x 9¼", cover
shows Statue of Liberty, Big Ben,
and planes flying above partial
view of globe, contains 6 colored metal airplanes and 2 spin-
ners, wooden box, c1924 . . . . . **140.00**
**Trap,** Ideal, strategy, board game,
cover shows man and woman
with gameboard and game pcs,
1972 . . . . . . . . . . . . . . . . . . **10.00**
**Trap the Rat,** Hasbro, generic,
board game, cover shows
mouse in spotlight with hands
extended, 1964 . . . . . . . . . . . **15.00**
**Trapped!, Ellery Queen's Great
Mystery Game,** Bettye B., mys-
tery/book, board game, cover
shows shadow of man in door-
way, 1956 . . . . . . . . . . . . . . **50.00**
**Traps and Bunkers—A Game of
Golf,** Milton Bradley, No. 4091,
golf, skill/marble game, 9⅛ x
17¾ x 1¼", golfing scenes on
cover, c1930 . . . . . . . . . . . . **110.00**
**Travel,** Gardner Games, travel,
travel game, cover shows waving woman, man wearing uni-

form cap using binoculars, and
suitcase, plane, bus, train, and
car in 4 corners, 1950s–60s       **30.00**
**Travel, Game of,** Parker Brothers,
travel, board game, 20½ x
13½", cover is map with game
name and mfg info bottom left
corner, wooden box with drawer
holding 25 cards, spinner, and
2 metal ships; ad inside drawer
reads "The Parker Game Board.
Patented Oct. 2, 1894, Took
Highest Awards, World's
Columbian Exposition Chicago,
1893," ©1894 . . . . . . . . . . . . **450.00**
**Travel America,** Harett–Gilmar,
Inc., No. 603, travel, electronic,
10 x 8 x 2", "With Wiry Dan The
Traveling Man," cover shows
Wiry Dan carrying suitcase, map
of U. S. in background, includes
gameboard with metal spinner,
and question cards, no date *see
illus* . . . . . . . . . . . . . . . . . . . **40.00**
**Treasure Island, Game of,** The
Gem Publishing Co., book,
board game, separate 16½" sq
board and 4 x 2½" pcs box,
patent and copyright info at lid
bottom, "Suggested By Robert
Louis Stevenson's Story," contains 2 dice cups and 2 wooden
counters, ©1922–23 . . . . . . . . **55.00**
**Treasure Island, Game of,** Stoll &
Edwards Co., Inc., board game,
8½ x 16⅜ x 1¼", cover shows
ship with furled sails, "games"
below bar connecting letters
"S" and "E" of mfg's name, mfg
info bottom center, contains
spinner, 4 wooden pcs, box of
16 checkers, and dual gameboard with checkerboard on
1 side, Treasure Island on other,
1923 . . . . . . . . . . . . . . . . . . **45.00**
**Trial Lawyer,** James N. Vail, law,
board game, cover shows judge,
witness, jury, man wearing jacket, and man holding glasses,
inset of game players top right
corner, "The Jurisprudence
Game," 1977 . . . . . . . . . . . . . **12.00**
**Tri–Ominos,** Pressman, skill,
10" sq x 1½", "The Triangle
Game," cover shows triangle

*Tri–Ominos*

with game pieces inside,
includes plastic triangle shaped playing pieces, no date *see
illus*. . . . . . . . . . . . . . . . . . .   **10.00**
**Trip Around The World, A,**
Parker Brothers, travel, 16³/₄ x
11¹/₂ x 1¹/₂", cover shows ship,
circle with buildings, and circle
with men wearing long robes,
c1920 . . . . . . . . . . . . . . . . .   **55.00**
**Trip Round The World, Game of,**
McLoughlin Brothers, travel,
board game, 22¹/₂ x 16", cover
shows river with passenger
laden boat and other boats,
building, and globe, contains
4 dice cups, 4 dice, 6 lead
yachts, wooden box, ©1897 . . .   **1,500.00**
**Trip Through Our National Parks,**
**A,** Cincinnati Game Co.,
No. 1122, travel/educational,
card game, 6⁵/₈ x 5¹/₈ x 1", cover
shows scroll design below game
name, contains cards with
various park scenes, c1910. . . .   **30.00**
**Trip–Trap,** Remco, generic, action
game, cover shows mfg logo
upper right corner, inset of players upper left corner, and hand
aiming whale shooter at bottom,
contains 2 whale shooters,
3 steel balls, and 5 obstacles,
1969 . . . . . . . . . . . . . . . . . .   **40.00**
**Triple Play,** National Games Inc.,
No. D3902, sports, board game,
9 x 11¹/₄ x 1¹/₈", cover shows
gameboard surrounded by ath-

letes, directions at bottom,
c1930s. . . . . . . . . . . . . . . . .   **10.00**
**Tripoly,** Cadaco, generic,
board/card game, De Luxe
Edition, cover shows king and
queen in circle, 4 card suits
above game name, "The Game
of Kings and Queens," 1965 . . .   **8.00**
**Tripoly, The Game of,**
Cadaco–Ellis, generic, board/
card game, folded board with
"The Game of, Tripoly, Kings
and Queens" in diamond, 1936   **15.00**
**Tripoly, The Game of,**
Cadaco–Ellis, Service Edition,
generic, board/ card game,
cover shows square with game
info on checkered background,
"The Game of, Tripoly, Kings
and Queens" in diamond, 1942   **20.00**
**Trips of Japhet Jenkens & Sam**
**Slick,** Milton Bradley, travel,
card game, 4³/₄ x 3³/₄", cover
shows ship with furled sails and
man with top hat, contains cards
and booklet, c1871 . . . . . . . . .   **30.00**
**Trolley,** Snyder Bros. Game Co.,
Inc., travel, card game, 4¹/₄ x
2³/₄", cover shows mfg info
beneath trolley on tracks, "The
Great Card Game," contains
60 cards with light brown and
white trolley backs and black
and white faces, ©1904 . . . . . .   **45.00**
**Trolley Ride, The Game of The,**
The Hamilton–Myers Co.,
Publishers, travel, cover shows
passengers on trolley, pedestri-
ans, horse and carriage, bicycle,
and buildings, mfg info bottom
right corner, unknown date. . . .   **65.00**
**Trump The Game,** Milton Bradley,
celebrity/real estate, Donald
Trump on cover, "It's not
whether you win or lose, it's
whether you win!" 1989. . . . . .   **8.00**
**Truth or Consequences,** Gabriel,
TV/game show, quiz game,
cover shows "Question Counter"
and "Talley Board," Amelia
Earhart top left corner, Thomas
Jefferson upper right corner,
1955 . . . . . . . . . . . . . . . . . .   **30.00**
**Tryce,** 3M, generic, card game,
cover shows circle with game

*TV Guide's TV Game*

*Twenty–One*

name and sketch of king and faces at left, 3 dots at top of circle, 1969 . . . . . . . . . . . . . **10.00**

**Tumble Bug,** Schaper, generic, action game, cover shows animated bugs around playing surface with starting gate and ramp, 1950s . . . . . . . . . . . . . **15.00**

**Turbo,** Milton Bradley, auto racing, board game, divided cover shows men with race car at bottom right and race cars on track at upper left, based on Sega arcade game, 1981 . . . . . . . . . **10.00**

**Turn Over,** Milton Bradley, generic, board game, 11⅝ x 5", cover shows clown and row of animals, contains 2 aluminum cylinders each filled with steel ball, and green target board, ©1908 . . . . . . . . . . . . . . . . . . **35.00**

**TV Guide's TV Game,** Trivia, Inc., TV/trivia, board game, 14½ x 10½ x 2¾", cover shows various TV Guide covers, includes fold–out game board, 4 question and answer booklets, paper game points, cards, dice, plastic game pieces, and rules, ©1984 Triangle Publications, Inc. *see illus.* . . . . . . . . . . . . . . . . . **10.00**

**TV Jackpot Game,** Milton Bradley, TV/game show, board game, cover shows woman with outstretched arms standing on circular platform, "As Seen on TV," 1975 . . . . . . . . . . . . . . . **10.00**

**12 O'Clock High Card Game,** Milton Bradley, TV/military, card game, cover shows plane gunner shooting at planes, game name in circle upper right, 1965 **20.00**

**12 O'Clock High Game,** Ideal, TV/military, board game, cover shows planes flying in formation, show star Robert Lansing in military uniform at left, and mfg logo bottom right corner 1965 . . . . . . . . . . . . . . . . . . **30.00**

• Second cover version with Paul Burke, 1965. . . . . . . . . . . . . . **20.00**

**Twentieth Century Limited,** Parker Brothers, railroad, 21½ x 14½ x 1", cover shows "Limited" above steam train, wooden box, c1910 **425.00**

**20,000 Leagues Under the Sea Game, Walt Disney World,** Lakeside, Disney, board game, cover shows sailors, windows with ocean views, octopus, island, vehicle with pointed front, and 2 divers, contains plastic boats, 1980s . . . . . . . . . **15.00**

**20 To 2,** Dearborn Industries, generic, strategy game, cover shows boy between man and woman, "A New Game Sensation for You and You and You!," 1949 . . . . . . . . . . . . . **25.00**

**Twenty–One,** Lowell, TV/game show, quiz game, cover shows 2 contestants in booths, game host Jack Berry at podium, "Educational and Entertaining," 1956 *see illus.* . . . . . . . . . . . . . **30.00**

*Two Game Combination,
Messenger Boy and Checkers*

*Uncle Jim's Question Bee*

**Twiggy,** Milton Bradley, fashion/celebrity, board game, cover shows Twiggy's face and poses of her in striped dress and hat and wearing plain dress in seated pose, "The Queen of Mod," 1967 . . . . . . . . . . . . . .    **35.00**

**Twilight Zone, The,** Ideal, TV/space, board game, cover shows open door, "E=Mc²," eye, window, and flying figure, mfg logo bottom left corner, 1964 . . . . . . . . . . . . . . . . . .    **50.00**

**Twister,** Milton Bradley, generic, action game, cover shows 3 people watching 2 players on playing surface, "The Game That Ties You Up In Knots," 1966 . . .    **15.00**

**2 For the Money,** Hasbro, TV/game show, cover shows stacks of currency and coins, large "2" at left, 1955 . . . . . . . .    **15.00**

**Two Game Combination, Messenger Boy and Checkers,** Milton Bradley, generic, board games, 8¾ x 17", cover shows messenger boy on bicycle, contains 4 colored wooden

men, spinner, and 24 red and black checkers, unknown date *see illus* . . . . . . . . . . . . . . . .    **65.00**

**Two Game Combination, U.S. Mail and Checkers,** Milton Bradley, No. 4904, generic, board games, 17 x 8¾ x 1½", cover shows train with steam engine passing under trestle, c1920 . . . . . . . . . . . . . . . . . .    **145.00**

**Tycoon,** Wattson Games, business, board game, cover shows woman and dog next to convertible, man with folded arms in front of brick steps, partial view of large house in background, "The Rags To Riches Game,"1976 . . . . . . . . .    **10.00**

–U–

**Ultimate Golf,** Ultimate Golf Inc., golf, board game, cover shows gameboard, "The Ultimate Game," 1985 . . . . . . . . . . . . .    **20.00**

**Ultimate Trivia Game, The,** Quizviz, generic, quiz game, cover shows "Presented By *Newsweek*" below game name, 1984 . . . . . . . . . . . . . . . . . .    **10.00**

**Uncle Jim's Question Bee,** Lowell, radio, quiz game, inside cover shows man holding paper in left hand standing at microphone, row of question marks, "Enjoyed by Millions as played over the NBC Blue Net Work," 1938 *see illus*. . . . . . . . . . . . .    **30.00**

*Game of Uncle Sam's Mail*

**"Uncle Sam's Farm," Game of,**
Parker Brothers, travel, card
game, 6½ x 5" cover shows
2 circles with waterfalls and
bridge, mfg info bottom right
corner, contains 35 multicolored litho cards with U.S.
landmarks, ©1895 . . . . . . . . .     **35.00**
**Uncle Sam's Mail, Game of,**
McLoughlin Bros., board game,
21½ x 9½ x 1¾, includes game
pieces, letters for delivery, cards,
dice, and dice cups, 1893 *see
illus.* . . . . . . . . . . . . . . . . . .     **200.00**
**"Uncle Wiggily" Game,** Milton
Bradley, story, board game, separate board and pcs box, cover
shows Uncle Wiggily wearing
top hat walking on path toward
house and carrying case, circle
with printing and "Made in
U.S.A." bottom right, based on
bedtime stores by Howard R.
Garis, 1920s . . . . . . . . . . . . .     **35.00**
**Uncle Wiggily Game,** Milton
Bradley, story, board game,
cover shows Uncle Wiggily with
hat in left hand and cane in
right hand, 1954 . . . . . . . . . .     **20.00**
**Undercover,** Cadaco–Ellis, espi-
onage, board game, cover
shows man wearing hat and
raincoat with hands in pockets,
pair of glasses, 2 uniformed
men with rifles wearing high
boots, and message "To: Secret
Agents," includes special
"Infra–Scope Goggles," 1960 . .     **25.00**
**Underdog,** Milton Bradley,
TV/cartoon, board game, cover
shows flying Underdog wearing
cape with "U" on shirt, female

dog tied to chair, and mad sci-
entist holding syringe, 1964 . . .     **25.00**
**Underdog To The Rescue Game,**
Whitman, TV/cartoon, board
game, cover shows flying
Underdog carrying woman over
buildings and trees, figure on
rooftop, 1975 . . . . . . . . . . . . .     **15.00**
**Underdog's Save Sweet Polly
Game,** Whitman, TV/cartoon,
board game, cover shows flying
Underdog carrying woman, man
tied to tree, mfg logo upper left
corner, 1972 . . . . . . . . . . . . .     **30.00**
**Undersea World of Jacques
Cousteau,** Parker Brothers,
travel/educational, board game,
cover shows deep–sea diver,
coral, and fish, 1968. . . . . . . .     **25.00**
**United Nations, A Game About
the,** Payton Products, educational, board game, cover shows
exterior of United Nations
building, mfg info bottom left
corner, 1961 . . . . . . . . . . . . .     **20.00**
**United States Geographical Lotto,**
The Statler Manufacturing Co.,
Inc., educational, lotto game,
11¾ x 6 x 1", cover shows stars
around world globe, contains
map, playing cards, and
240 lotto city disks, c1930s . . .     **20.00**
**Universe,** Parker Brothers, movie/
space, board game, cover shows
Keir Dullea playing game with
HAL 9000 computer, inset of
man with gameboard, 1967 . . .     **15.00**
**Untouchables, Eliot Ness and
the,** *see Eliot Ness and The
Untouchables*
**Uranium,** Saalfield, adventure,
board game, cover shows men
at campfires, tents, Geiger counters, and instructions for "A
Game for Two to Four
Prospectors," 1955 . . . . . . . . . .     **30.00**
**Uranium Rush,** Gardner Games,
adventure, electric game, cover
shows desert scene with cowboy
leading donkey and carrying
Geiger counter probe, uranium
symbol at right, "Your 'Geiger
Counter' Lights Your Way To Fun
and Fortune," 1950s . . . . . . . . .     **60.00**

*Video Village*

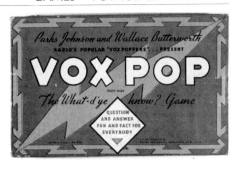

*Vox Pop*

# –V–

**Varsity,** Cadaco–Ellis, sports, board game, cover shows football player carrying ball framed in "V," "The Scientific Football Game," 1945 . . . . . . . . . . . . .    **15.00**

**Vegas,** Milton Bradley, game of chance, skill/luck game, cover shows round playing surface, cards, chips, and players' hands, 1973 . . . . . . . . . . . . . . . . . .    **10.00**

**Venture,** 3M, generic, card game, cover shows game name and highrise buildings in circle, diamond shaped design background, "A 3M Card Game," 1968 . . . . . . . . . . . . . . . . . .    **10.00**

**Victory Bomber,** Whitman, military, target game, cover shows plane dropping bombs, game name at top, contains wooden bombs, 1940s . . . . . . . . . . . .    **25.00**

**Video Village,** Milton Bradley, TV/game show, board game, cover shows woman in jail cell, 3 people walking on paths, bridge, and town buildings including bank and jewelry store, woman and man pointing finger bottom right corner, 1960 *see illus* . . . . . . . . . . . . . . . .    **25.00**

**Vignette Authors,** Selchow & Righter, educational, portrait of bearded man on easel, bust of man on pedestal, books background, mfg info bottom center, unknown date . . . . . . . . . . . .    **15.00**

**Virginian Game, The,** Transogram, TV/western, board game, cover with 4 show stars inset bottom left corner, cowboy facing second cowboy holding rifle, 1962 . . . . . . . . . . . . . . . . .    **40.00**

**Voice of the Mummy,** Milton Bradley, mystical, board game, cover shows playing surface and Mummy saying "Listen to My Voice," miniature record player concealed in Mummy's tomb, 1971 . . . . . . . . . . . . . . . . . .    **25.00**

**Volley,** Milton Bradley, sports, action game, cover shows players' hands at playing surface, 2 volley ball players at net upper left, 3 pictures inset at bottom right corner, "The Fast Action Random Shot Game," 1976 . . .    **10.00**

**Voodoo Doll Game,** Schaper, mystical, action game, cover shows voodoo doll with pins, witch doctor in front of thatched hut, game name down left side, 1967 . . . . . . . . . . . . . . . . .    **30.00**

**Vox Pop,** Milton Bradley, No. 4121, radio show, quiz game, $11^3/_4$ x $7^3/_8$ x $1^1/_4$", cover shows lightning bolt behind game name, "Question and Answer Fun and Fact for Everybody" in triangle, jagged line for lid border, based on Parks Johnson and Wallace Butterworth 1938 "Vox Poppers" radio show *see illus* . . . . . . . .    **20.00**

**Voyage of Fear Game,** Whitman, space, board game, cover shows tower above illuminated area,

*WWF Wrestling Stars Game*

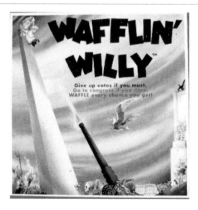

*Wafflin' Willy*

"Race to the Edge of the Unknown," based on Walt Disney Production "The Black Hole," 1979 . . . . . . . . . . . . . .    **15.00**

**Voyage Round the World, Game of,** Milton Bradley, No. 4189, travel, 16³/₈ x 11⁷/₈ x 1¹/₂", cover shows airship leaving hangar, game name top left corner, c1930s . . . . . . . . . . . . . . . .    **125.00**

**Voyage to the Bottom of the Sea Game,** Milton Bradley, TV/adventure, board game, cover shows helicopter flying over submarine, car, and motorcycle, 1964 . . . . . . . . . .    **20.00**

**Voyage to the Bottom of the Sea Card Game,** Milton Bradley, TV/adventure, card game, cover shows 2 divers approaching octopus, third diver caught in tentacles, 1965 . . . . . . . . . . .    **25.00**

–W–

**W.C. Fields How To Win* At Bridge,** The Game Keepers, celebrity, card game, cover shows Fields in top hat, "*Cheat" below game name, 1972 . . . . . . . . . . . . . . . . . .    **10.00**

**WWF Wrestling Challenge Game,** Milton Bradley, sports, board game, 19¹/₈ x 9⁵/₈ x 1¹/₂", cover shows inset pictures of wrestlers, wrestling ring in lower right hand corner, "Featuring 9 of Your Favorite World Wrestling Federation Superstars," includes game board, dice, tokens, cards, chips, and instructions, 1990 . .    **10.00**

**WWF Wrestling Stars Game,** Milton Bradley, sports, board game, 19¹/₈ x 9⁵/₆ x 1¹/₂", cover shows Hulk Hogan, 11 inset pictures of wrestlers, "Featuring 12 of the World Wrestling Federation's Stars," includes game board, cards, plastic pegs, cardboard wrestler tokens, dice, plastic marker, 1985 *see illus* . .    **12.00**

**Wackiest Ship in the Army Game, The,** Standard Toykraft, TV/military comedy, board game, cover shows 3 uniformed figures on sailboat, 2 with binoculars, faces of 2 men wearing military caps on each side of sailboat, 1964–65 . . . . . . . . . . . . . . . .    **45.00**

**Wacky Races Game, The,** Milton Bradley, TV/cartoon, board game, cover shows cartoon villain with hand on dynamite detonator standing behind tree with dog and watching race cars driving on mountainside road, 1969 . . . . . . . . . . . . . . . . . . .    **20.00**

**Wafflin' Willy,** Right Angle, Inc., political, board game, 12¹/₄ x 12¹/₄ x 1¹/₄", cover shows cannon firing, eagle flying, contains game board, spinner, game pieces, die, cards, and game rules, 1993 *see illus* . . . . . . . .    **10.00**

**Wagon Train Game,** Milton Bradley, TV/western, board game, cover shows cowboy holding rifle and cowboy with guns atop wagon train, series

*The Waltons Game*                *Welcome Back, Kotter*

starred Ward Bond and Robert
Horton, 1960. . . . . . . . . . . . .    **30.00**

**Wally Gator Game,** Transogram,
TV/cartoon, cover shows Wally
Gator running with knapsack
and map being chased by zoo
curator carrying net, "Help Mr.
Twiddle Find the Runaway,"
1962 . . . . . . . . . . . . . . . .    **40.00**

**Walt & Skeezix Gasoline Alley
Game,** Milton Bradley,
No. 4516, comic strip, 19¼ x
10 x 1⅝", cover shows large figure with hat flying running in
front of small open cart driven
by second figure, dog running
alongside cart, c1920. . . . . . .    **120.00**

**Walt Disney's Donald Duck's
Party Game for Young Folks,**
Parker Brothers, Disney, board
game, 19¼ x 9¾ x 1¾", lid
shows "Walt Disney's Own
Game" next to Donald Duck,
mfg info bottom right corner,
1938 . . . . . . . . . . . . . . . .    **65.00**

**Walt Disney's Uncle Remus
Game,** Parker Brothers, Disney,
17½ x 10 x 1¾", cover shows
Remus and friends looking at
playing surface, "Zip" bottom
left corner, c1930s . . . . . . . . .    **125.00**

**Waltons Game, The,** Milton
Bradley, TV/family, board game,
cover shows family members'
faces, pickup truck and house in
background, 1974 *see illus*. . . .    **10.00**

**Watch On De Rind,** Alderman,
Fairchild Co., black collectibles,
target game, cover shows Mose,
Sambo, and Rastus eating
watermelon, 1931 . . . . . . . . .    **250.00**

**Waterworks,** Parker Brothers,
generic, card game, cover

shows game name on a man-
hole cover, inset circle with
players, "Leaky Pipe Card
Game," 1972 . . . . . . . . . . . .    **8.00**

**Way to The White House, The,
Game of Electing The President,**
Alderman–Fairchild (All–Fair),
No. 304, politics, 15½ x 12",
cover shows White House in
inset circle, large picture of
Capitol, 1927 . . . . . . . . . . . .    **55.00**

**Weird–Ohs Game,** Ideal, toy,
board game, cover shows figures
in racing carts at finish line,
figure with striped shirt holding
checkered flag, 1963–64. . . . . .    **40.00**

**Welcome Back, Kotter,** Ideal, TV,
board game, cover shows 4 inset
pictures of show stars and large
picture of Kotter and Barbarino,
mfg logo bottom right corner
"Be Your Favorite Sweathog, the
up your nose with a rubber hose
game," 1976 *see illus* . . . . . . . .    **15.00**

**Welcome Back, Kotter Card
Game,** Milton Bradley, TV, card
game, cover shows Kotter,
Horshock, Washington, Epstein,
and Barbarino, game name
slanted in upper left corner,
1976 . . . . . . . . . . . . . . . .    **15.00**

**Welfare Game & A Modest
Solution, The,** St. Croix, Inc.,
society/economics, board game,
cover has game name over
newspaper background,
"Stop Spiraling Welfare Costs,"
1971 . . . . . . . . . . . . . . . .    **15.00**

**Wells Fargo Game,** Milton
Bradley, TV/western, board
game, cover with inset picture
of show star Dale Robertson

*What's My Line?*

*Wheel of Fortune TV Game*

bottom left corner, cowboys,
horses, and train in background,
1959 . . . . . . . . . . . . . . . . . .    **40.00**

**Wendy the Good Little Witch,**
Milton Bradley, TV/cartoon,
board game, cover shows
Casper following Wendy on
broom, house and crescent
moon in background, contains
spinner and colored playing
pcs, 1966 . . . . . . . . . . . . . .    **45.00**

**What D'ye Buy,** McLoughlin
Brothers, business, 6½ x 4⅞",
cover shows man standing with
hands on table holding numerous small items, 2 stacked
boxes and hanging small items
at left, 2 bottles at right, mfg
info center bottom, contains
12 large "trade" cards and
72 smaller merchandise cards,
©1887 . . . . . . . . . . . . . . . .    **45.00**

**What Shall I Be?,** Selchow &
Righter, careers, board game,
cover shows 6 women representing different careers including nurse and stewardess, game
name below girl's face, "The
Exciting Game of Career Girls,"
1966 . . . . . . . . . . . . . . . . . .    **15.00**

**What Shall I Wear?,** Selchow &
Righter, fashion, board game,
cover shows row of 6 women in
different outfits including
evening gown, tennis costume,
and bathing suit, game name
above girl's face, 1969 . . . . . . .    **10.00**

**What's My Line?,** Lowell,
TV/game show, quiz game,
cover shows 4 guests seated at
table, man seated at separate
table with small TV set, back

ground sketch of people in
different clothing representing
different occupations, contains
blinders, black and white guest
photos, and plastic TV, 1954–55
*see illus* . . . . . . . . . . . . . . . .    **40.00**

**What's My Name?,** Jay Mar
Specialty, radio program, quiz
game, 15¼ x 10¼ x 1⅞", cover
shows game name upper left
corner, microphone, "Played as
Broadcast Over the Nation, The
Exciting 'Clue' Game!," based
on Edward Byron and Joe A.
Cross radio show, c1940 . . . . . .    **35.00**

**Wheel of Fortune TV Game,**
Milton Bradley, TV/game show,
12¼ x 9½ x 1½", cover shows
man and 2 women standing
behind game wheel, another
woman standing in front of
letters on board, includes plastic
holder, cardboard letters, spinner, cards, paper money, and
instructions, 1975 *see illus* . . . .    **18.00**

**When My Ship Comes In,** George
S. Parker & Co., nautical, card
game, 5½ x 4", cover shows
ship with furled sails, shoreline,
mfg info bottom right corner,
contains 84 cards, ©1888 . . . . .    **25.00**

**Where's The Beef?,** Milton
Bradley, advertising, board
game, cover shows dialogue box
with game name, woman with
gray hair wearing necklace and
holding hamburger, based on

*Whirlpool Game*

Wendy's advertising, "The Fast Food Race Game," 1984 . . . . .   **10.00**

**Where's Willie?,** Milton Bradley, TV/stunt show, action game, playing pc has lever to open doors and find Willie, game name on roof, based on Shenanigans TV show stunt, 1966 . . . . . . . . . . . . . . . . .   **25.00**

**Which Witch?,** Milton Bradley, monster, 3–dimensional board game, cover shows youngsters, around playing surface with 3–dimensional haunted house, re–released in 1984 as The Real Ghostbusters Game, 1970 . . . .   **20.00**

**Whirlpool Game,** McLoughlin Brothers, No. 408, nautical, board game, 7¼" sq, cover shows figures in small boats behind sinking ship, printed info bottom right corner, contains 12 round wooden counters and spinner, c1899 *see illus* . . . . . .   **25.00**

**Whirly Bird,** Schaper, generic, action game, cover shows girl throwing dart at large bullseye shield, man and boy holding bullseye shields with darts, "Play Catch Game," 1958 . . . . .   **15.00**

**White Glove Girl,** American Publishing Corp., business/ careers, board game, cover shows 2 hands in white gloves, White Glove Girl Company adv, and maid for hire company, 1966 . . . . . . . . . . . . . . . . .   **15.00**

**White Squadron,** The Fireside Game Co., No. 1108, military, card game, 2⅝ x 3⅝", cover shows circle inset with naval ship, 2 faces in scroll design surrounding circle, chain link border, contains 52 cards with U.S. Navy ships, ©1896 . . . . . .   **35.00**

**Whiz Bowl,** Zenith, sports, skill game, cover shows boy pointing to pins set up on playing surface, girl holding ball, "New Bowling Game," 1950s . . . . . . .   **15.00**

**Who?,** Parker Brothers, generic, board game, cover shows 4 people seated at table with playing surface and looking at row of 6 people, "A Game of Hidden Identity," 1951 . . . . . . . . . . . .   **30.00**

**Who Can Beat Nixon?,** Dynamic Design, politics, cover shows eagle atop question mark, 4 stars below game name, "Presidential Sweepstakes," 1970 . . . . . . . . . . . . . . . . .   **10.00**

**Who What or Where Game,** Milton Bradley, TV/quiz show, quiz game, cover shows oval frame with 2 men and women seated at panel, game name with assigned values (Who=30, What=40, Where=50) in front of each contestant, question marks in squares background, "NBC TV Quiz Game" in square at left, 1970 . . . . . . . . . . . . . . .   **10.00**

• "New 2nd Edition," cover shows 2 women and man separate circles, game name with assigned values (Who=30, What=40, Where=50) in front of each contestant, "NBC TV Quiz Game" bottom right . . . .   **10.00**

**Whodunit?,** Cadaco–Ellis, mystery, board game, cover shows "Murder in the Village" card with silhouette figure against circle, moon behind buildings, 2 cards behind first card, "The Game of Evidence," printed info bottom right corner, 1959 . . . . .   **20.00**

**Whoopee!,** Milton Bradley, western, No. 4314, 5⅜ x 4 x 1", cover shows cowboy riding bucking horse, mfg and copy-

Whoopee!

Willow

right info, and "Made in U.S.A." along bottom edge, ©1929 *see illus.* . . . . . . . . . . . . . . . . . . .   **20.00**

**Whosit?,** Parker Brothers, mystery, guessing game, cover shows game name bordered by lights, group of people at bottom include boy with glasses, man with right hand over heart, girl wearing hat, and man smoking pipe, 1976. . . . . . . . . . . . . . .   **10.00**

**Why,** Milton Bradley, mystery, board game, "Presented by Alfred Hitchcock," cover shows profile of Hitchcock in circle, top of house, fence, and trees, game name letters cracked in half, 3 different cover versions, 1961. . . . . . . . . . . . . . . . . . .   **15.00**

**Wicket the Ewok, Star Wars,** Parker Brothers, movie, board game, cover shows large winged figure flying over smaller figures among trees, "Star Wars Return of the Jedi" upper left corner, "Food Gathering Adventure Game," 1983. . . . . . .   **10.00**

**Wide World of Sports–Auto Racing,** Milton Bradley, sports, board game, cover shows #70 race car next to film strip with slides of game name and racing car, 1974. . . . . . . . . . . . . . . . .   **15.00**

**Wide World of Sports–Golf,** Milton Bradley, sports, board game, cover shows film strip with slide of game name and slide of golfer swinging club, golfers on course background, 1974 . . . . . . . . . . . . . . . . . . .   **15.00**

**Wide World of Sports–Tennis,** Milton Bradley, sports, board game, cover shows film strip with slide of game name and slide of player serving tennis ball, players on court background, 1974 . . . . . . . . . . . . .   **15.00**

**Wide World Travel Game,** Parker Brothers, travel, board game, cover shows 4 scenes of famous sites above and below "World," globe at left, contains metal jet playing pcs, 1957 . . . . . . . . . . .   **20.00**

**Wild Bill Hickok's The Cavalry and The Indians Game,** Built–Rite, western, board game, cover shows Hickok with Indian in headdress, cavalry riding toward fort, "Plus the Old Favorite India Game" bottom left corner, "Game of India" on back . . . . . . . . . . . . . . . . . . .   **50.00**

**Wild Life,** E.S. Lowe, travel/education, conservation, board game, cover shows elephant, map, and "An Ecology Game that Fosters Wild Animal Conservation," 1969–71 . . . . . .   **20.00**

**Willow,** Parker Brothers, movie, board game, 17½ x 9¼ x 2", cover shows characters from movie, "The Game of Heroes, Villains and Magic," includes game board, cards, tokens, and two dice, 1988 *see illus* . . . . . .   **10.00**

**Win, Place & Show,** 3M, horse racing, board game, cover shows 3 jockeys riding horses along track rail, 1966 . . . . . . . .   **15.00**

*Winnie–The–Pooh Game*

**Wine Cellar,** Marina Enterprises, educational, wine tasting game, cover shows grapes, mountains, vineyards, wine bottle, and 2 glasses of wine, game name on barrel bottom, 1971 . . . . . .   **10.00**

**Wings,** Parker Brothers, No. 789, aviation, card game, 5½ x 4", cover shows biplane with propeller, patent info lid top, "The Air Mail Game," mfg info bottom right corner, contains 99 pink and white backed cards with air mail plane pictures, ©1928. . . . . . . . . . . . . . . . . .   **20.00**

**Winnie–The–Pooh Game,** Parker Brothers, book, board game, 17⅛ x 8⅞", picture square shows Pooh with friends in front of tree with open door at base, line connecting squares under picture, "A New Kind of Game...Moving By Colors" bottom left, mfg info bottom right corner, ©1933 by Stephen Slesinger, Inc. *see illus* . . . . . . .   **65.00**

**Winnie–The–Pooh,** Parker Brothers, book, board game, 17 x 9", cover shows Pooh with friends walking toward tree with open door at base, "colorful game," mfg info bottom right corner, contains 4 cardboard counters in wooden supports, and cloth bag containing colored markers, ©1933 . . . . . . . .   **75.00**

**Winnie the Pooh Game, Walt Disney's,** Parker Brothers, Disney/book/movie, board game, cover shows Pooh and friends in field, seated Christopher Robin, mfg logo below "Pooh," 1964 . . . . . . . . .   **20.00**

**Winnie the Pooh Game, Walt Disney's,** Parker Brothers, Disney/book, cover shows Pooh, Christopher Robin, and others walking on path, 1979 . . . . . . .   **10.00**

**Wipe Off Target Game,** Milton Bradley, generic, board game, cover shows boy carrying box standing with girl in short dress, *Parents* and *Good Housekeeping* seals bottom right corner, 1959 . . . . . . . . . . . . . . . . . .   **12.00**

**Wizard, The,** Fulton Specialty Co., educational, quiz game, 8⁷⁄₁₆ x 8³⁄₈ x 1¼", cover shows figure wearing pointed hat in circle center, bats and cats in lid's 4 corners, "Educational... Instructive," contains cardboard insert, directional arrow, and question disk, ©1921 . . . . . . . .   **35.00**

**Wizard of Oz, The Game of the,** Whitman, book/movie, cover shows Dorothy and friends on Yellow Brick Road headed for castle, 1939 . . . . . . . . . . . . . .   **35.00**

**Wizzer Wheel, Walt Disney's Official Mouseketeer,** Ideal, spinner game, cover shows Mickey Mouse in circle surrounded by small cards with Disney character pictures, "The Exciting Spin–A–Picture Game," mfg logo bottom right corner, 1964 . . . . . . . . . . . . . . . . . .   **25.00**

**Wogglebug Game of Conundrums, The,** Parker Brothers, based on Oz books character, card game, 6½ x 5", cover shows pumpkin face and creature with pointed nose and 4 long tentacles wearing jacket

*Woman & Man*

*The Wonderful Game of Oz*

and short pants, contains gray
and buff question and answer
cards, ©1905 . . . . . . . . . . . . .    **95.00**

**Wolfman Mystery Game,** Hasbro,
monster, board game, cover
shows arrows pointing in different directions around Wolfman
picture, 4 inset pictures, 1 of
tree branches, 1963 . . . . . . . .    **125.00**

**Woman & Man,** Psychology
Today, society, board game,
cover shows large man wearing
belted jacket and ascot patting
"little" woman's head, kneeling
figure with dynamite at bottom
left, "The Classic Confronta-
tion," 1971 *see illus* . . . . . . . .    **10.00**

**Wonderbug,** Ideal, generic, board
game, cover shows open cars
with large headlights, "The
game that lets you turn 'Schlep'
into Wonderbug," elongated
oval bottom left corner, circle
with mfg logo bottom right
corner, 1977 . . . . . . . . . . . . .    **12.00**

**Wonderful Game of Oz, The,**
Parker Brothers, book, board
game, 10 x 19", cover shows
Dorothy, lion, tin man and
scarecrow, castle in background, mfg info bottom left
corner, contains dice cup,
6 wooden Wizard cubes,
4 pewter figures of Dorothy and
friends, later game replaced
pewter figures with plain wood-
en disks, ©1921 *see illus* . . . . .    **950.00**

**Wonderful World of Color, Walt
Disney's,** Parker Brothers,
"Professor Ludwig Von Drake
Presents, A Game Based on the
TV Program," board game, cover
shows Professor pointing stick at
game announcement against
colored squares background,
1962 . . . . . . . . . . . . . . . . . . . .    **35.00**

**Wonderful World of Color Game,
Walt Disney's,** Whitman,
Disney, board game, cover
shows Donald Duck, Pluto, and
others around playing surface,
spinning globe upper left corner,
1961 . . . . . . . . . . . . . . . . . . . .    **45.00**

**Woody Woodpecker Game,**
Milton Bradley, TV/cartoon,
board game, cover shows
Woody with friends including
boy wearing hat, *Parents* and
*Good Housekeeping* seals at
left, 1958 . . . . . . . . . . . . . . . .    **40.00**

**Woody Woodpecker's Game Box,**
Saalfield, TV/cartoon, 4 board
games, cover shows "Walter
Lantz" upper right corner,
Woody surrounded by 4 game
cards and colored circles,
"Saalfield Artcraft" bottom left
corner, 1964 . . . . . . . . . . . . .    **25.00**

*Wordy*

*World Trivia Game, Series 4*

**Woody Woodpecker, Travel With,**
Cadaco–Ellis, TV/cartoon, travel,
cover shows Woody in prop
plane and clusters of spired
buildings, printed info bottom
right corner, "By Walter Lantz"
top right, 1956 . . . . . . . . . . . .    30.00

**Word For Word, Merv Griffin's,**
*see Merv Griffin's Word for*
*Word*

**Wordy,** Pressman Toy Corp.,
generic, word game, 14 x 14 x
1", cover shows letter tiles in
squares and on tile holder, tiles
spell out "fun, fast, exciting,
new," hand with pointing finger
and "the new cross word game"
inset top right corner, exclamation point and "with dictionary" inset bottom left corner,
©1938 *see illus* . . . . . . . . . . .    25.00

**World Educator and Game, The,**
W.S. Reed Toy Co., educational,
word game, 14 x 6⅝ x 1¼",
cover shows game name in
shape with scrolled edges,
"Educational and Entertaining,"
1919 . . . . . . . . . . . . . . . . . .    45.00

**World of Wall Street, The,**
Hasbro, stock market/investing,
cover shows 4 people holding
strips of tape coming from old
tickertape machine, "NBC" and
peacock logo upper right
corner, 1969 . . . . . . . . . . . .    15.00

**World Trivia Game, Series 4,**
Hoyle Products, trivia, card

game, "pocket trivia," cover
shows Abraham Lincoln, Mona
Lisa, Albert Einstein, space shut-
tle, and men carrying American
flag, includes cards, 1984 *see*
*illus* . . . . . . . . . . . . . . . . . .    8.00

**World's Championship Baseball**
**Game,** National Indoor Game &
Novelty Co., sports, 13 x 19",
cover shows umpire calling play,
player holding bat, baseball at
top center, unknown date . . . . .    30.00

**World's Fair Game, The Official**
**New York,** Milton Bradley,
event, board game, cover shows
aerial view of world's fair buildings and circular hemisphere pc,
skyline of highrise buildings in
background, "includes 9 full–
color scenes of the fair
1964–1965," 1965 . . . . . . . . .    35.00

**Wow Pillow Fight Game for**
**Girls,** Milton Bradley, generic,
action game, cover shows girls
tossing pillows, 1964 . . . . . . . .    20.00

**Wrestle Around Game,** Ideal,
generic, action game, cover
shows players' hands on handles
of playing pc, inset of 4 players,
mfg logo bottom right corner,
1969 . . . . . . . . . . . . . . . . . .    15.00

**Wyhoo!,** Milton Bradley, generic,
9¼ x 5", cover shows man
with open mouth wearing
bowtie in oval frame with scroll

*X–Men Alert! Adventure Game*

*Yahtzee*

design, "Novel, Amusing. Easy. Instructive. No Knowledge of Music Required to Play this Game," mfg info in rectangle at bottom right, contains 110 litho black and white cards, ©1897, "©1906" on rules. . . . . . . . . . .   **25.00**

### –X–

**X–Men Alert! Adventure Game, The Uncanny,** Pressman, comic book, adventure, board game, 20 x 11³/₄ x 2¹/₄", cover shows 4 X–Men in action, contains game board, 18 collectible figures, cards, dice, chips, movers, and instruction booklet, 1992 . . . . . . . . . . . . . . . . .   **10.00**

**X–Plor US,** Alderman–Fairchild, No. 3, educational, board game, separate 17¹/₂" sq board and 5³/₄ x 4" pcs box, multicolored litho U.S. map on board, directions printed bottom center, contains 4 metal airplanes and score pad, c1922. . . . . . . .   **85.00**

### –Y–

**Yacht Race,** Clark & Sowdon, nautical, board game, 15 x 7¹/₂", cover shows 2 yachts and ships, mfg info bottom right corner, contains 4 cardboard yachts in wooden stands and spinner, c1895 . . . . . . . . . . . . . . . . .   **55.00**

**Yacht Race,** Milton Bradley, nautical, board game, 8 x 14¹/₈", cover shows yacht with full sails riding ocean waves, game name at top, mfg info bottom left corner, contains 4 round colored wooden markers and spinner . . . . . . . . . . . . . . . .   **55.00**

**Yacht Race,** Parker Brothers, nautical, board game, cover shows steering wheel in center of map diagram and again at lid bottom above mfg info, contains large metal boats, 1961 . . . . . .   **30.00**

**Yahtzee,** E.S. Lowe, generic, dice game, cover shows man wearing graduate's hat and bowtie, 5 dice, and dice cup, "The Game That Makes Thinking Fun!," 1956 . . . . . . . . . . . . . .   **10.00**

**Yahtzee,** E.S. Lowe, Deluxe Edition, generic, dice game, lid center shows sketch of man wearing graduate's hat and bowtie next to game name and above mfg info, 1961 . . . . . . . .   **15.00**

**Yahtzee,** E.S. Lowe, generic, 9³/₄ x 7³/₄ x 2³/₄", cover shows Yahtzee cup spilling dice, includes plastic cup, dice, plastic chips, score pad, and instructions, ©1975 Milton Bradley *see illus* . . . . . . . . . . . . . . . . .   **10.00**

**Yahtzee, Challenge,** E.S. Lowe, generic, dice game, cover shows playing surface, dice, and dice cup, endorsed by "The Odd

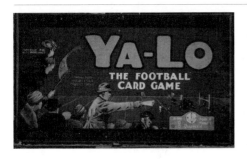

Ya–Lo

Yoda the Jedi Master Game, Star Wars

Couple" with Tony Randall and Jack Klugman upper right corner, 1974. . . . . . . . . . . . . . . .   10.00

**Yahtzee Score Pads,** E.S. Lowe, generic, game accessory, same cover as Yahtzee, 1956. . . . . . .   4.00

**Ya–Lo,** E.J. Graber, 16³/₄ x 10 x 1", sports, educational, cover shows fans watching football game, includes game board, defense and offense cards, metal football, and instructions, 1925 *see illus.* . . . . . . . . . . . . . . . . . . . .   85.00

**Yankee Doodle,** Parker Brothers, U.S. History/educational, board game, 21¹/₄ x 14¹/₈", cover shows naval battle scene in bottom right corner, picture of man in circle in upper right corner, 3 drummers and "1775" in upper left corner, and soldiers with rifles in battle in lower left corner, contains spinner, 4 colored wooden counters, and red and yellow cardboard disks, wooden box, ©1895 . . . . . . . .   625.00

**Yankee Doodle!,** Cadaco–Ellis, Deluxe Edition, U.S. History/ educational, word game, cover shows man wearing cap playing with letter tiles, game name placed above exclamation point, 1940 . . . . . . . . . . . . . .   25.00

**Yankee Trader,** Corey Games, business/trading, board game, cover shows ships, men working on docks, highrise buildings, and "A Game of Trading Skill," 1941 . . . . . . . . . . . . . . . . . .   30.00

**Ye Peculiar Game of Ye Yankee Peddler,** George S. Parker & Co.,

generic, card game, 6³/₈ x 4³/₄", cover shows woman standing with hands on hips on porch talking with man wearing top hat carrying suitcase, cart loaded with wares, mfg info on fence board bottom right corner, contains printed cards, ©1888 . . . . . . . . . . . . . . . . .   30.00

**Yertle, The Game of,** Revell, book, balancing game, cover shows turtles standing atop each other, "By Dr. Seuss," 1960. . . .   50.00

**Yoda the Jedi Master Game, Star Wars,** Kenner, movie, board game, cover shows space creature on back of boy, face of space creature upper right corner, seated man talking with space creature lower right corner, man in battle lower left corner, 1981 *see illus* . . . . . . . .   15.00

**Yogi Bear Game,** Milton Bradley, TV/cartoon, board game, cover shows Yogi in open car holding picnic basket in left hand followed by group of people led by ranger, 1971 . . . . . . . . . . .   20.00

**Yogi Bear Go Fly A Kite Game,** Transogram, TV/cartoon, board game, cover shows friends watching Yogi flying kite with "Go Fly A Kite" clipped to kite's string, "A Fascinating Game of Perception," mfg info upper left corner, 1961 . . . . . . . . . . . . .   35.00

**Yogi Bear Score–A–Matic Ball Toss,** Transogram, TV/cartoon, action game, cover shows ball going into Yogi's mouth, arrow pointing to numbered values

*Groucho's You Bet Your Life*

*Walt Disney's Zorro*

ranging from 20 to 60, contains
20" high Yogi target with auto-
matic ball return, 1960. . . . . . . **45.00**
**You Bet Your Life, Groucho's,**
Lowell, TV/quiz show, quiz
game, 18 x 12", cover shows
"NBC" below Groucho smoking
a cigar, small circle with
"DeSoto" and "Plymouth"
framing picture of Groucho,
contains multiple choice
questions cards, answer card,
and cardboard letters, 1955
*see illus* . . . . . . . . . . . . . . . **55.00**
**You Don't Say Game,** Milton
Bradley, TV/game show, cover
shows 4 players at table, 1 man
scratching head, and "Plastic
Bonus Board," 1964–69 . . . . . . **10.00**
**Young Folks Historical Game,**
McLoughlin Brothers, educational, card game, 6¼ x 4½",
cover shows eagle, shield, and
men, mfg info bottom right corner, flowered border, contains
36 cards, c1890. . . . . . . . . . . **30.00**
**Yours For A Song,** Lowell,
TV/game show, action game,
cover shows "Automatic–Song–
Selector," man on knees,
woman with raised arms standing next to man holding
Selector, and inset of Bert Parks
in upper right corner, 1961. . . . **25.00**

## –Z–

**Zaxxon,** Milton Bradley, arcade
game, board game, cover shows
game name with jagged letters
upper right corner, small circle
upper left, "Based on the Action
Packed Arcade Game by SEGA"
lower left, 1982 . . . . . . . . . . . **10.00**
**Zippy Zepps Air Game,**
Alderman–Fairchild Co., aviation, board game, cover shows
large zeppelin, contains metal
zeppelins and zeppelin cards,
unknown date . . . . . . . . . . . . **400.00**
**Zok,** Hasbro, generic, action
game, cover shows 4 players
playing game on giant vinyl
playing mat, contains mat and
super game cards, 1967 . . . . . . **20.00**
**Zorro Game,** Whitman, movie/
Disney, board game, cover
shows 2 girls and 2 boys playing
game in foreground, Zorro in
background, mfg logo bottom
right corner, 1965. . . . . . . . . . **20.00**
**Zorro, Walt Disney's,** Whitman,
movie/Disney, board game, lid
shows Zorro at left of buildings
and street, 1959 *see illus* . . . . . **40.00**
**Zorro Game, Walt Disney's,**
Parker Brothers, movie/Disney,
board game, cover shows Zorro
on rearing horse, mission building lower right, mfg logo bottom
left corner, 1966. . . . . . . . . . . **30.00**

# PUZZLES

*Einson–Freeman Co., Inc., L. I. City, N.Y.,*
*Every Week Jig–Saw Puzzle Series, "Young Jig–Saw Makers," No. 33,*
*Orson Lowell illus, litho diecut cardboard, 14¹/₄ x 10³/₈", 228 pcs,*
*©June 15, 1933, $40.00*

# ADULT JIGSAW PUZZLES

## HAND CUT

**A–1 Puzzle Club,** untitled Impressionist landscape by August Renoir, wood, woman strolling along shady road, 24 x 20", c1910, box missing . . **10.00**

**Bliss, R. W.,** Wallaston, MA,
- The Arab Raiding Party, A.D., Schreyer print of armed horsemen riding at dusk, 12 x 9", 153 pcs, early 20th C, black and orange box . . . . . . . . . . **20.00**
- The Flower Market, Van Vreeland print of Dutch flower market by canal, interlocking cut, 9 x 12", 200 pcs, c1930, period box. . . . . . . . . . . . . . **25.00**

**Milton Bradley**
- Premiere Jigsaw Puzzles Moon Beam's Princess, evening scene with Indian princess, 300 pcs, boxed . . . . . . . . . . **75.00**
Port of Heart's Desire, kneeling mother holding daughter, 8 x 10", 168 pcs, 1920s, orig box . . . . . . . . . . . . . . . . . . **40.00**
Tyrolean Waters, alpine scene with castle, lake, and mountains, 15 x 11", 300 pcs, 1937, orig box . . . . . . . . . . . . . . **25.00**
Why The Guests Were Late, country scene of rescue of snow–bound coach, Talbert Wright artist, 19 x 12", 500 pcs, 37 pcs figurals, orig box. . . . . . . . . . . . . . . . . . . **40.00**
- Untitled, attributed to Gaston Roulle, large boats sailing on Venice Grand Canal in blustery wind, wood, 482 pcs, 62 figurals, 23 x 16", box missing . . . . . . . . . . . . . . . . . . . **65.00**

**Chad Valley Co.,** The Autocar Jig–Saw Puzzles, wood, Meteors of Road and Track, F. Gordon Crosby, No. 2 of series of 12, "Leyland (J.G.P. Thomas) and

*The Nelson Touch*

Fiat (E.A.D Eldridge)," 10⁵⁄₈ x 7¹⁄₈", 200 pcs, period box . . . . . **80.00**

**Cooke, Frances A.,** Weston, MA, No. 23, "Speak for it!," grassy meadow scene with girl and dogs, 13¹⁄₈ x 8¹⁄₂", 213 pcs, c1910, orig box . . . . . . . . . . . **35.00**

**Cotton, Robert,** "Soldier Boy," soldier surrounded by ammunition, 76 pcs, cut January 22, 1943, back of puzzle is cigar box lid, boxed . . . . . . . . . . . . **25.00**

**Damon** (attributed to), Lunch–time, wood, Norman Price print of boy sharing lunch with puppy, 11 x 16", 178 pcs, 32 figurals, color line cutting, pre–1930 . . . . . . . . . . . . . . . . **35.00**

**Falls Puzzles,** Cleveland Heights, OH, wood, No. 2140, "The Nelson Touch," Admiral and aide at table, wood, 358 pcs, many intricate figurals, 11⁵⁄₈ x 15¹⁄₂", boxed *see illus*. . . **85.00**

**F. B.,** Shenandoah Valley, VA, "Tap–Tap," multicolored magazine photo of chorus line rehearsing on stage, 8³/₄ x 5³/₄", 132 pcs, mid–1930s, contains cloth bag . . . . . . . . . . . . . . .   **30.00**

**Fretts, Alden L.,** The Yankee Cut–ups, Home Memories, English cottage and garden, Thompson illus, 23 x 16", 676 pcs, 24 figurals, c1930s . . .   **65.00**

**Full o' Cheer Picture Puzzles,** Boston, MA, "Contentment Cottage," T. Noel Smith country scene of cottage and garden by stream, color line cutting, 12 x 9", 132 pcs, 9 figurals, c1930s, period box missing . . .   **25.00**

**Gleason, H. A.,** Cheerio Jig Saw Puzzles, Mine's the Largest, pin–up girl with ten gallon hat, Holt Armstrong illus, 16 x 12", 720 pcs, 7 figurals, orig box . . .   **85.00**

**Glencraft/Glendex**
• Fishing Pier, New England harbor scene, 22 x 15", 720 pcs, c1960s . . . . . . . . . . . . . . .   **50.00**
• Sailing Off Block Island, wood, sailing yawl and Block Island Lighthouse, Y.E. Goldberg illus, 19 x 14", 512 pcs, 1960s, orig box . . . . . . . . . . . . . . . . . .   **45.00**
•Tree Island, New England landscape, interlocking, 14 x 10", 304 pcs, 1960s, orig cardboard box . . . . . . . . . . . . . .   **30.00**

**Grant, Robert,** North Epping, Newmarket, NH, "A Hot Argument," humorous picture of country men watching dispute, non–interlocking, some color line cutting, 12 x 9", 57 pcs, chocolate box presumed period, dated Nov 22, 1932 . . . . . . . . .   **20.00**

**Great Lakes Exposition,** Cleveland Centennial, June 27 to Oct 4, 1936, 2¹/₈ x 3¹/₈ x ³/₄", information stenciled on top of block in blue and red, 3–dimensional layered cutting . . . . . . . .   **60.00**

**Hale, Cushman & Flint,** PZ21, "The Boyhood of Raleigh," after Sir John Miles portrait in London's Tate Gallery, A Medici Picture Puzzle, 7¹/₂ x 8¹/₂" . . . . .   **20.00**

**Hammond's Leisure Hour Jig–Saw Puzzle,** C.S. Hammond

& Company, Brooklyn, NY, "An Old Sailor," sailor assembling ship model, approx 350 pieces, puzzle from rental library of Eugene Clark Book Shop, New Haven, CT, boxed . . . . . . . . . .   **45.00**

**Hanks Puzzle Shop,** Conway, NH
• A Colonial Sweetheart, portrait of Dutch colonial woman with vase of flowers, J. Van Vreeland artist, 16 x 20", 538 pcs, orig box . . . . . . . . . . . . . . . . . . .   **60.00**
• Over Field and Fence, wood, hunt scene with horses and hounds in pursuit, 16 x 20", 519 pcs, box missing . . . . . . .   **50.00**

**Hassett, Waman S.,** Pine Tree Puzzle, In Old Kentucky, Daniel Boone–style deerslayer sighting prey, 12 x 16", 410 pcs, orig box   **40.00**

**Hodges, William,** Mt. Desert, ME, Acadia National Park, photo of ocean surf on rocky Maine coast, 11 x 8", 334 pcs, c1970s, orig box . . . . . . . . . . . . . . . . .   **35.00**

**Houser, Glad,** The Rug Merchant, Near Eastern woman showing rug to elderly gentleman buyer, Balesio Roman Tivol artist, 8 x 6", 100 pcs, c1920, orig box   **15.00**

**Huvanco Jig Saw Puzzle,** English, "A Stream In The Highlands," Ernest Wilbourn autumnal landscape of trees and stream, random cut, 10 x 14", 203 pcs, c1940s, period box . . . . . . . . .   **20.00**

**Jewel Puzzle Company,** New Haven, CT, "The Father of His Country at Play," 214 pcs, boxed   **30.00**

**Jost, J. W. Jr.,** Jost Jig–Saw Puzzle, No. 107, "Their First Lesson," 16 x 12", 220 pcs, figural pcs include 2 stars, bird on branch, spaniel, horse, rooster, elephant, and letters D and G, some line cutting, orig box . . . . . . . . . . .   **35.00**

**Ken–Way Puzzle,** Greenwood, RI, "Home, Sweet Home," English cottage, interlocking difficult cut, 16 x 20", 512 pcs, period box . . . . . . . . . . . . . . . . . .   **50.00**

**Kilborne Jig Saw Puzzle,** Trenton, NJ, The Mill Pond Has Gone to Sleep, Will Thompson print of

*The Stop at the Inn*

*A Connoisseur*

lakeside cottage at sunset,
200 pcs, 13 figurals, some color
line cutting, 10 x 12", orig box **40.00**

**Kingsbridge** (Sweden)

• The Arrival (A Hunting Morn),
hunters pause in Tudor town,
L. Cox illus, wood, 15 x 11",
400 pcs, 1960s, orig box . . . . **35.00**

• The Harbour, boats at village
dock, 11 x 9", 197 pcs, many
nearly identical shapes, 1960s,
orig cylinder container with
guide picture . . . . . . . . . . . . **20.00**

**Kingsbridge by Atlantic,**

• A Connoisseur, 9½ x 12",
approx 270 pcs, accompanied
by print measuring 10½ x
13⅝", and mkd "1310/96, F.R.
London *see illus* . . . . . . . . . **35.00**

• The Arrival (A Hunting Morn),
hunters pause in Tudor town,
L. Cury Cox artist, 15 x 11",
400 pcs, 1960s, orig box . . . . **37.50**

**Leisure Hour Puzzle Co.,** Paul
Revere's Ride, F.M. Stone artist,
16 x 19", 589 pcs, orig box . . . **60.00**

**Little Gem Jig–Saw Puzzle,** The
Evening Devotion, wood, bed-
side scene of mother with child
saying prayers, dog obliging,
10 x 12", 270 pcs, 1930s, orig
box . . . . . . . . . . . . . . . . . . . . **35.00**

**Macy's Jigsaw Puzzle**

• John Paul Jones, Revolutionary
war hero aboard ship saluting
sinking ship, 20 x 15",

497 pcs, 40 figurals, period
wood box with sliding lid
dated Dec. 10, 1932 . . . . . . . **70.00**

• On a Canal in Venice, gondola
at sunset, 10 x 12", 253 pcs,
1930s, wood slice–top box . . . **30.00**

**Madmar,** Interlox Puzzle

• Spoils of War, Prussian officers
enjoying leisurely evening of
music and relaxation in
European parlor, 20 x 16",
755 pcs, orig box . . . . . . . . . **65.00**

• The Marriage of Mary Stuart to
Francis Dauphin of France,
approx 160 pcs, boxed . . . . . . **25.00**

**Miller's Pharmacy,** Cumberland
Mills, ME

• Bowl of Roses, wood, multicolored still life, 12 x 10",
231 pcs, orig box . . . . . . . . . . **30.00**

• Cut for Fessenden's Library,
Venetian Revelers, harbor
scene at sunset, Moran artist,
13 x 10", 251 pcs, c1930s . . . **35.00**

**Mosaic Puzzles, The,** "The Stop at
the Inn," automobile stopped at
The George Inn, approx 17½ x
12", 368 pcs, cut on color lines,
c1908–10, boxed, *see illus* . . . . **225.00**

**Bessie J. Nowell,** Bangor, ME,
untitled (One of Us), J.H. Shard
picture of Native American
chieftans and white man in cere-
monial dress inside tent, composition board, 23 x 19", 434 pcs,
cutter's name stamped on back
of back, box missing . . . . . . . . **50.00**

**Par Company, Ltd.,** New York, NY,
Par Picture Puzzle

• Full Honors, Japanese samurai riding through village, numerous figural pieces include people, four medieval ladies each carrying a letter that spells "RUTH", and two seahorses, some color line cutting, rounding edges, 15³/₈ x 24³/₈", approx 750 pcs, orig box . . . .  **500.00**
• Sparkling Raiment, Slavic wedding march, interlocking, some color line cutting, 24 x 16", 730 pcs, 15 figurals, c1940s–50s, period box . . . . .  **450.00**

**Parker Brothers**
• Jig–a–Jig Picture Puzzle, The Stag, wood, F.F. English print of stag at sunset, 6 x 8", 82 pcs, 1905, orig box . . . . . .  **25.00**
• Pastime Contest, untitled, Indian painting hide before campfire, 4⁷/₈ x 3¹/₄", 27 pcs, 4 page rule booklet, orig box . . . . . . . . .  **20.00**
• Pastime Picture Puzzle
A Pioneer Christmas, wood, families returning to homestead with Christmas tree, 7 x 5", 104 pcs, 1932, orig box . . . . . . . . . . . . . .  **25.00**
A Shady Pathway, lakeside country scene with shepherd and sheep, 17 x 11", 350 pcs, 36 figurals, dated March 28, 1931, orig box . . . . . . . . . . .  **50.00**
Balcony in Palestine, man ascending stairs to balcony overlooking city, 13 x 17", 302 pcs, 34 figurals, dated May 1930, period box . . . . . .  **60.00**
Chess Players, drawing room scene of gentlemen at game table, 14 x 10", 200 pcs, 17 figurals, late 1930s, orig box . . . . . . . . . . . . . . . . . .  **30.00**
Coolidge's Birthplace, misty landscape of President's farm amidst fields and mountains, 21 x 16", 482 pcs, 48 figurals, dated January 28, 1932 . . . . .  **60.00**
Cottage By The Road, wood, autumn sunset scene of

*Pip and Estella in the Inn Yard*

early American homestead, 16 x 20", 400 pcs, 48 figurals, some color line cutting, 1933, orig box . . . . . . . . . . . . . . . .  **55.00**
In Colonial Days, over 425 pcs, some figurals, boxed . . . . . . .  **60.00**
Landscape with Mountains (untitled), American western scene of fertile valley with sandstone buttes and snow–capped mountains in background, 23 x 16", 523 pcs, 60 figurals, 1930s . . . . . . . . . . . . . . . . .  **75.00**
Mediterranean Harbor (untitled), young couple watching sunset and sailboats returning to mooring in small Mediterranean village, 37 x 29", 1,305 pcs, 148 figurals, orig box . . . . . . . . . . . . .  **175.00**
Pip and Estella in the Inn Yard, 19¹/₂ x 11¹/₂", approx 370 pcs, 16 figurals, period packaging missing, attributed to Parker Brothers base on cutting see *illus* . . . . . . . . . . . . . . . .  **50.00**
The Introduction, musician being introduced to Elizabethan lady in baronial hall, 13 x 10", 202 pcs, 35 figurals, 1940s . . . . . . . . .  **35.00**
The Jade Parure, Whitman Addett picture of woman seated at vanity, curlicued interlocking cut, 7 x 9", 105 pcs, 12 figurals, 1930, orig cardboard box . . . . . . . . . . . . . .  **20.00**

*Visiting the Invalid Dog*

Visiting the Invalid Dog, 11⁵/₈ x 10", over 150 pcs, cut on color lines, no figural pcs, sawed by "12," red box *see illus*. . . . . . . . . . . . . . . .    **35.00**

Winter Sunset, wood, country cottage by stream, village in background, M. Thompson illus,10 x 7", 122 pcs, 11 figurals, 1931, orig box . . . . . . . .    **20.00**

**Per–Plex Puzzles,** Boston, MA, Per–Plex Jig Saw Puzzles, "Washington Reviews Navy," Washington standing on wharf looking toward American Fleet, wood, 12 x 9", 157 pcs, box pictures family working puzzle    **30.00**

**Picture Puzzle Exchange,** Boston, The First Note of the Bell, colonial Philadelphia scene Liberty Bell's christening, 14 x 10", 196 pcs, 1916, orig box . . . . . .    **35.00**

**Homer F. Pike,** Washington's Headquarters at Valley Forge, 1915 print by Ketterlinus Litho Mfg., 11" sq, 266 pcs, orig "Old Homestead" chocolate box inscribed "Homer F. Pike, Mfr"    **30.00**

**Pine Tree Puzzle,** "Treasure Hunters," 64 pcs, strip cut, boxed . . . . . . . . . . . . . . . .    **15.00**

**Pixie Picture Puzzle,** Melrose, MA, Halting at the Inn, huntsmen enjoying quaff outside Tudor Tavern, 10 x 8", 175 pcs, orig box. . . . . . . . . . . . . . . .    **25.00**

**Bernard S. Rose** (Rental Library), Darkness Before Dawn: Emancipation Day, Abraham Lincoln and Mary Todd Lincoln at fireside, wood, 15 x 11", 318 pcs, c1930s, orig box. . . . .    **45.00**

**Charles W. Russell,** Auburn, MA, Sunset in Normandy, canal barge passing old farmstead, 16 x 12", 347 pcs, 37 figurals, some color line cutting, c1920s, orig box. . . . . . . . . . . . . . . . .    **50.00**

**S. & H. Novelty Co.,** Atlantic City, NJ, Spare Time Jig Saw Puzzles
•Oriental Traders in Venice, 50 pcs, boxed . . . . . . . . . . .    **15.00**

• Sulgrove Manor: Home of George Washington, 8 x 6", 75 pcs, some figurals, orig cardboard box . . . . . . . . . . .    **20.00**

**Selchow & Righter Co.,** New York, Pandora Jig Saw Puzzle, "The Tavern," 5⁷/₈ x 7⁷/₈", 72 pcs, several abstract figurals, orig box    **20.00**

**Shenandoah Community Workers** (Virginia), Audubon Bird Picture Puzzles, set of 3, Chickadee by Allen Brooks, and Scarlet Tanager and Belted Kingfisher by R. Bruce Hersfall, each 6 x 8" puzzle shows male and female of species and is encased in its own tray, approx 30 pcs per puzzle, 1930s, orig box . . . . . .    **45.00**

**Joseph K. Straus**
• Calm of Night, Frederick D. Ogden print of log cabin and mountain lake in moonlight, 12 x 16", 300 pcs, 1940s, orig box . . . . . . . . . . . . . . . . . .    **28.00**

• Guardians of Liberty, World War II scene of battleship and planes passing Statue of Liberty, T.J. Slaughter artist, 16 x 20", 482 pcs, mid–1940s    **25.00**

• Rural Beauty, Series No. 222, 11³/₄ x 8⁷/₈", over 200 pcs, interlocking, dark green wrapped cardboard box, orange end label, no Straus identification, early . . . . . . .    **45.00**

• Welcome Home, C. Moss & Co., wood, 1941 print of father and child in sleigh bringing

home Christmas tree, 21 x 16",
488 pcs, 1940s, orig box . . . .     **45.00**
• White Clipper, wood, 3 masted
square rigger under full sail, D.
Sherring illus, 16 x 12", 282
pcs, orig box . . . . . . . . . . . .     **25.00**

**Tuck's Famous Zig–Zag Picture
Puzzle,** English, The Band of the
Household Cavalry Passing the
King at Buckingham Palace,
13 x 9", 150 pcs, 17 figurals,
orig box. . . . . . . . . . . . . . . .     **30.00**

**U–Nit Puzzles,** West Caldwell,
NJ, Marina at Capri, fishing village, 21¹⁄₂ x 18", 600 pcs, orig
cardboard box . . . . . . . . . . . .     **80.00**

**Unidentified Cutters**
• A Melody of Old Egypt, Henry
Clive print of 1930s–style
glamour girl in evening gown
posed before great pyramids at
night, 16 x 20", 694 pcs, orig
box labeled #41 . . . . . . . . . .     **75.00**
• A Mother's Love, wood, Herst's
Boston American Sunday
Supplement, print of mother
tending child in cradle,
11 x 17", 160 pcs, ©1901, box
may not be orig . . . . . . . . . .     **25.00**
• A Serious Case, wood, Norman
Rockwell illus, village doctor
examining girl's doll, 9 x 12",
294 pcs, c1930s, orig box
missing . . . . . . . . . . . . . . . .     **35.00**
• Bust portrait of baby, cut on
color lines, stored in wooden
Hall's Cigars box . . . . . . . . . .     **15.00**
• Dined Well But Not Wisely,
English, Pears' print of English
"diners" discovering inebriated
friend, 12 x 18", 300 pcs,
c1910 . . . . . . . . . . . . . . . . .     **45.00**
• Fox & Ducks, wood, *Field and
Stream* type–picture of red fox
stalking mallards, 17 x 35",
415 pcs, late 1930s/early
1940s, box probably not orig     **40.00**
• General Electric Company,
Walter L. Greene Art Deco era
picture of GE plant/industrial
park, wood, 10 x 14",
252 pieces, 2 figurals, plain
box mkd "Old Rustic Bridge"
does not match . . . . . . . . . .     **40.00**

Ladies' Home Journal

• Hallowed Moment, European
flower vendor pausing to
honor remembered soul,
16 x 12", 296 pcs, dated
February 3, 1933 . . . . . . . . . .     **40.00**
• House for Sale, real estate–type
picture of modern Colonial
house, composition board,
18 x 15", 211 pcs, 1940s,
1942 Christmas card box . . . .     **30.00**
• Jig–Sawed Picture Puzzle,   No.
48–2108, untitled, Stuart painting Washington's portrait,
8 x 10", information about
painted from *The Literary
Digest* inside box lid, cardboard box with plain red paper
covering . . . . . . . . . . . . . . . .     **25.00**
• Keeping the Faith, British family
watching WWII planes returning at sunset, composition
board, 22 x 16", 537 pcs, box
missing . . . . . . . . . . . . . . . .     **50.00**
• *Ladies Home Journal,* magazine
cover, 8⁷⁄₈ x 12", 154 pcs, cut
on color lines, Jackson illus,
period packaging missing
*see illus* . . . . . . . . . . . . . . . .     **45.00**
• My Little Girl, elderly host intro-
ducing marriageable–age
daughter to young huntsman,
14 x 10", 495 pcs . . . . . . . . .     **45.00**
• Old Glory Forever, John Van
Arsdale's exploit at Ft. George,
November 25, 1783, Clyde  G.

*1933/34 World's Fair
Century of Progress, Chicago*

DeLand artist, 14 x 10",
200 pcs.................... **30.00**
• Pretty Country Scene, 15¼ x
11¼", box covered with
Christmas paper with winter
village and stagecoach scene **15.00**
• Quoits, cartoon image of
4 gentlemen playing quoits,
7¾ x 11¼", 123 pcs, print
mkd in lower left corner
"Copyright 1904, I. Austin Co.,
Chicago," R. Mattloch illus,
fleur–de–lis figural signature
pc, orig packaging missing... **25.00**
• Sulgrove Manor, The Ancestral
Home of George Washington,
20 x 16", 495 pcs ........ **40.00**
• The Birth of Our Country, Ben
Franklin at hearthside, Hy
Hintermeister artist, 13 x 9",
80 pcs, c1920 ........... **20.00**
• The Heart of Nature, stream
coursing through mountainous
countryside, 7 x 9", 101 pcs,
dated March 12, 1933 ...... **40.00**
• The Tuneful Monk, violinist in
monastery garden, 12 x 15",
308 pcs, c1930s, box missing **30.00**
• Untitled
1933/34 World's Fair, Century
of Progress, Chicago, 6¼ x
8½", 124 pcs, period packag-
ing missing *see illus*........ **35.00**

Woman reclining on couch rests
head on lover's shoulder, 16th
C costumes, tiger skin on floor,
12⅛ x 5⁵⁄₁₆", 126 pcs, Gilbert
4686 Alarm box reads "Old
Ladies Home, Two Lovers,
pretty Mrs. W.P. Lunt, over
100 pieces," first quarter
20th C................. **20.00**
Woman seated at Art Deco
vanity looking into hand mirror, non–interlocking,
7⅜ x 10⅜", c1925, box missing .................. **25.00**
World War I soldier holding
girl in white dress with red,
white, and blue ribbon, playing with campaign hat, 9⅜ x
12⅛", approx 135 pcs, Gayle
Hoskins illus, orig packaging
missing ................ **30.00**
• Whistling in the Dark, *Saturday
Evening Post*–type picture
of young boy and dog sneak-
ing away at night, 7 x 9",
125 pcs, 2 figurals, 5 reverse
swastikas, early 1940s, orig
box .................. **25.00**
• Wing and Wing (untitled), lead
sloop sailing with the wind,
9 x 10", 64 pcs, c1940s ..... **15.00**
**Victory Artistic Wood Jigsaw
Puzzle, English**
• Calvi, Mediterranean harbor
scene, M. Buzzle artist,
20 x 15", 500 pcs, orig box... **40.00**
• Mountain Retreat, color photograph of Alpine couple and
goats, 14 x 12", 300 figural,
post–1950 .............. **20.00**
• The Lobster Pot, fishing boats
beached in Old World harbor,
13 x 10", 200 pcs,12 crudely
cut figurals, orig gold box.... **25.00**
• The Unexpected Party, V. De
Beuvoir Ward print of mounted
gentlemen and servants outside Tudor inn, 19 x 15",
500 pcs, 27 figurals, 1940s,
orig gold box............ **60.00**
**West, W. Frank,** Newport, RI,
Picture Puzzles, In a Japanese
Store, 1920s print of 2 American

*Queen's Page*

*No Nudes is Bad Nudes*

women persuing wares at
Japanese bazaar, Ethel Pennewill
Brown illus, 11 x 9", 130 pcs,
c1930s, orig box . . . . . . . . . . **25.00**

## DIECUT

### American News Company and Branches
• Jig of Jigs, No. 1, Queen's
Page, Maxfield Parrish illus,
drawing from The Knave of
Hearts, 9½ x 12", over
250 pcs *see illus* . . . . . . . . . . **150.00**
• Miss America Puzzle Series,
No. 4, "In Blossom Time,"
13¼ x 10", over 300 pcs,
1933 . . . . . . . . . . . . . . . . . . **25.00**

**Automatic Products Company,**
Transportation building,
Indianapolis, IN, Tip–Top Jigsaw
Puzzle, "Paradise Valley," garden terrace with mountains in
background, 11⅝ x 15¾",
391 pcs, orig box . . . . . . . . . . **20.00**

**Ballyhoo Magazine,** Ballyhoo,
"No Nudes is Bad Nudes,"
10½ x 15½", 333 pcs, 1930s,
cardboard box *see illus* . . . . . . **40.00**

**E.J. Brach & Sons Art Study Jigs
Saw Puzzles** "For Study and
Recreation, Featuring Six
Famous Paintings By World
Famous Artists, Price 15¢ Each,
Produced Exclusively For E.J.

Brach & Sons, Chicago," untitled, Dutch girl selling flowers
by doorway, 10¾ x 8", 98 pcs,
paper envelope . . . . . . . . . . . **10.00**

**Milton Bradley**
• Buckingham Jig Picture Puzzle,
Hector, the Protector, over
240 pcs, guide picture on box **12.00**
• Mayfair Jig Picture Puzzle
A Scene in Venice, No. 4934,
over 200 pcs, cardboard box **8.00**
Grand Canyon, No. 4934, over
200 pcs, boxed . . . . . . . . . . **10.00**
• Moonbeam's Princess,
No. 4934, pin–up–style picture
of Indian Princess in moon-
light, over 200 pcs, orig box . . **20.00**
• Piccadilly Jig Picture Puzzle,
No. 81, "On the Loire," over
200 pcs, 1930s, box with blue
and white ground . . . . . . . . . **12.00**
• Santa Inez Valley, No. 4730,
approx 22 x 16", 468 pcs,
mid–1930s, orig box . . . . . . . **10.00**
• The Dover Jig Picture Puzzle,
No. 4728, "The Circus," over
300 pcs, 1930s, guide picture
on box . . . . . . . . . . . . . . . . . **15.00**

**Brooms & Herbig Company,**
Coshocton, OH, Jig of the Hour
Picture Puzzle, No. 1, "Boulder
Canyon," approx 300 to 400
pcs, boxed . . . . . . . . . . . . . . **20.00**

*Big 10, Romance Canyon*

**J.R. Brundage**, Empire Jig Picture Puzzle, "A Canadian Landscape," over 400 pcs, box features sketch of Empire State Building . . . . . . . . . . . . . . .   **8.00**

**Built–Rite,** Interlocking Picture Puzzle, "Hospitality," approx 19⅝ x 15⅝", over 350 pcs, guide picture on box . . . . . . . .   **5.00**

**Century Novelty Company,** Souvenir of 1933 Century of Progress buildings, Chicago, Tom Saw Puzzle, "Fort Dearborn Building," over 225 pcs, boxed . . . . . . . . . . .   **35.00**

**Consolidated Paper Box Co.,**
• Big Star
   "After The Hunt," 13½ x 10", over 250 pcs, boxed . . . . . . .   **8.00**
   "School Patrol," No. 1010, approx 10 x 13½", late 1930s, guide picture on blue–tone box   **8.00**
• Big 10
   A Colonial Sweetheart, 10¼ x 15¼", 280 pcs, mid–1930s, orig box . . . . . . . . . . . . . . .   **10.00**
   Grandma's Birthday, approx 15½ x 10¼", over 275 pcs, boxed . . . . . . . . . . . . . . . .   **8.00**

Romance Canyon, 10½ x 15⅝", 280 pcs, R. Atkinson Fox illus, mid–1930s *see illus* . . . . . . . .   **30.00**
• Big 10 Perfect Picture Puzzle, No. 1010, "Millstream in Winter," approx 13½ x 10", over 250 pcs, late 1930s, box   **6.00**
• Big 10 No. 10, Statue of Liberty, 15⅛ x 10⅛", 280 pcs, box with light blue and white checkerboard ground . . . . . . .   **15.00**
• Perfect Double
   Anxious Guardian/Country Gentleman, No. 102, 15 x 10", over 275 pcs, boxed. . . . . . .   **12.00**
   Brookside Manor/Canal in Belgium, 10¼ x 15½", 280 pcs, orig box . . . . . . . . . .   **10.00**
• Perfect Picture Puzzle
   "Away We Go," No. 1611, child sledding down snow covered hill, approx 10⅛ x 15½", over 275 pcs, guide picture on box   **8.00**
   "Catch 'Im Gramps," No. 1410 series, grandfather and boy tangled in fishing line in boat, Hintermeister illus, approx 11 x 14½", over 250 pcs, guide picture on box . . . . . . . . . . .   **10.00**
   "Cool and Silence, No. 211," No. 2016, over 450 pcs, guide picture on box . . . . . . . . . . .   **6.00**
   "Dawn's Early Light, No. 305," No. 25, approx 15½ x 19½", 375 pcs . . . . . . . . . . . . . . .   **10.00**
   Mountain Warfare, approx 19½ x 15½", over 375 pcs, c1943, eight stars on box . . . .   **25.00**
   Port of Hope, Spanish galleon, 10⅜ x 13¾", 266 pcs . . . . . . .   **10.00**
   Progress, No. 16, amphibious plane flying over 3–masted ship, 10¼ x 15½", orig box. . .   **10.00**
   Proof Positive, No. 250–29, boy photographing dog holding fishing float, approx 19½ x 15½", 375 pcs, c1950s   **6.00**
   Sentinels of Peace, approx 19½ x 15½", over 375 pcs, eight stars on box cover . . . . .   **8.00**

*In Conference*

*Eddie Cantor Jig–Saw Puzzle*

The First Covey, 13¼ x 10⅛",
252 pcs, mid–1930s, orig box   **8.00**

War at Sea, British Spitfire and
bomber battling Nazi planes
while sinking German fire-
fighter, 19½ x 15½", 378 pcs,
K. Graf illus, red, white and
blue box, central guide picture
flanked by four stars on left
and three stars and Savings
Bond logo on right, 1942–45   **30.00**

**Dell Publishing Company**
• All–American Picture Puzzle,
No. 2, "Wings in the Night,"
aerial combat over enemy harbor, approx 280 pcs, 1942,
guide picture on box . . . . . . .   **25.00**
• Movie Mix–Up!, Clark Gable,
black and white head and
shoulders photo, 8½ x 12",
paper envelope . . . . . . . . . .   **75.00**

**Einson–Freeman,** Long Island
City, NY
• Every Week Jig–Saw Puzzle
No. 12, Peter Pan, Pan sitting on
rocky outcropping holding
flute and looking at nest of
young birds, Eggleston illus,
10½ x 14½" . . . . . . . . . . . . .   **15.00**
No. 17, Abraham Lincoln, Ray
Morgan illus, 10⅝ x 14½", orig
box . . . . . . . . . . . . . . . . . . .   **18.00**
No. 22, First Lesson, dog teach-
ing four pups to hunt peasant,
10½ x 14½", Lynn Bogue Hunt
illus . . . . . . . . . . . . . . . . . .   **20.00**

No. 24, Sails and Sea Gulls, racing yacht at full sail surrounded by sea gulls, 10½ x 14½",
1933, cardboard box . . . . . . .   **20.00**
No. 27, The Cradle Maker,
mother with baby looks over
shoulder of young boy making
cradle from carton scraps,
10½ x 14¼", 165 pcs, Walter
Beach Humphrey illus . . . . . .   **18.00**
No. 30, In Conference, 14¼ x
10¼", over 200 pcs, Ray
Morgan illus, photo by Seaf,
Stamford, Conn *see illus*. . . . .   **25.00**
• Radio Stars
Series No. 1, Eddie Cantor
Jig–Saw Puzzle, 10 x 14¾",
over 200 pcs, 1933 *see illus*. .   **30.00**
Series No. 2, Kate Smith
"Jig–Saw Puzzle: The Song Bird
of the South!," Smith's face,
insert images in right corners,
10⅛ x 14¾", 228 pcs . . . . . . .   **35.00**

**E. E. Fairchild Corporation,**
No. 647, Finesse Picture Puzzle,
"Gypsy Love Call," approx
11 x 14", over 250 pcs . . . . . . .   **6.00**

**Fort Wayne Paper Co.,** Ft. Wayne,
IN, Wayne Jig–A–Jig Puzzle,
No. 23, Bringing Home The
Flock, over 300 pcs, Van
Truesdael illus, orig box . . . . . .   **10.00**

*Sky Fighters, Curtiss P40F Warhawk*

**Gebhart Folding Box Co.,**
Dayton, OH, Wonder Picture
Puzzle, "The Cascade," over
300 pcs, orig box. . . . . . . . . . **8.00**
**Gelco Interlocking Puzzle
Company,** Chicago, IL, Weekly
Interlocking Jigsaw, No. 2, The
Old Fort, 11³/₄ x 8³/₄", approx
150 pcs. . . . . . . . . . . . . . . . **15.00**
**Hallmark Cards,** Springbok,
"Super Bowl Sunday,"
18 x 23¹/₂", over 500 pcs, boxed **5.00**
**Hart, Harter Publishing Co.,**
Cleveland, OH, H–131 Series,
approx 11 x 15", over 200 pcs
• No. 3, Series 5, Castle Rock . . . **5.00**
• No. 4, Series 3, Fishin' and
Wishin', green tone box. . . . . **6.00**
• No. 5, Series 2, Puppy Love,
Annie Benson Muller illus . . . **8.00**

• No. 10, Series 2, Red Demon of
the Forest, Philip R. Goodwin
illus. . . . . . . . . . . . . . . . . . **10.00**
• Village in the Hills, 15³/₄ x 11³/₄",
mid–1930s, orig box . . . . . . . **10.00**
**Hart, Leo,** Sky Fighters, Curtiss
P40F Warhawk, 12¹/₈ x 10",
180 pcs, 3 pcs missing, price for
puzzle complete *see illus* . . . . . **30.00**
**Jaymar Specialty Company,**
Hobby Jig Saws, Grizzly Bear,
approx 14 x 22", over 300 pcs,
small guide picture on box,
green ground, treasure chest
motif . . . . . . . . . . . . . . . . . . **10.00**
**Jig 'A Word Manufacturing Co.,**
St. Paul, MN, Jig 'A Word Series,
No. 1–A, 12" sq, over 300 pcs,
jigsaw puzzle and clues on box
lid, puzzle provides solution to
crossword puzzle . . . . . . . . . **30.00**
**Kindel–Graham,** San Francisco,
CA, The Jigger Picture Puzzle
Weekly, Series 104, Mission
Dolores, over 300 pcs, box
design similar to Viking
Manufacturing Company's
Picture Puzzle Weekly . . . . . . . **25.00**
**Knobby–Cut Picture Puzzle,** The
Limit of Wind and Sail, Spanish
galleons on raging sea,
11⁷/₈ x 9³/₄", orig box. . . . . . . . **10.00**
**Lutz & Sheinkman,** Merry Mood
Jig Saw Puzzle, "After The
Hunt," by R. Jlinek, approx
18¹/₂ x 14¹/₂", over 400 pcs,
1930s, 4³/₈ x 10³/₈ x 2³/₈" box . . . **12.00**
**Middletown Distributing Co.,**
Middletown, OH, Everybody's
Picture Puzzle, "The
Christening," over 300 pcs,
boxed . . . . . . . . . . . . . . . . . . **10.00**
**Midwest Distributors,**
Minneapolis, Screen Books
Magazine, Tarzan of the Apes
Jig–Saw, Johnny Weissmuller on
elephant, 10³/₄ x 8¹/₂", paper
envelope . . . . . . . . . . . . . . . . **150.00**
**Movie Cut–Ups,** Peabody, MA
• No. 3, Face In The Sky, starring
Marian Nixon, 13¹/₈ x 9⁷/₈",
over 225 pcs, boxed. . . . . . . . **40.00**

*So This Is Africa*

*National Jigsaw Puzzle*

- No. 6, Air Hostess, featuring Evalyn Knapp, Columbia, 10 x 13½", 320 pcs . . . . . . . .   **35.00**
- No. 7, Bitter Tea of General Yen, Columbia, starring Barbara STanwyck and Nils Asther, 9⅞ x 13⅛", over 225 pcs, box   **25.00**
- No. 9, So This Is Africa, Columbia, featuring Wheeler and Woolsey, 13¼ x 9⅞", 275 pcs *see illus* . . . . . . . . .   **35.00**
- No. 14, Secrets, United Artists, Mary Pickford and Leslie Howard, 10 x13¼", 304 pcs, wrapped in label from Pippins Cigars reading "IT'S A PIPPINS JIG" . . . . . . . . . . . . . . . . . .   **40.00**

**National Novelty Manufacturing Co.,** Allentown, PA, National Jig–Saw Puzzle, pastel landscape scene, over 165 pcs, guide picture on box *see illus*   **10.00**

**Novelty Distributing Company,** Newark, NJ, "Famous Comics" Jig Saw Puzzle, No. 2, The Gumps, manufactured by Stephens Kindred & Co., NY, back of box contains three portions of cartoon strip, puzzle completes panel, 13 x 11¾", 250 pcs . . . . . . . . . . . . . . . .   **40.00**

**Once–a–Week Dime Jig–Saw Puzzle,** Puzzle No. 3, The Love Nest, 7⅜ x 9½", William Thompson illus, period envelope . . . . . . . . . . . . . . . . . .   **15.00**

**Playboy Playmate Puzzles,** AP115, "Miss May Jennifer Liano," American Publishing Co., can container . . . . . . . . .   **12.50**

**J. Pressman & Co., Inc.,** Victory Picture Puzzle, No. 20, "Flying Fortresses Bombing Enemy Base," approx 19¼ x 15¼", over 375 pcs, c1945 . . . . . . . . . . .   **27.50**

**R–M Sales Corporation,** New York, NY

- Duo Jig Puzzle, set of 2, B–4 Morocco and B–5 Masquerade, 7¼ x 9¼", 154 pcs each puzzle, different color backs . . . . . . . . . . . . .   **20.00**
- Swellelegant Jig–Cartoon, No. 1, At The Opera, over 300 pcs, boxed . . . . . . . . . . . . . . . . .   **25.00**

**Regent Specialties, Inc.,** Rochester, NY, DeLuxe Picture Puzzle

- Day Dreams, Western couple riding in moonlight, approx 20 x 16", about 400 pcs, boxed . . . . . . . . . . . . . . . . .   **17.50**
- Shall We Go Sailing?, 19⅛ x 15½", 391 pcs . . . . . . .   **12.00**
- Silver Moon, approx 16 x 20", approx 400 pcs, 1930s, cardboard box . . . . . . . . . . . . . .   **15.00**
- Snow Capped Peaks, approx 20 x 16", approx 400 pcs, 4¾ x 9¾ x 2½" box . . . . . . . .   **12.00**

**The Reynolds & Reynolds Co.,** Dayton, OH, The American Individual Pictured Puzzle,

"19B A Bit of French Tapestry,"
over 350 pcs, orange–tone box    **8.00**

**Santway Photo–Craft Company,
Inc.,** Watertown, NY

• The Muddle, The New Jig
Puzzle, Fine Art Series B–2,
The Fishing Fleet, 15 x 11",
300 pcs. . . . . . . . . . . . . . . . .    **15.00**

• The Muddle: The Jig Puzzle with
the Interlocking Border, "Fine
Art Series L–Lake Louise
Campfire," over 300 pcs, orig
box. . . . . . . . . . . . . . . . . . .    **8.00**

**Geo. P. Schlicher & Sons,**
Allentown, PA

• No. 5, The Essell Picture Puzzle,
Street Scene, 14⁵/₁₆ x 8⁷/₈", over
200 pcs, J.E. Berninger illus . .    **17.50**

• No. 10, Black and White
Picture Puzzle, The Bridge,
14¹/₄ x 8⁵/₈", over 200 pcs, E.
Berninger illus, cardboard box    **15.00**

**A. Schoenhut Co.,** Philadelphia,
PA, "Schoenhut" Picture Puzzle,
"Let's Go," over 200 pcs,
10 x 22" box . . . . . . . . . . . . .    **20.00**

**Simkins Paper Box Mfg. Co.,**
Philadelphia, PA, Simco Jig
Puzzle, "The Landing," approx
16 x 12", over 300 pcs, box
marked "Par 4 Hours" . . . . . . .    **10.00**

**Smoller–Mazur Co.,** Madison,
WI, Gamo–Jig "The Gamest
Game of Them All, New Subject
Weekly, Over 325 Pieces,
Interlocking," No. 34, A Gift
From Heaven, orig box. . . . . . .    **15.00**

**Tichnor Brothers, Inc.,**
Cambridge, MA, See America
First, No. 39, Natural Bridge,
VA, over 300 pcs, boxed . . . . .    **15.00**

**Tower Press,** Queen Elizabeth
and Prince Charles, 9¹/₂ x 14",
204 pcs, mid–1950s, orig box    **20.00**

**Tuco, Upson,**

• ABC's Wide World of Sports,
No. 8244, Baseball, 15 x 11",
252 pcs, early 1970s, orig box    **8.00**

• Bell Airacobras, "BELL AIRACO-
BRAS" printed on puzzle,
14³/₄ x 19¹/₈", 320 pcs,
Schieder illus, guide picture
on lid . . . . . . . . . . . . . . . . .    **10.00**

*Pal O' Mine*

• Bridal Veil Falls, approx
12 x 16", over 200 pcs, orange
box, c1935 . . . . . . . . . . . . .    **30.00**

• Pal O'Mine, 19¹/₂ x 15",
320 diecut pressboard pcs,
9³/₄ x 7¹/₄" box, c1940 *see illus*    **15.00**

• Peonies, 14³/₄ x 19", 357 pcs,
picture copyrighted 1937,
guide picture on box . . . . . . .    **10.00**

• "Quietude," approx 16 x 12",
over 200 pcs, box with gold
stripes on red ground . . . . . . .    **8.00**

• Religious Interlocking Picture
Puzzle, Christ's Entrance Into
Jerusalem, painting by
Plockhorst, diecut cardboard,
approx 16 x 20", 300 to 500
pcs, guide picture on card-
board box . . . . . . . . . . . . . .    **8.00**

• Soap Opera Puzzles, No. 8857,
"General Hospital," diecut
cardboard, approx 15 x 11",
over 350 pcs, portraits of Alan,
Monica, and Susan, guide picture on cardboard box,
unopened . . . . . . . . . . . . . .    **8.00**

• "The Last Roundup," approx
20 x 16", over 300 pcs, horizontal maroon bands across
lid, guide picture . . . . . . . . . .    **10.00**

**University Distributing Company,**
Cambridge, MA, Jig of the Week

• No. 4, The Prairie Fire, portion
of Currier and Ives print,
13³/₈ x 10¹/₈", 300 pcs . . . . . . .    **25.00**

*Kittens*

*Home on Leave*

- No. 16, Between Two Fires, 20 x 15", paper insert, boxed **12.00**
- No. 17, Milday of the Tavern, two cavaliers sitting at tavern table, serving girl approaches with bowl of fruit, 13¹/₈ x 10", 300 pcs . . . . . . . . . . . . . . . **12.00**
- No. 23, Hunters, 13¹/₈ x 10¹/₈", insert, box . . . . . . . . . . . . . . **12.00**
- No. 25, So Near, Yet So Far, paperboy holding papers in one hand and money in other looking in pet shop window at terrier, "FOR SALE $25.00" sign, 10¹/₈ x 13¹/₄", 300 pcs, Hy Hintermeister illus . . . . . . **10.00**

**Unknown Manufacturer**
- Roosevelt–Garner, jugate, card-board, red, white, and blue, "Together To Revive Prosperity," dated March 4, 1933, orig glassine envelope **20.00**
- Souvenir, 1933 inaugural, Roosevelt and Garner flanking Capitol, "TOGETHER WE PROSPER," 9⁵/₈ x 7⁷/₈", orig cellophane envelope . . . . . . **40.00**
- The Puzzle of Watergate, black and white cover, shrink–wrapped, ©1973 . . . . . . . . . . **35.00**

**Viking Manufacturing Company,** Boston, MA, Picture Puzzle Weekly

- Series A–4, Lions at Sunset, 13⁷/₈ x 10", box . . . . . . . . . . . **25.00**
- Series B–7, Kittens, 10 x 13³/₄" *see illus* . . . . . . . . . . . . . . . . **15.00**
- Series C–1, Caravels of Columbus, 13⁷/₈ x 10¹/₈", paper insert advertising puzzle tray, boxed . . . . . . . . . . . . . . . . . . **20.00**
- Series C–3, The Breath of Spring, elderly man removing fishing gear from attic trunk, cat watching, 10 x 13¹/₂", orig box **25.00**
- Series C–5, Static, dog howling as two hunters in cabin listen to radio, 10 x 13³/₄" . . . . . . . . **20.00**
- Series D–1, The Olde Kentucky Home, Blacks surrounding banjo player, white woman listening in background, 14¹/₂ x 10⁵/₈", box . . . . . . . . . . **25.00**
- Series E–1, A Party At Murano, group embarking from Venetian gondola onto terrace, 14¹/₂ x 10¹/₂" . . . . . . . . . . . . . . **30.00**

**Whitman Publishing Co.** Guild Picture Puzzle, No. 2900
- Series RR, "Millpond," approx 18 x 15¹/₂", 304 pcs, guide picture on box . . . . . . . . . . . **4.00**
- Series T, Home on Leave, 20 x 15³/₄", over 300 pcs, Hy Hontermeister illus *see illus* . . **28.00**

**Wilkie Picture Puzzle Company,** Everybody, No. 24, A Winter Day, G Fleissner illus, 15³/₄ x 11⁷/₈", 310 pcs, mid–1930s, orig box . . . . . . . . . **10.00**

# CHILDREN/JUVENILE JIGSAW PUZZLES

*Smashed Up Locomotive*

*The Ark Puzzle*

## PRE–1915

**James W. Barfoot,** London, England, wood, Story of the Arctic Ship Resolute, hand colored, c1850, wood box, 9 x 7"    **350.00**

**Milton Bradley Company,** Springfield, MA

• Dissected Outline Map of the United States of America, wood, reversible, U.S. map and scenes, c1880, 8 x 9³/₄" wood box . . . . . . . . . . . . . .    **125.00**

• Fire Department Puzzle Box No. 4144, 3 puzzle set, 18 pcs each puzzle, c1910s, 1 view on box lid  . . . . . . . . . . . . .    **275.00**

• Model Ship Puzzle, c1880, box 7 x 9" . . . . . . . . . . . . . . . .    **225.00**

• Sectional Steamer & Hose, c1880, 5 x 7" box . . . . . . . . .    **250.00**

• Smashed Up Locomotive, 9 x 7", wood box *see illus* . . .    **285.00**

**George H. Chinnock,** New York, NY, wood, Centennial Exhibition Puzzle Blocks, set of 5 hand cut puzzles, 4 guide pictures, fifth on lid, Art Gallery, Machinery Hall, Horticultural Hall, Agricultural Hall, and Main Building, 20³/₄" w puzzles vary in height from 4" to 6", approx 30 pcs each puzzle, 1875, 22 x 11¹/₂" wood box . . .    **500.00**

**Rev. E. J. Clemens,** Clayville, NY, wood, Clemens Silent Teacher, U.S. map poster for White Sewing Machines on reverse, c1885, 7 x 9" box . . . . . . . . . .    **165.00**

**Charles Crandall,** Brooklyn, NY, wood, Expression Blocks, c1870, 8 x 4" wood box . . . . . .    **250.00**

**Wallie Dorr,** frame tray, The B.B.B.B. Puzzle, Brooklyn Bridge and East River with boats, 17³/₄ x 5¹/₄" 30 hand cut wooden blocks, copyright 1889, 18 x 6" box . . . . . . . . . . . . . . . . . . .    **1,500.00**

**S. L. Hill,** Williamsburgh (Long Island), NY, wood, Carrying Corn to the White Settlement, hand colored, c1860, 8 x 6" wood box . . . . . . . . . . . . . . .    **250.00**

**E. J. Horsman,** New York, NY

• Prize Birds, wood strip, c1885, 7 x 11" wood box . . . . . . . . .    **100.00**

• Prize Mother Goose Pictures Dissected . . . . . . . . . . . . . .    **75.00**

**W. & S.B. Ives,** Salem, MA, mahogany, French Puzzle Brain, 4³/₈ x 2³/₈", 18 pcs, 1851 . . . . . .    **65.00**

**Seymour Lyman,** New York, NY

• Tally Ho Puzzle, 28¹/₂ x 13³/₄", 30 sliced pcs, litho stagecoach crash on box *see illus*. . . . . . .    **30.00**

• The Ark Puzzle, c1880, 7 x 10" box *see illus*. . . . . . . . . . . . .    **275.00**

*CrissCross Spelling Strips*

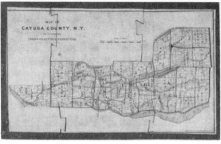

*Sectional Map, Cayuga County NY*

**Charles Magnus,** New York, NY,
   The Glorious Finale of the War
   Dissected, hand colored, 1865,
   5 x 7" box . . . . . . . . . . . . . . .   **300.00**
**Mason, G. E.,** Weedsport, NY,
   sectional map, map of Cayuga
   County, NY, lithograph by
   Weed, Parson & Co., 27 pcs,
   12½ x 7⅝", boxed *see illus* . . .   **85.00**
**McLoughlin Brothers,** New York,
   NY
• Composition Board Puzzles
   A New Dissected Map of the
   United States, 12 x 8", c1887,
   wood box . . . . . . . . . . . . . .   **60.00**
   A Peep at the Circus Picture
   Puzzle, 1887, 12 x 10" box . .   **450.00**
   Brownie Puzzle Blocks, Palmer
   Cox illus, hexagonal puzzle
   with booklet, 1891, 11 x 15"
   box . . . . . . . . . . . . . . . . . . .   **750.00**
   CrissCross Spelling Strips,
   c1880, 10 x 9" box see *illus* . .   **100.00**

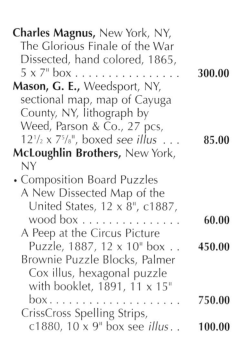

Dissected Map of the United
   States, world on reverse, 1884,
   10 x 7" box . . . . . . . . . . . . . .   **80.00**
Home Scroll Puzzle, 7¼ x 9¼",
   multicolored litho interlocking
   pcs, c1897 . . . . . . . . . . . . . .   **80.00**
Locomotive Picture Puzzle,
   locomotive at station,
   24¾ x 18", 1887 . . . . . . . . . .   **350.00**
Mother Goose Scroll Puzzle,
   7½" x 9¾", several multicolored litho interlocking pcs,
   c1882, wood box . . . . . . . . . .   **85.00**
Old Woman & Pig Picture
   Puzzle, 20 x 12", copyright
   1890, 9 x 13" box . . . . . . . . .   **250.00**
Picture Puzzle, The Werra,
   steamship, 1886, 12 x 9" box   **150.00**
Picture Puzzle Steamship,
   19¼ x 7¾", multicolored litho
   interlocking pcs, includes
   wooden box, c1896 . . . . . . . .   **225.00**
Santa Claus Scroll Puzzle, multi-
   color color litho box, 1899 . .   **350.00**
St. Nicholas Picture Puzzle,
   Young America Series, Santa in
   sleigh pulled by reindeer racing through night sky above
   rural Victorian homestead,
   19 x 12", copyright 1890,
   12 x 8" box . . . . . . . . . . . . . .   **550.00**

*The Young Blue Jackets*

*The Blow Up Steam Boat*

The Young Blue Jackets, set of 2,
18 pc 10 x 6" United States
Cruiser *Columbia* and 15 pc
9 x 6½" United States Cruiser
*San Francisco*, litho box with
3 sailors around naval gun
*see illus.* . . . . . . . . . . . . . . .   **250.00**
Up the Heights of San Juan
Scroll Puzzle, 1898, 13 x 18"
box . . . . . . . . . . . . . . . . . .   **400.00**
• Wood Puzzles
Aunt Louisa's Cube Puzzles,
Aesop's Fables 6 sided, book-
let, 1891, 11 x 15" box . . . . .   **600.00**
Dame Trott and Her Cat,
6 puzzle set, each puzzle
7¼ x 5½", 20 pcs, c1880,
11 x 8" wood box . . . . . . . .   **250.00**
Picture Puzzle, Early Rising,
4¾ x 6¾", multicolored litho
interlocking pcs, c1885 . . . . .   **50.00**
**Novelty Game Co.,** New York,
NY, After Dinner Puzzle, c1870,
6 x 9" box . . . . . . . . . . . . . .   **125.00**
**J. Ottmann Lithography
Company,** New York, NY
• Dissected A.B.C., 11½ x 10",
red, yellow and white alpha-
bet pcs, c1910. . . . . . . . . . .   **55.00**
• Dissected Circus, 18½ x 12¾",
sliced pcs . . . . . . . . . . . . . .   **125.00**
• Dissected Map of the United
States, 10 x 11½", 20 multicolored litho pcs cut on straight
lines, c1910 . . . . . . . . . . . .   **75.00**

**Parker Brothers,** Salem, MA
• Little People's Picture Puzzle,
2 puzzle set, multicolored
litho, signed by Alice
Hirschberg, c1915 . . . . . . . . .   **75.00**
• Picture Puzzle: Wild Domestic
Animals, multicolored litho
animal pcs, 16½ x 14½",
c1899 . . . . . . . . . . . . . . . .   **95.00**
• Robber Kitten, 2 multicolored
litho cat puzzles, 1 pictured on
lid, other shows cats before
fireplace and grandfather
clock,10½ x 7¾", c1895–
1900, 8 x 11" box . . . . . . . . .   **125.00**
**Parkhurst, V.S.W.,** Providence, RI,
metamorphosis, hand colored
on paper, c1860. . . . . . . . . . .   **135.00**
**Selchow & Righter,** New York, NY
• Dissected Map of the United
States, multicolored litho,
9½ x 11½", c1910 . . . . . . . . .   **50.00**
• Sliced Nations, 1875, 8 x 9" box   **75.00**
**Jacob Shaffer,** Philadelphia, PA,
wood, New Dissected Puzzle of
the United States, hand colored,
c1865, 7 x 8" wood box . . . . . .   **150.00**
**Peter G. Thomson,** Cincinnati,
OH
• The Blow Up Steam Boat,
Queen City, going up the
Ohio River, sliced format,
16¼ x 12¼", 28 pcs, c1880s,
6½ x 5½" cardboard box with
guide picture *see illus.* . . . . . .   **325.00**

- The Cut Up Punch & Judy Puzzle, sliced stiff board, 12¼ x 16", 44 pcs, c1880s, guide picture, 6½ x 5½" cardboard box . . . . . . . . . . . . . .   **400.00**

**Unknown Maker,** English, wood, United States New Double Puzzle, hand colored, c1845, 7 x 9" wood box . . . . . . . . . .   **300.00**

**Frederick Warne,** London & New York, Jack and Jill, double sided, book, c1890, 11 x 8" wood box   **175.00**

## 1915–1945

**Army–Navy Combat Picture Puzzles,** set of 4, c1945, 9 x 8" box . . . . . . . . . . . . . . . . . . . .   **45.00**

**Milton Bradley Company,** Springfield, MA
- Farm Friends Puzzle Box, 3 puzzle set, 1913–35, 13 x 17" box   **75.00**
- Four Picture Puzzles for Children, H. Boylston Dummer artist, c1935, 10 x 7" box . . . . . . . . . . . . . .   **35.00**
- Funny Animal Puzzle Box, 3 puzzles, 1913–17, 10 x 15" box . . . . . . . . . . . .   **75.00**
- Little Worker's Scroll Puzzle, girl helping young child off donkey, 15 pcs, box shows girl leading donkey with young boy and dog on donkey's back   **45.00**
- Old Mother Hubbard Puzzle Box, No. 4212, 3 puzzle set, 1913–35, 9 x 13" box . . . . . .   **100.00**
- Santa Claus Puzzle Box, contains 3 puzzles, c1920, 9 x 13" box . . . . . . . . . . . . .   **300.00**
- Three Little Kittens, reversible, 1931, 10 x 7" box . . . . . . . . .   **50.00**
- Uncle Wiggily, 3 puzzles, 1949, 10 x 13" box . . . . . . . . . . . .   **65.00**
- Wee Willie Winkie, 4341, double sided, 7¼ x 10", 30 pcs, 1 guide picture on box . . . . . .   **40.00**

**Cadaco–Ellis,** Chicago, IL, Tableau: The Picture Puzzle Game, 1941, 9 x 10" box . . . . .   **35.00**

*Captain Marvel Picture Puzzle*

**Consolidated Paper Box Co.,** Somerville, MA
- Big 4 Circus Puzzles Jig–Saw Type, Set No. 1, 3 puzzle set, each puzzle approx 9⅜ x 7¼"   **20.00**
- Children's Puzzles, No. 200, "Cleanliness" and "Kiddie Orchestra," diecut cardboard, 2 puzzle set, each puzzle 103/4x 83/4", approx 50 pcs per puzzle, c1930s, cardboard box . . . . . . . . . . . . . . . . . .   **20.00**
- 2 Perfect Jig Saw–Type Inter-locking Children's Puzzles, No. 41, diecut cardboard, No. 5 The Swing/Skating, 2 puzzle set, 7¼ x 9¼", 50 pcs each puzzle, early 1940s, United States Savings Bonds and Stamps stamp on cardboard box. . . . .   **15.00**

**Daintee Toys, Inc.,** Brooklyn, NY, Red Riding Hood, masonite tray puzzle, c1940 . . . . . . . . . . . .   **15.00**

**E.E. Fairchild Corporation,** Rochester, NY, All–Fair Puzzle, Children of American History Picture Puzzle, No. 680, Series 3, 2 puzzle set, each puzzle 9½ x 6¾" . . . . . . . . . . . .   **12.00**

**Fawcett Publications Inc.,** Minneapolis, MN, Captain Marvel Picture Puzzle: One

*Famous Art Picture Puzzles*

*Princess Cut–Out Picture Puzzle*

Against Many, c1941, 10 x 7"
paper envelope *see illus*. . . . . .    **60.00**

**Samuel Gabriel Sons & Co.,** New
York, NY, Our Defenders
Puzzles, set of 3, 1940s,
12 x 16" box . . . . . . . . . . . . .    **50.00**

**Graphicut Corp.,** New York, NY,
Eureko: The Great New Jig–Saw
Puzzle Game 1942, 10 x 13"
box. . . . . . . . . . . . . . . . . . .    **30.00**

**C.S. Hammond,** Brooklyn, NY,
Little Folks Picture Puzzles:
Happy Hour, set of 4, c1920,
8 x 10" box . . . . . . . . . . . . . .    **40.00**

**Harter Publishing Co.,** Cleveland,
OH, diecut cardboard, H–110
Cinderella Puzzles, 4 puzzle
set, Fern Bisel Peat illus,
$7^1/_2$ x $^1/_2$", 40 pcs each puzzle,
1931, cardboard box with
1 guide picture . . . . . . . . . . .    **40.00**

**G.J. Hayter,** England, Victory
Farmyard Wood, 1930–70,
10 x 16" box . . . . . . . . . . . . .    **35.00**

**George Leis,** Newark, NJ, Noah's
Ark, wood, c1945, 12 x 17" box    **30.00**

**Madmar Quality Co.,** Utica, NY
• Air Fleet Picture Puzzle, set of
  3, 1930s, 10 x 8" box. . . . . . .    **60.00**
• Dissected Map: New York, State,
  1930s, 12 x 16" box. . . . . . . .    **30.00**
• Dissected Map Puzzle, Junior
  Series, No. 773, California,
  guide picture on box . . . . . . .    **35.00**
• Granny Goose Picture Puzzle,
  Series 318A, diecut cardboard,
  3 puzzle set, fairy tale themes,
  Mary LeFetra Russell illus,

$7^7/_8$ x $9^7/_8$", 12 pcs each puzzle,
1930s, cardboard box . . . . . .    **40.00**

• Princess Cut–Out Picture
  Puzzle, Series No. 420,
  saw–cut 5–ply cardboard, double sided, The Royal Outlaw,
  R. Atkinson Fox illus, 1 side
  with tiger image, other with
  3 children descending staircase
  in Victorian mansion with
  St. Bernard at bottom,
  $6^5/_8$ x $8^5/_8$", 36 pcs, c1930s,
  cardboard box, tiger guide pic-
  ture on lid *see illus*. . . . . . . .    **40.00**

**Louis Marx & Co.,** New York, NY,
wood, Cottage of Dreams/Moon
Mullins, double sided, double
set, $9^1/_2$ x $6^3/_4$", 145 pcs, cardboard box mkd 150 pcs . . . . . .    **85.00**

**McLoughlin Bros.,** Picture
Puzzle, Little Bo–Peep, wood,
$5^1/_2$ x $7^1/_4$", 20 pcs, guide picture
on cardboard box. . . . . . . . . .    **45.00**

**J. Ottmann Lithography
Company,** New York, NY,
Dissected Circus Puzzle, c1900,
10 x 13" box . . . . . . . . . . . . .    **75.00**

**Parker Brothers,** Salem, MA
• Circus Picture Puzzles, set of 3,
  c1925, 8 x 11" box . . . . . . . .    **35.00**
• Famous Art Picture Puzzles,
  saw–cut cardboard, 2 puzzle
  set, untitled, 1 with Arabian
  horsemen in desert, other with
  Dutch children returning from
  harbor, $12^1/_2$ x $8^5/_8$", 15 pcs
  each puzzle, Doge's Palace in
  Venice on lid *see illus* . . . . . .    **20.00**

*Just Kids Picture Puzzles*

*Movie Squarecut Puzzle*

- Old Dobbin Picture Puzzles, set of 2, c1925, 12 x 9" box . . . . **25.00**
- Robber Kitten Picture Puzzles, set of 2, 10¼ x 7¼", 15 pcs each, robber kitten guide picture on box . . . . . . . . . . . . . **60.00**
- United States Puzzle Map, wood, cut on state lines, 8 x 13" box . . . . . . . . . . . . . **25.00**

**Perfect Picture Puzzles,** diecut cardboard, Percy Crosby's Skippy in Jig Saw, No. 740, No. 7, "Gawd help anybody that spits on the flag to–day," 1 of series of 8, 13¾ x 10⅛", over 250 pcs, boxed. . . . . . . . . **30.00**

**Saalfield Publishing Co.,** Akron, OH
- Bringing Up Father Picture Puzzles, No. 909, diecut cardboard, various diecut variations, 4 puzzle set, 9½ x 7½", 1933, Jigg slipping on banana guide picture on cardboard box . . . . . . . . . . . **65.00**
- Just Kids Picture Puzzles, No. 910, 4 puzzle set, each puzzle approx 93/4 x 8", 1 guide picture on box *see illus*. . . . . . . . . . . . . . . **45.00**
- Kitty–Cat Picture Puzzle Box, No. 567, 6 puzzle set, Fern Biesel Peat illus, each puzzle approx 77/8 x 97/8". . . . . . . . **50.00**

- Mother Goose, set of 3, 1943, 12 x 10" box . . . . . . . . . . . . **20.00**

**Selchow & Righter,** New York, NY
- Pandora Picture Puzzles, Bunny Rabbit Series, set of 3, c1940, 11 x 8" box . . . . . . . . . . . . . . **60.00**
- Sliced Flowers, c1920, 9 x 10" box . . . . . . . . . . . . . . . . . . **25.00**

**Squarecut Puzzle Co.,** New York, NY, Movie Squarecut Puzzle, Keeper of the Flame, 2 sections, 22 x 16¾", more than 500 pcs, small guide picture on box *see illus* . . . . . . . . . . . . . . . . . **45.00**

**Peter G. Thomson,** Cincinnati, Sliced Objects, 72 strips each measuring approx 7 x 1¼", children playing with sliced puzzle on box lid . . . . . . . . . . **75.00**

**Transogram Co., Inc.,** New York, NY
- Patriotic Jig Saw Puzzles, The Yanks in Action on Land, Sea, and Air, diecut cardboard, 2 puzzle set, 1943, interlocking . . . . . . . . . . . . . . . . . . . **20.00**
- Tony Sarg's Puzzles, 1930s, 9 x 17" box . . . . . . . . . . . . . . **45.00**

**Upson Company,** Tuco Work Shops, Lockport, NY, diecut cardboard, Puzzles For Good Health, series of 6; No. 4, I Use My Hankie/I Drink Water, Twelvetrees illus, orig box. . . . . **30.00**

*Movie–Land Cut Ups*

*Edgar Bergen's
Charlie McCarthy Picture Puzzles*

**Whitman Publishing Company,**
Racine, WI
• Edgar Bergen's Charlie
McCarthy Picture Puzzles,
No. 3932, 2 puzzle set,
approx 7¼ x 10", 1938 copy-
right *see illus* . . . . . . . . . . . .    **40.00**
• Tarzan Big Little Book Picture
Puzzles, 1938, 11 x 8" box. . .    **150.00**
**Wylder,** St. Louis, MO
• Combination Ocean Liner and
World Map Puzzles, saw–cut
composition, double sided,
*Berengaria* entering New York
Harbor on obverse, world map
on reverse, 12¼ x 9", 28 pcs,
c1930s . . . . . . . . . . . . . . . .    **40.00**
• Movie–Land Cut Ups, set of 4,
12 to 20 pcs each 10 x 8"
puzzle, diecut cardboard,
scenes from movies "Our
Gang, Harry Langdon, Mickey
(Himself), McGuire," and
"Only the Brave," ©1930, orig
box *see illus* . . . . . . . . . . . .    **120.00**
• "There was an old woman
who lived in a shoe...," 7½ x
5¾", 25 pcs. . . . . . . . . . . . .    **15.00**

## POST–1945

**American Publishing Corp.**
• Suzanne Somers as Chrissy in
Three's Company Jigsaw
Puzzle, No. 1509, diecut
cardboard, swimsuit pose,
11¹¹/₁₆ x 17¹/₁₄", 204 pcs, late
1970s, cardboard box with
guide picture . . . . . . . . . . . .    **15.00**
• The Bionic Woman Jigsaw
Puzzle, No. 1245, 17¼ x 11",
204 pcs, canister . . . . . . . . . .    **16.00**
**Milton Bradley Company,**
Springfield, MA
• Captain Kangaroo Puzzles, No.
4501–5, diecut cardboard,
4 puzzle set, each puzzle
approx 6¼ x 10", 20 pcs each
puzzle, cardboard box with
2 partial guide pictures. . . . . .    **25.00**
• Dr. Kildare Jigsaw Puzzle, 4318,
No. 2, We are going to call
him Jimmy, includes 14 x 12"
color portrait for framing,
over 600 pcs, 1962 copyright,
guide picture on box . . . . . . .    **20.00**
• Huckleberry Hound, 4 puzzle
set, 1960, 14 x 11" box . . . . .    **40.00**
• James Bond 007 Jigsaw Puzzle,
4691-1, Thunderball, No. 1,
Spectre's Surprise, approx
24 x 14", over 600 pcs, partial
guide picture on cover . . . . . .    **30.00**

*Weird–Ohs Picture Puzzle*

*Blondie and Dagwood Interchangeable Blocks*

• Raggedy Ann Picture Puzzles, No. 4855, diecut cardboard, late 1940s, guide picture on box . . . . . . . . . . . . . . . . . .   **35.00**

**Built–Rite: made by Warren Paper Products,** Lafayette, IN, Junior Picture Puzzle, Famous TV Stars, Robin Hood, No. 1229, Set 101, Robin Hood's Merry Men, cardboard box with guide picture . . . . . . .   **18.00**

**Cadaco–Ellis,** Jingo: The Jigsaw Bingo Game, first player to fit 5 pieces vertically, horizontally, or diagonally into Jingo Board wins round, 1941, $13^{1}/_{4}$ x 10 x 1" box . . . . . . . . . .   **35.00**

**Chilcote Company,** Cleveland, OH, diecut cardboard, Barney's Bungling Circus, No. 2, Under the Big Tent, series of 6, paper insert with poem relating to view, $15^{1}/_{2}$ x $11^{1}/_{2}$", over 300 pcs, Barney the elephant on box . . . . . . . . . . . . . . . . .   **15.00**

**Consolidated Paper Box Company,** Somerville, MA

• No. 2, Children of all Nations, cardboard, 3 puzzles, approx 50 pcs each, cardboard box with children's parade theme   **8.00**

• No. 41, 2 Perfect Jig Saw Type Interlocking Children's Puzzles, No. 5, boy preventing girl from crossing street and boy and grandfather in rowboat, Hintermeister illus, each puzzle $7^{1}/_{8}$ x $9^{1}/_{4}$", boy and girl waving puzzle boxes on cover   **10.00**

**Hermann Eichhorn,** West Germany, Mickey Mouse Picture Cubes, c1980, 6 x 7" wood suitcase–type box . . . . . . . . . . .   **15.00**

**E.E. Fairchild Corp.,** Rochester, NY

• Lariat Sam Puzzle, diecut cardboard, 14 x 10", 60 pcs, c1978, guide picture on box. .   **15.00**

• Weird–Ohs Picture Puzzle, 1652, Freddy Flameout: The Way Out Jet Jockey, diecut cardboard, Freddy in jet, approx 15 x $10^{1}/_{2}$", 108 pcs, 1963, cardboard box with guide picture *see illus*. . . . . . .   **30.00**

**Samuel Gabriel Sons & Co.,** New York, NY

• Animal Puzzles, No. T218, diecut cardboard, c1940s, mother cat and two kittens playing in shoe on box . . . . .   **15.00**

• Pinky Lee, 3 Funny Picture Puzzles, 1955, 12 x 9" box. . .   **40.00**

**Gaston Manufacturing Co.,** Cincinnati, OH, Blondie and Dagwood Interchangeable Blocks, c1950, 7 x 11" box *see illus* . . . . . . . . . . . . . . . .   **65.00**

*Kaptain Kool and The Kongs*

*The Beatles Yellow Submarine*

**Golden, Western Pub. Co. Trademark,** Racine WI, diecut cardboard, No. 4605–46, Masters of the Universe Jigsaw Puzzle, fighting water monster, approx 11½ x 15", 100 pcs, cardboard box . . . . . . . . . . . .  **4.00**

**H–G Toys,** Long Beach, NY

• Evil Knievel, Ring of Fire, No. 475–04, diecut cardboard, Knievel on Harley flying through fiery ring, 10 x 14", 150 pcs, 1974, 3⅝" d, 6⅞" h cardboard, metal, and plastic cylinder mkd "Hardcord, Jersey City, NH". . . . . . . . . .  **18.00**

• Happy Days, Featuring The Fonz, No. 46502, approx 14 x 10", 150 pcs, guide photo on box . . . . . . . . . . . . . . . .  **8.00**

• Kaptain Kool and The Kongs, diecut cardboard, approx 10 x 14", 70 pcs, c1977, guide picture on box *see illus*  **10.00**

• Laverne and Shirley, No. 425–01, diecut cardboard, 4 scenes, 2 of Laverne and Shirley at playground, 10 x 14", 150 pcs, guide picture on cardboard box. . . .  **12.00**

• Showgun Warriors, No. 455–04, Great Mazinga, diecut cardboard, 10 x 14", 150 pcs, late 1970s, guide picture on cardboard box . . . . . . . . . . . . . .  **5.00**

• Star Trek Jigsaw Puzzle, No. 496–02, Attempted Hijacking of USS Enterprise and its Officers, approx 14 x 18", over 300 pcs, guide picture on box . . . . . . . . . . .  **15.00**

**Leo Hart Company,** Rochester, NY, Wings of Victory...Three Hart Picture Puzzles of War Planes, Curtiss Commando, Curtiss Dive Bomber, and Grumman Skyrocket, Series 200, each puzzle 9⅝ x 7", 40 pcs, 5 figurals each puzzle, ©1943, orig box. . . . . . . . . . . . . . . . .  **45.00**

**Jaymar Specialty Co.,** New York, NY

• Bedtime Story Picture Puzzle, Puss in Boots, guide picture on box . . . . . . . . . . . . . . . . . .  **5.00**

• Beetle Bailey Picture Puzzle, Potato Artist, diecut cardboard, 13¹⁵⁄₁₆ x 9¾", 63 pcs, guide picture on cardboard box . . . .  **12.00**

• Dick Tracy Kiddies Jigsaw Puzzle, 1950s, 8 x 10" box. . .  **35.00**

• King of the Royal Mounted Jig Saw Puzzle, diecut cardboard, large pcs, c1950, guide picture on box. . . . . . . . . . . . . . . .  **25.00**

• The Beatles Yellow Submarine, "Sgt. Pepper Band," 19 x 19", 650 pcs, unopened box, ©1968 King Features Syndicate *see illus*. . . . . . . . . . . . . . . .  **5.00**

*Walt Disney's Mickey Mouse*

*Walt Disney's Mickey Mouse
Comic Picture Puzzle*

- The Beverly Hillbillies, No. 8672, diecut cardboard, Jed, Elly May, and Granny leaning on railing, approx 10 x 14", 63 pcs, mid 1960s, guide picture on cardboard box. . . . . . . . . . . . . . . . . .  **20.00**
- Walt Disney's Interlocking Jig Saw Puzzle, Three Little Pigs, diecut cardboard, 22 x 14", over 300 pcs, late 1940s, guide picture on cardboard box. . . . . . . . . . . . . . . . . .  **25.00**
- Walt Disney's Mary Poppins Picture Puzzle, diecut cardboard, approx 14 x 10", over 60 large interlocking pcs, 1964 boxed. . . . . . . . . . . . .  **15.00**
- Walt Disney's Mickey Mouse, diecut cardboard, Mickey fishing from trailer while Goofy drives, approx 22 x 14", over 300 pcs, 1950s, boxed *see illus*. . . . . . . . . . . . . . .  **20.00**

**Kenner,** diecut cardboard, No. 40100, Star Wars, Artoo–Detoo/See–Three Pio, approx 14 x 18", 140 pcs, 1977, guide picture on cardboard box  **10.00**

**M.T. Matthews Publishing Co.,** frame tray, 3D Picture Puzzle, 2 puzzle set, mother and young zebra in cage and amusement park train ride, stereo glasses, 8¹/₂ x 11³/₄", 30 pcs each puzzle, cardboard box. . . . . . . . . . . .  **30.00**

**National Biscuit Company,** New York, NY, Straight Arrow Indian Jig Saw, series of 12, Straight Arrow with Packy and Fury, To the Rescue, 9 x 7", 1949 copyright, envelope with glassine window. . . . . . . . . . . . . . . . . .  **15.00**

**Parker Brothers Inc.,** Salem, MA
- Happy Birthday Miss Jones, Norman Rockwell illus, 11 x 14", 1973. . . . . . . . . . . .  **10.00**
- Walt Disney's Mickey Mouse Comic Picture Puzzle, set of 4, 1950s, 7 x 18" box *see illus* . .  **60.00**

**Platt & Munk,** New York, NY
- Little Brown Bear Puzzles, set of 6, 1950, 11 x 9" box . . . . . . .  **30.00**
- Pinocchio Picture Puzzles, No. 140, diecut cardboard, set of 6, Tony Sarg illus, each puzzle 8 x 10⁵/₈", 1 guide picture on box . . . . . . . . . . . . . . .  **50.00**

*Gunsmoke*

*Doc Savage*

**Saalfield Publishing Co.,** Akron, OH
Happy Friends Picture Puzzles, No. 7352, diecut cardboard, 3 puzzle set, Lajos Segner illus, 83/4 x 101/4", 1949, 1 guide picture on cardboard box  . . . .    **20.00**

**B. Shackman,** New York, NY, wood, No. 3713, Dimensional Donkey Puzzle, Shackman paper label on puzzle bottom, made in Japan, 4 x 3¼ x 1½", 14 pcs, c1950s, cardboard box with paper label. . . . . . . . . . .    **5.00**

**Sifo Company,** St. Paul, MN
• Little Black Sambo, masonite tray puzzle, 9 x 12", c1965  . .    **20.00**
• Sammy Sun tells the Days and Months, frame tray, clock with months and numbers in outer circle and days of week in inner circle, sun in center. . . .    **15.00**

**Joseph K. Straus,** Brooklyn, NY, wood, Transportation and Home Life in the U.S. 60 Years Ago, 3 puzzle set, c1950, 10 x 13" box . . . . . . . . . . . . . . . . . .    **35.00**

**Time, Inc.,** Life Puzzles, New York, NY, diecut cardboard, Journey To The Moon series, A Giant Leap for Mankind, poster, approx 13 x 20", approx 500 pcs, guide photo on box . .    **15.00**

**Transogram,** Funny Page Jig–Saw Puzzle, Series No. 6, "Fritzi Ritz in Mistaken Identity," approx 10 x 14", late 1930s, cartoon characters on box cover . . . . . .    **40.00**

**John Waddington,** Leeds, England, diecut cardboard, No. 929, Captain Scarlett and the Mysterons, Colonel White Briefing Captains Scarlet, Blue, and Grey, 13 x 10½", 251 pcs, guide picture shown on cardbard box . . . . . . . . . . . . . . .    **50.00**

**Whitman Publishing Co.,** Racine, WI
• A Big Little Book Jigsaw Puzzle, No. 4657-11, Hanna– Barbera Frankenstein Jr., 10 x 13", 99 pcs, book format box. . . . .    **20.00**
• Authorized Jr. Jigsaw Puzzle, No. 4404, Series No. 303, Gunsmoke, diecut cardboard, Matt leaning against wall loading gun, 63 pcs, guide picture on cardboard box *see illus* . . .    **25.00**
• Doc Savage Jigsaw Puzzle, No. 4610, diecut cardboard, Doc Savage with clenched fists,    14 x 18", 100 pcs, guide picture on cardboard box *see illus*. . . . . . . . . . . .    **10.00**
• Jigsaw Puzzle, No. 4429, Series No. 302, diecut cardboard, untitled, events associated with life of President Theodore Roosevelt, approx 15 x 11½",

*Cheyenne*

*Li'l Abner*

63 pcs, guide picture on card-
board box . . . . . . . . . . . . . .    **8.00**
• Little Golden Picture Puzzle
Johnny's Machine, book
cover, 1949, box with guide
picture . . . . . . . . . . . . . . .    **16.00**
Tottle, 2991, 6⅛ x 7½", 1946
copyright, guide picture on
box . . . . . . . . . . . . . . . . . .    **20.00**
**J.L. Wright, Inc.,** Chicago, IL,
Lincoln Log Historical Jig Saw
Puzzle, No. 503, The Rail
Splitter, Lincoln, approx 50 pcs,
orig box. . . . . . . . . . . . . . . .    **15.00**

## FRAME TRAY

**Milton Bradley Company,**
Springfield, MA
• Cheyenne, 14 x 10", 1957
see illus . . . . . . . . . . . . . . .    **20.00**
• Son of Hercules, No. 4572–X8,
Hercules stopping Roman
chariot, 14¼ x 10⅛", 43 pcs,
©1966 . . . . . . . . . . . . . . . .    **20.00**
• The Official New York World's
Fair 1964–1965, No.
4435–X3, Greyhound at the
Fair, 14¼ x 10¼", 28 pcs . . . .    **18.00**
**Built–Rite: made by Warren
Paper Products,** Lafayette, IN
• Dagwood and children rushing
out door while Blondie watch-
es, No. 1129, Sta–N–Place

Inlaid Puzzle, 13½ x 10⅝",
early 1960s . . . . . . . . . . . . .    **15.00**
• Jungle Jim, No. 1229, chimp
rubbing Jungle Jim's hair,
10¾ x 13½", ©1956. . . . . . . .    **20.00**
• Rusty Riley, No. 18,
Sta–N–Place,  five hidden ani-
mals and clown, 12½ x 8¾",
24 pcs, ©1949 . . . . . . . . . . .    **15.00**
**E.E. Fairchild Corporation,**
Rochester, NY, Little Roquefort
and Percy Puss, 1600–2, A
Terry–Toon Puzzle, Percy hold-
ing Roquefort, 11 x 8½" . . . . . .    **12.00**
**Great Lakes Press,** Rochester, NY,
Your Congressman Frank Horton
36th Congressional District of
New York, 11 x 14", 35 pcs, por-
tion of orig cellophane wrap . . .    **15.00**
**Jaymar Specialty Company,** New
York, NY
• Bugs Bunny Inlaid Puzzle,
No. 2389–3, Bugs dressed as
Indian confronting brave hold-
ing Porky and Petunia Pig
hostage, 12¾ x 9¾", 30 pcs . .    **15.00**
• Li'l Abner, 14  x 11", 35 diecut
pcs *see illus* . . . . . . . . . . . . .    **20.00**
• Rudolph the Red–Nose
Reindeer, Rudolph leading
sled, 11 x 14", ©1950 . . . . . .    **18.00**
• Walt Disney's 101 Dalmatians,
birth of pup, 12¾ x 9¾",
30 pcs . . . . . . . . . . . . . . . . .    **12.00**

*Crusader Rabbit and Rags the Tiger*

*Top Cat*

• Walt Disney's Pinocchio,
No. 2576, whale attacking
raft, 14 x 11", 35 pcs . . . . . . .    **18.00**

**National Fire Protection
Association,** Boston, MA,
A Clean House Seldom Burns!,
Sparky sweeping basement,
$8^{1}/_2$ x $10^{1}/_2$" . . . . . . . . . . . . . . .    **15.00**

**Saalfield Publishing Co.,** Akron,
OH

• Angela Cartwright, America's
Little Darling on Nationwide
TV, The Danny Thomas Show,
$10^{1}/_2$ x 14", 27 pcs, ©1962 . . .    **30.00**

• Artcraft, 7042, Diver Dan, Dan
on ocean floor surrounded by
3 fish, mermaid in back-
ground, $10^{1}/_2$ x 14", ©1957 . . .    **20.00**

• Authorized Edition, "Would you
Believe?," Don Adams in Get
Smart, Adams lighting match
near TNT boxes, $10^{1}/_2$ x 14",
©1965 . . . . . . . . . . . . . . .    **30.00**

• Bonny Braids: Dick Tracy's New
Daughter, No. 7319,
$10^{1}/_4$ x $11^{1}/_2$", 28 pcs . . . . . . .    **35.00**

**Thumbs–Up Enterprises, Inc.,**
One For the Thumb in 81, Joe
Greene in Steeler's uniform
wearing 4 Super Bowl rings,
10 x $12^{1}/_2$", 48 pcs . . . . . . . . .    **30.00**

**Unknown Maker**

• Crusader Rabbit and Rags the
Tiger, Crusader Rabbit sitting
on Rags' stomach floating
down river, frog on dock,
$13^{1}/_4$ x $9^{7}/_8$" *see illus* . . . . . . .    **6.00**

• Mustang Running, cowboy on
horse lassoing mustang while

others chase herd in back-
ground, $14^{1}/_2$ x $10^{1}/_4$" . . . . . . .    **18.00**

**Upson Company,** Tuco Work
Shops, Baby Huey the Baby
Giant Puzzle, Huey floating on
back while two ducks sit on his
stomach and paddle,
$10^{3}/_8$ x $14^{3}/_8$" . . . . . . . . . . . . . .    **15.00**

**A.M. Walzer,** Dover, NJ, No. 75,
untitled, young baby drinking
milk from bottle assisted by terrier, Charlotte Becker illus,
$10^{7}/_8$ x 14", 34 pcs . . . . . . . . .    **15.00**

**Whitman Publishing Co.,** Racine,
WI

• Captain Kangaroo Frame Tray
Puzzle, Captain Kangaroo
assembling puzzles,
$11^{1}/_4$ x $14^{3}/_8$", 48 pcs . . . . . . . .    **15.00**

• Gunsmoke, 15 x 11", 1958 . . . .    **35.00**

• Hanna–Barbera Top Cat,
No. 4457, policeman watching
Top Cat in trash can sipping
milk from bottle, $11^{3}/_8$ x $14^{3}/_8$",
©1961 *see illus* . . . . . . . . . . .    **20.00**

• Little Beaver Picture Puzzle, No.
2628, Little Beaver fishing,
$11^{3}/_8$ x $14^{7}/_8$", ©1954 . . . . . . .    **18.00**

• Pip the Piper Frame Tray Puzzle,
TV show characters photo,
$11^{3}/_8$ x $14^{1}/_2$", 17 pcs, torn orig
cellophane wrap with 29¢
price sticker . . . . . . . . . . . . .    **16.00**

• Rifleman, No. 4427, Al
Andersen cartoon drawing of
Lucas and Mark hiding behind

rocks, Indians on horseback approaching in distance, 11³/₈ x 14¹/₂", 18 pcs, ©1960, portion of orig cellophane wrap . . . . . . . . . . . . . . . . .   **25.00**

• Rip Foster Picture Puzzle, No. 2606, mother, father, and son in spacesuits flying among planets, rocket ship in background, 11³/₈ x 14⁷/₈", 36 pcs, airplane, battleship, and handgun figurals . . . . . . . . . . . . .   **35.00**

• Roy Rogers Picture Puzzle, No. 4427, Roy preparing to mount Trigger, 11³/₈ x 14¹/₂", 25 pcs . .   **25.00**

• Santa hanging ball on Christmas tree, Eileen Fox Vaughn illus, 11³/₈ x 14⁷/₈". . . . . . . . . . . . .   **15.00**

• Santa seated among toys and sack reading to reindeer from "Good Boys and Girls" book, No. 4424, 11¹/₄ x 14¹/₂", 26 pcs   **15.00**

• Tales of Wells Fargo, No. 4427, hero drawing gun while entering saloon, 11¹/₄ x 14¹/₂", ©1958 . . . . . . . . . . . . . . . .   **25.00**

• Tennessee Tuxedo, Tennessee and Walrus in diving helmets

finding treasure chest at bottom of sea, 11³/₈ x 14⁷/₁₆", 16 pcs, telephone handle, bell, and flying bird figurals . . . . . .   **20.00**

• Tweety & Sylvester, No. 4514A, Sylvester trying to catch Tweety as he parachutes from nest in tree, 8¹/₄ x 11" . . . . . . . . . . .   **4.00**

• Wagon Train, No. 4427, wagon master and scout hunting buffalo, 11³/₈ x 14¹/₂", ©1961 . . . .   **20.00**

• Walt Disney's Babes in Toyland, No. 4454, couple sharing drink, large Queen of Hearts card in background, 11¹/₄ x 14³/₈", ©1961 . . . . . . . .   **15.00**

• Walt Disney's Cinderella Picture Puzzle, No. 2975, Cinderella carrying wood to stove, 14⁷/₈ x 11¹/₂", ©1950, wrapper with guide picture on front and puzzle piece lines and unmarked picture on back, suitable for framing . . . . . . . .   **20.00**

• Walt Disney's Fantasyland, No. 4420, Donald and Mickey on aerial ride, 11¹/₄ x 14¹/₂", ©1957. . . . . . . . . . . . . . . . .   **15.00**

# MISCELLANEOUS JIGSAW PUZZLES

## ADVERTISING PUZZLES

**American Bakers Association,** "What Enriched Bread Does For Me," diecut cardboard, frame tray, loaf of bread with each part containing information about nutritional value, 9¹/₂ x 5¹/₂", 1955 copyright, orig packaging missing . . . . . . . . . . . . . . . . .   **15.00**

**American Bank and Trust Co. of PA,** BankAmericard, "Takes the puzzle out of your banking," diecut cardboard, 4 x 5", 16 pcs, bank and credit card symbols superimposed over photograph of coins on wire mesh, orig packaging missing . .   **10.00**

**Armstrong Cork Company,** Lancaster, PA, Armstrong

Quaker Rugs, children in nursery playing with building blocks, large insert advertising products, 8¹/₂ x 5¹/₂",15 pcs, c1933 . . . . . .   **40.00**

**Birds Eye,** "Birds Eye Puts It All Together Jigsaw Puzzle," diecut cardboard, unopened, lid shows "Clarence Birdseye..the man who started an industry" standing in front of Birds Eye Frosted Foods freezer in old–fashioned country store, 9 x 6 x 2" box. . .   **10.00**

**Black Cat Hosiery Co.,** Kenosha, WI, diecut cardboard, 5 x 7", 60 pcs, shows young boy and girl stacking building blocks c1908, paper envelope . . . . . . .   **85.00**

*Sparkalong Burgess*

*Picking Coffee Berries*

**Burger Chef,** "Dragon Wagon,"
part of Timetraveler Funmeal
Fest, frame tray, 9¹/₂ x 6⁵/₈",
16 pcs, 1980 . . . . . . . . . . . . .  **10.00**

**Burgess Battery Co.,** "Sparkalong
Burgess," young cowboy riding
animal that is part horse and
part zebra jumping wooden
fence, 5¹/₂ x 4", glassine envelope rubber stamped with dis-
tributor's name *see illus* . . . . . .  **20.00**

**Burlington Socks,** "Guess whose
show is selling Burlington Socks
on TV this fall?," diecut cardboard, black and white, pair of
feet wearing Burlington socks,
answer to question is Dean
Martin, 8 x 10³/₈", 21 pcs, textile
mailing sack with applied paper
label . . . . . . . . . . . . . . . . . . .  **35.00**

**Camel Laird Picture Puzzles,** Find
the Camel, "CAM–BRU–MAC,"
Reversible Puzzle, No. 4,
"Casting A Large Ingot, Sheffield
and Birkenhead," wood,
6⁷/₈ x 4⁷/₈", reverse with camel
on plain field, labeled "Thos.
Forman & Sons, Nottingham
and London," orig box . . . . . . .  **75.00**

**Campfire/Angelus Marshmallows,**
series of 4
• No. 1, "Fishing Boats," boats
tied at wharf, 9³/₄ x 6³/₄",
48 pcs, paper envelope . . . . .  **10.00**
• No. 4, "Spanish Galleon,"
6⁵/₈ x 9⁵/₈", 1933, paper enve-
lope . . . . . . . . . . . . . . . . .  **15.00**

**Captain Crunch,** cereal premium,
hidden scene, Captain Crunch

looking into ship's doorway,
4¹/₂ x 3", 10 pcs, orig wrap . . . .  **15.00**

**Chase & Sanborn,** Chase &
Sanborn's Puzzle Picture
• Old Fashioned New England
Country Store, men lounging
around potbelly stove, 1 of
series of 4, 8 x 6", 63 pcs,
cardboard box, 3¹/₄ x 2¹/₂ x 1",
c1909 . . . . . . . . . . . . . . . . .  **35.00**
• Picking Coffee Berries, 1 of
series of 4, 8 x 6", 63 pcs,
cardboard box, 3¹/₄ x 2¹/₂ x 1",
c1910 *see illus.* . . . . . . . . . . .  **30.00**

**Chevrolet**
• 60's Chevys: For 1960 Chevy's
Got 'Em All!, 12 pcs, 5¹/₂ x 3¹/₄"
cardboard puzzle with 1960
Corvair in front of U.S. Capitol
on, 5 x 5" plastic bag with
4⁷/₈ x 2" cardboard top flap,
Shilling Chevrolet Company
adv on back of flap . . . . . . . .  **30.00**
• "Superior Chevrolet Utility
Coupe" and "Superior
Chevrolet 5 Passenger
Touring," boxed set of
2 puzzles, each 6¹/₂ x 4¹/₂" puzzle has 12 pcs, box shows
Superior Chevrolet
5–Passenger Sedan, 1923–24     **200.00**

**Chicago Mail Order Co.,**
"Glorious Girl" Jig–Saw Puzzle,
free with any Glorious Girl dress
or coat purchased from Spring
and Summer catalog, offer
expired July 31, 1993, cardboard, cartoon drawing of children playing, 6⁵/₈ x 6¹/₈", 40 pcs,

*The Flying Family*

*Singing in the Rain*

paper envelope with guide picture . . . . . . . . . . . . . . . . . . .    **20.00**
**Cocomalt,** R B Davis Co.
• "Buffalo Bill," Buffalo Bill standing on rock, covered wagon in background, 6½ x 10", 65 pcs, c1933, paper envelope with guide picture . . . . . . . . . . . .    **18.00**
• "The Flying Family," diecut cardboard, Col. Hutchinson and family superimposed on map of western part of US showing route family traveled, accompanied by 4 pg pamphlet on how to become a Flight Commander, 6½ x 9⅞", 1933, paper envelope
  Puzzle and envelope . . . . .    **15.00**
  Puzzle, pamphlet, and envelope *see illus* . . . . . .    **25.00**
• "The Windmill Jig–Saw Puzzle," windmill and harbor at low tide, 10 x 6½", 65 pcs, paper envelope . . . . . . . . . . . . . .    **10.00**
**College Inn Food Products Co.,** Hotel Sherman, Chicago, No. 1 of series of 4, At Anchor, sailing ships moored in harbor, paper envelope, 7⅛ x 9½", early 1933    **15.00**

**Cruikshank Brothers Co.,** Pittsburgh, PA, Cruikshank's Little Cooks, double sided, front shows parading cartoon cooks holding food products, reverse with "No thanks," said Banks, "I want Cruikshanks," 7 x 9¾", approx 25 pcs, paper envelope, 7¼ x 10" . . . . . . . . . . . . . . .    **60.00**
**Cunningham Radio Tubes,** frame tray, Kate Smith and Rudy Vallee bust portraits, printed biographical comments about each, adv in border, cardboard, 12 x 10", orig packaging missing . . . . . . .    **75.00**
**Curtis Candy Company,** "Singing in the Rain" Jig Saw Puzzle, double sided, front shows boy and girl under umbrella, reverse shows Curtis 1¢ candies, 5⅝ x 7½", paper envelope *see illus* . . . . . . . . . . . . . . . . .    **35.00**
**Dayton Tires,** frame tray, "The Big Sport," tire cartoon of man's head, 9 x 12", 18 pcs, 1950s. . .    **15.00**
**Dearborn Truck Company,** Chicago, IL, "For Every Job the Dearborn Truck," stake body truck, 10½ x 7", 30 pcs, paper envelope . . . . . . . . . . . . . . . .    **65.00**
**DeMartini Macaroni Co.,** Martini Brand Spaghetti, The Zoo in Puzzles, Series No. 1, "Giraffe," 5⅝ x 8" including top and bottom labels, complete . . . . . .    **20.00**

*Psyche*

*The Goodrich Silver Fleet
at Niagara Falls*

**DIF Washing Powder**
- First in War, Washington leading troops, cardboard, 8¹/₂ x 12", Einson–Freeman, S–131, ©1933, paper envelope with guide picture . . . . .   **15.00**
- Psyche, 9¹/₂ x 12", paper envelope, small guide diagram *see illus*. . . . . . . . . . . . . . .   **12.00**

**Dunlop Tire & Rubber Corp.,** Dunlop Circular Picture Puzzle, outer border is Dunlop tire, center is picture looking up through hole on tee at group of golfers, one golfer removing Dunlop golf ball from hole, 19" d, 10¹/₂ x 7¹/₂ x 1¹/₂", approx 600 pcs, cardboard box, c1970   **30.00**

**Esso,** English, Save The Tiger Campaign, bust portrait of Tiger pointing finger, portion of "Save The Tiger" button in lower right, 5 x 7", 35 pcs, cardboard, 1970s, no packaging . . . . . . . .   **20.00**

**Essolube,** "The Five Star Theatre Presents Foiled By Essolube: A Jig–Saw–Melodrama," features series of characters including Zero–Doccus, Karbo–Nockus, Moto–Muchus, Oilio–Gobelus, and Moto–Raspus in jungle setting, Dr. Seuss illus, 17 x 11¹/₄", 150 pcs, 1933, paper envelope   **100.00**

**Everett Piano Co.,** Boston, MA, The Everett Piano, two women

at piano, "An Honest Piano At An Honest Price," 8¹/₂ x 6¹/₂", 16 pcs, John Church Co., Cincinnati, OH, c1890, cardboard folder, 3³/₄ x 5¹/₂". . . . . . .   **85.00**

**Fischer Baking Company,** Fisher's Vitamin "D" Bread, No. 4 from series of 6, diecut cardboard, untitled, parade of children featuring young boy riding St. Bernard carrying basket with loaf of Fischer's bread, 9¹/₄ x 7", 1933, paper envelope with guide picture on front and instructions and adv on back. . .   **18.00**

**Folger's Coffee Co.,** Folger's can with ocean liner in center medallion, 8 x 10¹/₂", 56 pcs, 1980, cardboard and metal container resembling coffee can . . .   **5.00**

**Fritz Company,** Lawrence, KS, "Home For The Yuletide," stock puzzle by Thos. D. Murphy Co., Red Oak, IA, Fritz Company applied label, gasoline service station, 8¹/₈ x 6¹/₈ x ³/₄", box . . . .   **15.00**

**General Electric,** Portable Appliances, kitchen scene with appliances, 15 x 10¹/₂", 104 pcs, c1960, guide picture, plastic bag . . . . . . . . . . . . . . . . . . .   **30.00**

**Goodrich Tire,** Akron, OH, The Goodrich Silver Fleet at Niagara Falls, 9³/₄ x 7¹/₂", 10 x 8", approx 50 pcs, paper envelope with "Stock No.4091–GT" *see illus*. .   **25.00**

*Green Spring Dairy*

*Heinz 57 Varieties*

**Green Spring Dairy,** Baltimore, MD, dairy processing machinery, 10³/₄ x 9", envelope missing *see illus* . . . . . . . . . . . . . . . . . . 30.00

**Greyhound Jig Saw Puzzle Cartoon Map of the United States,** historical data and 250 4–color illus on map, 20 x 13¹/₂", over 300 pcs, cardboard box, 8¹/₂ x 6¹/₄ x 1¹/₂" . . . . 35.00

**Heinz 57 Varieties,** children playing store with all 57 products displayed on shelf, 10¹/₈ x 12", paper envelope *see illus* . . . . . . 45.00

**Hi–C Super Fruits,** Coca–Cola Co., Zowie Powie Punch, 9³/₄ x 8", rounded corners, 28 pcs, orig packaging missing 30.00

**Hood, C. I.,** Lowell, MA
• A Wedding in Catland and Hood's Bridge Puzzle, Louis Wain illus, 14¹/₂ x 9⁷/₈", 35 pcs, orig box . . . . . . . . . . . . . . . 275.00
• Hood's Panama Canal Puzzle, double sided, front shows canal scene, reverse with topographic map, both sides, 5¹/₂ x 14", 22 pcs, c1914, cardboard box, 5 x 3³/₄" . . . . . 90.00
• Hood's Rainy Day and Balloon Puzzles, double sided, sales man in buggy and Hood's factory, reverse shows hot air balloon, 10 x 15", ©1891, cardboard box, 7¹/₂ x 5", with guide pictures and brochures 120.00

**Howard Clothes,** gentleman in modern suit superimposed over gentleman wearing early 19th C suit, 4¹/₄ x 6¹/₂", 50 pcs, dates "1833" to "1933," period packaging missing . . . . . . . . . . . . . 30.00

**International Salt Co.,** A Family Reunion, young boy holding puppy in center, puppy's mother in front of dog house on left, Alfred Gulloy illus, 12 x 9", 125 pcs, 12³/₈ x 9¹/₂" paper enveloope, c1933 . . . . . . . . . . 15.00

**Jack and Jill Jell,** Special Offer, 5 Boxes of Jack & Jill Jell and a 100 pc The Fisher Bros Co. Picture Puzzle, No. 17, "Modern Beauty," 2 1930s beauties, 10¹/₄ x 8", paper envelope . . 20.00

**Jerry's Restaurants,** chef holding tray with Jerry's Restaurants take–home box, 6¹/₈ x 9", 20 pcs, c1960, plastic envelope with "Join Jerry's Birthday Club" on cardboard flap . . . . . . . . . . 35.00

**Johnson Wax,** Raid Picture Puzzle, diecut cardboard, bugs interrupted in their feasting, Don Pegler illus, 11³/₄" sq, 156 pcs, 2⁷/₈" d cardboard, metal, and plastic tube can . . . . . . . . . . . 20.00

**Johnston's Chocolates,** "Garden No. 1," formal garden setting with 3 colonial couples,

*Chew Tobacco Puzzle*

7¹⁵/₁₆ x 5", mid–1930s, 6½ x 9³/₈"
paper envelope . . . . . . . . . . .    **45.00**
**Kolynos Company,** New Haven,
CT, "Just Plain Bill," David, Bill,
and Nancy in barbershop,
12 x 9", 150 pcs, paper enve-
lope . . . . . . . . . . . . . . . . . .    **20.00**
**Lambert Pharmacal Co.,**
Listerine, 3 children in bath-
room gargling with Listerine,
dog taking part, Frances Tipton
Hunter illus, 13³/₄ x 10³/₄",
paper envelope, Phillips Lord,
The Country Doctor radio show
premium . . . . . . . . . . . . . . .    **45.00**
**Law Lottier,** "Chew Tobacco
Puzzle," young male dressed in
sailor's suit in Victorian parlor,
10 x 10¹/₄", 16 pcs, c1900–10,
cardboard box with engraved

sheet on lid, notation on lid
reads, "Richmond Engraving
Co.," 10½ x 10³/₈" lid *see illus.* .    **325.00**
**Lucus Paints and Varnishes,**
"Giant Painter Puzzle," painter
kneeling in miniature village,
can of paint by right knee, hold-
ing house in left hand, 5½ x 7",
c1920s. . . . . . . . . . . . . . . . .    **125.00**
**Lux Toilet Soap**
• My Island of Dreams,
    Mediterranean harbor,
    12¹/₄ x 9", 150 pcs, c1933,
    paper envelope with guide pic-
    ture . . . . . . . . . . . . . . . . .    **8.00**
• The Wayside Inn, 12¹/₄ x 10",
    150 pcs, 1930s, paper enve-
    lope with guide picture,
    12½ x 10½". . . . . . . . . . . .    **12.00**
**Majestic Publishing Company,**
"Majestic Movie Star Puzzle,
Compliments of Paramount
Theater, Coming! Saturday,
March 18th, 'The Vampire Bat'
with Lionel Atwell and Fay
Wray," Wallace Beery, sepia,
7 x 8⁷/₈", figural pcs, c1933,
glassine envelope . . . . . . . . . .    **35.00**
**Maxwell,** "Build A Maxwell Piece
By Piece," diecut cardboard,
8 x 5", 28 pcs, block format,
double sided, family in car in
oval with information in 4 cor-
ners on front, car priced $595,
alphabet features for car includ-
ing "A for ABLE That's Easy To
See" on back, 5½ x 3¹/₈" enve-
lope with "New Prices Effective,
January 1st, 1917: Roadster—
$620; Touring Car—$635; FOB
Detroit" on back. . . . . . . . . . .    **150.00**
**McKesson & Robbins,** Bridgeport,
CT
• McKesson's "Our Gang" Jig–Saw
    Puzzle, drugstore and soda
    fountain scene, chamfered cor-
    ners, 14 x 10³/₄", 80 pcs,
    ©1932, 11 x 14" paper enve-
    lope with guide picture . . . . .    **65.00**
• McKesson's Products, chemist
    and research scientist at work,
    14 x 10½", 150 pcs, ©1933,
    paper envelope, 14¹/₄ x 11",
    includes crossword puzzle and
    first aid book . . . . . . . . . . . .    **45.00**

*Personal Finance Co.*

*Toy Carnival*

**Metropolitan Property and Liability Insurance Company,** "Met Works," diecut cardboard, features Peanuts Linus, Lucy, Schroeder, and Snoopy playing atop child's block, 7" sq, 36 pcs, 1988, orig shrink wrap ........ **15.00**

**Miller Rubber Products Co.,** Akron, OH, Toy Carnival, circus scene, 9³/₄ x 7¹/₂", approx 50 pcs, 1933, paper envelope, 10 x 8" *see illus* ............ **30.00**

**R. J. Mrizek Co.,** makers of Mrizek's Bohemian Rye Bread, Chicago, "Washington's Childhood Home," 7 x 8⁵/₈", paper envelope ............ **12.00**

**MS Neum Amsterdam,** map of Western Caribbean with insert of ship in upper right quadrant, promotion for DDA "You're Part Of It," Travel Award Winner, cardboard, 13¹/₁₆ x 9⁷/₈", 100 pcs, 1980s, cardboard can **20.00**

**New Jersey Bell,** "The Answer To Your Communication Puzzle: BELL," 8 x 8", 9 pcs, period packaging missing .......... **8.00**

**Olympic Airways,** "Catch Olympics flying Greek party to Paris, Any night," cardboard, 5³/₄ x 9", 18 pcs, orig box ..... **10.00**

**Orange Disc Anthracite Coal,** free with purchase of ton of coal, Summer, Einson–Freeman, S115, Welsh illus, cardboard, 8⁵/₈ x 12¹/₈", paper envelope with guide picture .......... **30.00**

**Our Gang Gum,** Puzzle No. 8, 1 of series of 25, aerialist dangling from wire using mouth grip, 3⁹/₁₆ x 5¹/₈", c1933 ....... **8.00**

**Pacific Coast Borax Co.,** "Hauling 20 Mule Team Borax Out Of Death Valley," 20 mule head figural pcs, 10³/₄ x 8¹/₄", 1933, paper envelope with newsprint cartoon insert. ............. **20.00**

**Penick & Ford,** Vermont Maid Syrup, 2 Jig–Saw Puzzles, "Home" and "Ready For The Pasture," 7³/₈ x 9¹/₄" each, 49 pcs per puzzle, paper envelope with green lettering "New Series" ... **18.00**

**Pennzoil,** snowball fight behind freezing snowman, line cut, 5³/₄ x 8", 16 pcs, paper envelope **15.00**

**Personal Finance Co.,** Springfield, MO, 4 block comic strip of couple applying for loan, 9 x 6", 49 pcs, ©R. E. Tucker 1933, paper envelope *see illus* ...... **35.00**

**Philadelphia Sunday Inquirer,** "Blondie" Jig–Saw Puzzle, 10 x 7⁷/₈", uncut border, issued as Sunday supplement, ©1933 King Features Syndicate, Forbes–Boston ............. **20.00**

**Phillips Petroleum Company,** double sided, Alaska and Hawaii, central map of each state surrounded by scenes from state, 15 x 11", 1973 ............. **12.00**

**Plee–Zing Palm Oil Soap,** Free Jig–Saw Puzzle with 4 Bars, oceanliner entering New York harbor, 9⁷/₈ x 7³/₄", paper envelope. ................... **20.00**

*Adventures of Professor Oscar
Quackenbush:Chasing Pink Elephants*

*His Master's Voice*

**Poll–Parrot,** frame tray, Howdy Doody Magic Show, Howdy pulling Poll–Parrot from hat, 8¼ x 7¼", c 1950s, paper envelope with guide picture . . . . . .    **50.00**

**Proctor and Gamble,** Adventures of Professor Oscar Quackenbush: Chasing Pink Elephants, Oscar riding mouse chasing elephant, 1 of series of 4 puzzles, African native by tree in background, 9¾ x 7½", c1933, glassine envelope *see illus* . . . . . . . . . . . . . . . .    **15.00**

**Psychodynamic Consultants, Inc.,** Clayton, MO, "We Have Moved Reb 1st 1980 Parkway Tower," diecut cardboard, Clayton, MO map showing office move from one location in the city to another, 10⅞ x 8½", 28 pcs, orig packaging missing . . . . . . .    **10.00**

**Quaker Oats Company,** "The Quaker Oats Company, Makers of Puffed Wheat and Puffed Rice, Presenting Dick Daring," cardboard, schematic drawings of Dick Daring's city headquarters, insert of puzzle surface, 12 x 8¾", 100 pcs, paper envelope . . . . . . . . . . . . . . . . . .    **30.00**

**RCA Victor**
• "All that the Victrola gives to others it will give to you," seated couple in front of record player surrounded by miniature musicians, folk singers, and opera singers, RCA logo lower right, 8⅞ x 8", dated 1932, paper envelope . .    **150.00**

• "His Master's Voice" Jig Saw Puzzle, classic Nipper listening to phonograph, 13 x 10", approx 165 pcs, 3 figural pcs, ©1933, 5¼ x 3¼" cardboard box with radio image *see illus*    **175.00**

**Richfield Golden Gasoline/ Richlube Motor Oil,** "Goofy Golf," Jig–Saw Puzzle, No. 2 in series of 6, "In Hawaii–And How!," 7 x 9", 49 pcs, paper envelope with Alex Morrison golf lesson on front. . . . . . . . . .    **30.00**

**Rold Gold Butter Pretzels,** boy and girl in nursery, girl feeding dog pretzel from Rold Gold box, boy playing with Rold Gold truck, 9⅞ x 7¾", 40 pcs, c1933, paper envelope . . . . . . . . . . .    **75.00**

**C. F. Sauer Co.,** Richmond, VA, Sauer's Vanilla and Duke's Home Made Mayonnaise, Sauer's Gardens, multicolored garden setting, blue border, 8 x 10¼", 8¼ x 10½" paper envelope, c1933 . . . . . . . . . .    **20.00**

**Scott & Bowne,** "Scott's Emulsion Of Cod Liver Oil," diecut cardboard, 13¼ x 10⅝", 60 pcs, Scott fisherman standing in harbor at Balstad, Lofoten Islands, Norway, Site of Scott & Bowne's Cod Liver Oil Refinery, 7 pcs spell out "SCOTT'S," 1933–35, orig packaging missing . . . . . . .    **50.00**

*A Bully Time in Spain*

**Service Coal Company,** Wm. H. Gross, Prop., Allentown, PA, Cross Creek Coal, Genuine Jedda Coal, rectangular insert of coal yard above rural harvest and cabin scene at twilight, 7½ x 9⅝", 49 pcs, c1933, paper envelope . . . . . . . . . . . . . . . .    **15.00**

**Shultz's Pretzels,** Hanover, PA, winter scene featuring stone arch bridge, adv info on puzzle, 3 x 6", paper envelope . . . . . . .    **10.00**

**Springmaid,** frame tray, Abdullah Bulbul Amir defending his sheet, battle scene on front between Abdullah Bulbul Amir and Ivan Skavinsky Skivar, poem on back, 14 x 11", c1951 . . . . .    **15.00**

**Standard Oil Company of Ohio,** Radio Jig Saw Puzzle
- No. 2, In Dutch with Gene & Glenn and Jake and Lena, 14½ x 11", 252 pcs, guide picture with adv on back, boxed    **18.00**
- No. 3, A Bully Time in Spain, double sided, Lena fighting bull in Spanish bullring on front, reverse with head and shoulder portraits of Gene and Glenn, 14½ x 11", 252 pcs, adv sheet with guide picture, cardboard box, 6¾ x 8¼", c1933 *see illus* . . . . . . . . . .    **25.00**

**Sundial Bonnie Laddie Shoes,** Sundial "Lucky Pup" Jig Saw Puzzle, frame tray, Bonnie Laddie on right, features charac-

ters from Lucky Pup television show, 10¾ x 8¾", 1948, guide picture on envelope . . . . . . . .    **40.00**

**Sunshine Lone Star Sugar Wafers,** child pushing wheelbarrow filled with children, Twelvetrees illus, 9¼ x 7", 40 pcs, 1932, guide picture on paper envelope    **35.00**

**Swift & Company,** "Milking Time at a Brookfield Dairy Farm," dancing cows at center above oval with info about "Brooksie" the famous white cow and her pals, figural pcs spell "SWIFT & CO," 12 x 12" box . . . . . . . . . .    **65.00**

**Taco Bell,** fast food premium, frame tray, Parasaurolophus, 5 x 8", 15 pcs, 1 of series, 1993    **4.00**

**Timken Silent Automatic Burner Co.,** Canton, OH, 8 x 8½", 87 pcs, paper envelope. . . . . . .    **25.00**

**Toddy, Inc.,** "Circus Parade," cartoon format, 1 of series of 6, elephant leading parade, tent in background, 13½ x 10", 75 pcs, some figural, 1932, paper envelope. . . . . . . . . . . . . . . . . . . .    **20.00**

**Trans World Airlines,** "The airport waiting game and how to beat it," diecut cardboard, 15¼ x 10¼", 35 pcs, photo of gameboard with airplane, passengers, and TWA personnel, TWA personnel motif, 2⅞" d, 7½" h cardboard and metal can mkd "Hardcord, Jersey City, NJ" . . . .    **20.00**

**John Wanamaker,** New York, NY, double sided, E.J. Meeker etching of Grace Church and Wanamaker's New York City store on front, 25 line description of Wanamaker's store entitled "The Great Stores Of The World" on back, 40 pcs, c1933, orig packaging missing . . . . . . .    **65.00**

**Ward's Baking Co.**
- Patriotic Jig–Saw Puzzle (United States Military Academy), aerial view of academy, 10 x 8", approx 100 pcs, c1943, paper envelope, 10½ x 8½" . . . . . . .    **35.00**
- Tip–Top Circus, circus parade, 7¼ x 8¼", 36 pcs, ©1951, paper envelope, 7¾ x 8½" . . .    **25.00**

*Jack O'Brien and the Penguins*

**Wausau Insurance Company,** The
Famous Wausau Depot, 4" d,
5¹/₁₆" h unopened can with
guide picture . . . . . . . . . . . .     **15.00**

**Weinberger's Cut Rate Drugs,**
Co–Operation, kitchen scene
with young Dutch boy and girl
baking, 3¹/₄ x 4³/₄", 15 pcs, paper
envelope labeled "Weinberger's
Gift Picture Puzzle for Boys and
Girls," c1933 . . . . . . . . . . . . .     **25.00**

**Wendy's International,** "Where's
The Beef?," diecut cardboard,
4 x 5¹/₂", 9 pcs, Clara Peller's
face, 1984, orig packaging miss-
ing . . . . . . . . . . . . . . . . . . . .     **10.00**

**Westinghouse Mazda Lamps,**
Jigsaw Puzzle, A–1498,
"General Washington and
General Lee at the Battle of
Monmouth," 1 of series of 12,
figural pcs spell "Westinghouse,
Mazda Lamps," 11¹/₂ x 12¹/₄",
c1933, paper envelope. . . . . . .     **35.00**

**WFSB,** Eyewitness News, "We fit
right into your day!, NEWS
5 o'clock, 3," diecut cardboard,
5 x 6³/₄", 15 pcs, news anchors,
2⁷/₈" d, 2" h cylindrical can . . . .     **10.00**

**Wheaties,** Jack O'Brien Jig Saw
Puzzle, "Jack O'Brien and the
Penguins," 1 of series of 4, dog
sled and penguins, 7 x 6",
approx 30 pcs cut from back of
Wheaties box, 1930s *see illus.* .     **25.00**

**White Baking Company,** Jig–Saw
Puzzle, No. 8, Girl and Bird,
1 of series of 10, 9³/₄ x 11³/₄",
135 pcs, c1933 . . . . . . . . . . .     **15.00**

*Birthday Card*

**White Rose Tea,** Puzzle No. 1,
untitled, cardboard, boy taking
sick dog to vet, 7¹/₁₆ x 9¹/₁₆",
49 pcs, 1932–33, envelope with
guide picture . . . . . . . . . . . . .     **20.00**

## MULTIPURPOSE PUZZLES

**Birthday Card,** Volland, B–1,
"Birthday Greetings," verse
beneath arch, 2 knaves carrying
cake lower left corner, cover
sheet featuring seated dog,
"Happy Birthday" in puzzle pcs,
and verse, 5¹/₄ x 4¹/₄" puzzle,
1932 *see illus.* . . . . . . . . . . . .     **15.00**

**Book,** Sam See, Let's Play
Together: The Second Eye–Cue
Builder Book, S.C. Platt, Series
200, 4 puzzle set, diecut frame
tray format, popular internation-

al children's games theme, 9½ x 11¾", 1945, plastic spiral bound . . . . . . . . . . . . . . . . . **30.00**

**Business Card,** Monarch Coal, sold by S.P. Morris, Baltic & Kentucky Aves., Atlantic City, NJ, diecut poster board, 2 deer in winter forest scene, duplicate picture top and bottom, top picture with business card info on back, bottom 14 pc punchout puzzle with frame remaining, 3½ x 3⅞" full size, at least 3 known Monarch Coal examples, each with different scene   **15.00**

**Candy,** Puzzle Pumpkin, unknown maker, colored white chocolate, 3 pcs. . . . . . . . . . . . **15.00**

**Christmas Card,** unknown manufacturer, "Wishing you a full–of–fun Christmas!, From Aunt Lizzy, Uncle Joe, Joey & Richy 1980," squirrel, rabbit, and chipmunk building snowman, orig packaging missing. . .   **4.00**

**Game**
• Cadco–Ellis, Jingo: The Jigsaw Bingo Game, first player to fit 5 pcs vertically, horizontally, or diagonally into Jingo Board wins round, 1941, 13¼ x 10 x 1" box . . . . . . . . . . . . . . . . . **35.00**
• Ideal Toy Corporation, No. 2017–2–100, Skooz–It Heckle and Jeckle Pick–A–Picture Game, pick pcs to complete puzzles, 1963, 4¼" d, 8¼" h cardboard and metal cylinder . . . . . . . . . . . **50.00**
• KLM, Skill, "Form a circle with these 8 parts. You will be able to read the words 'Fly KLM'," coated stiff cardboard, 8" d, 8 pcs, 2⅛ x 3⅞" envelope, instructions on back of envelope in English, Spanish, and Dutch . . . . . . . . . . . . . . . **10.00**
• Oxford Specialty Co., Boston, MA, "Budge: Sports," diecut cardboard, 17 x 17", cardboard box contains instructions for 4 players to race to assemble their quarters first . . **35.00**

*The Man From U.N.C.L.E.*

• Toddy Travel Series, Two Game Puzzle, puzzle converts to gameboard, "Calcutta Sweepstakes," No. 5 of 6 in series, diecut cardboard, 13 x 9¾", 50 pcs, 1933, 10 x 13¾ x ⁷⁄₁₆" cardboard box   **35.00**

**Mystery**
• Milton Bradley, Mystery Jigsaw Puzzle, The Man From U.N.C.L.E., No. 4581–4, "The Impossible Escape," 24⅛ x 14", 612 pcs, 8 pg story booklet, partial guide picture on box *see illus* . . . . . . . . . . **40.00**
• Einson–Freeman Lithograph Co., Mystery–Jig Puzzle, No. 2 in series of 4, "By Whose Hand," 19⅞ x 14", approx 300 pcs, booklet enclosed, 1933 cardboard box . . . . . . . . . . . . . **30.00**
• Janus Games, Inc., The Janus Mystery Jigsaw Puzzle Ellery Queen, "The Case of His Headless Highness," No. 3, cardboard, 21½ x 14¾", 510 pcs, gun and dagger figurals, mystery story on back of box . . . . . . . . . . . . . . . . . **22.00**
"The Case of the Snoring Skinflint," by Henry Slesar, No. 1 of 4, approx 22 x 15", over

*Dick Tracy's 2 in 1 Mystery Puzzle*

500 pcs, 1973, story on back
of cardboard box . . . . . . . . .     **20.00**
• Jaymar Specialty Company, Dick
Tracy's 2 in 1 Mystery Puzzle,
2 puzzles, 10⁷/₈ x 13⁷/₈", 24 pc
problem puzzle in vertical format, 10⁷/₈ x 13⁷/₈", 99 pc solution puzzle in horizontal format, copyright 1948, period
box *see illus* . . . . . . . . . . . .     **50.00**
• Pearl Publishing Company,
Brooklyn, NY, Mystery Puzzle
of the Month, No. 2, Case of
the Duplicate Door, 11¹/₂ x
13¹/₂", 208 pcs, 16 pg story
booklet with mystery solution     **25.00**
**Photograph Puzzle**
• American Studios, LaCrosse, WI,
personalized, individual's
home, 1965, boxed . . . . . . .     **15.00**
• E. J. Curtis, Inc., Pittsfield, MA,
Jig Saw Puzzle Enlargement
from your negative, wood,
Mildred Carlson taken c1933
at Sulfield Academy, CT,
7³/₄ x 9³/₄", 128 pcs, 5³/₈ x 6³/₄
x 1" cardboard box . . . . . . .     **25.00**
**Postcard,** souvenir
• Statue of Joseph Warren, Picture
Puzzle Post Card, U.S. 616,
Roxbury, Mass, 3¹/₂ x 5¹/₂",
18 pcs, perforated, mailing
envelope . . . . . . . . . . . . . . .     **15.00**
• Washington In A Sack Jig Saw
Puzzle, Washington
Monument and Japanese
Cherry Blossom, postcard
glued to wood and then cut,

*Squirrel Jig Puzzles*

canvas mailing sack, 5¹/₂ x 3¹/₂"
card, late 1930s . . . . . . . . . .     **20.00**
**Premium,** Squirrel Brand Co.,
Cambridge, MA, Squirrel Jig
Puzzles, "One Free with every
Penny Purchase," cut out pcs
from card and assemble into
puzzle, 4 different cards including No. 1 Queer Fellow (clown
face), No. 2 Singing Sam from
the Sunny South, No. 3 A Fine
Old Ship, and No. 4 Squirrel,
individual card 3¹/₂ x 5³/₈",
c1930, box of 100 contains
25 of each view, 8¹/₈ x 6¹/₈ x 1"
cardboard box
•No. 2, black theme . . . . . . . . .     **10.00**
•Nos. 1, 3, or 4 *see illus (No. 3)*     **5.00**
**Stationery,** World War II,
No. 23, Fresno Art Novelty Co.,
Fresno, CA, red and blue letter-
head of GI in prone position
shooting machine gun, "I'm
Shootin' This To You In A
Hurry!," orig envelope . . . . . . .     **10.00**
**Talking Puzzle,** Whitman, Sound
A Round Talking Puzzle Master
Unit, durable frame holding
talking record and large piece
puzzle, self adjusting magic
tonearm, hard cover story book,
"Choo–Choo at the Zoo" . . . . .     **25.00**

# JIGSAW PUZZLE EPHEMERA

*Washington's Fairwell to New York*

*Jigsaw Puzzles—and how to make 'em*

### Advertising Tear Sheet
- *Miss America,* Vol. 5, No. 6, April 1947, Page 8, Noxzema jigsaw puzzle theme adv . . . .   **5.00**
- *Playboy,* May 1981, back cov features Crown Royal jigsaw puzzle adv . . . . . . . . . . . . .   **8.00**

### Booklet
- Graffam, Perry S., editor, *50 Jigsaw Projects,* published as part of The Home Workshop Library by General Publishing Co., pgs 5–14 devoted to jigsaw puzzle cutting, 1949 . . . .   **15.00**
- Perry, L. Day, editor, T.K. Webster, Jr., consultant, *Jigsaw Puzzles – and how to make 'em,* Mack Publications, 1933, 32 pgs, 8½ x 11½", compilation of articles that appeared in *Popular Homecraft see illus*   **75.00**

### Broadside
Einson–Freeman
- Every Week Jig–Saw Puzzle, No. 18, Washington's Fairwell to New York, 14³/₁₆ x 10⁵/₁₆" *see illus*. . . . . . . . . . . . . . .   **20.00**
- Problem Jig–Saw Puzzle, Princess and Peasant Problem, cardboard, 12³/₄ x 15½" . . . . .   **35.00**

- University Distributing Company, Jig of the Week, No. 22, Boyhood of Sir Walter Raleigh, paper, 14 x 10³/₄" . . .   **40.00**
- Viking Manufacturing Company, Picture Puzzle Weekly, Series D–3, "The Chariot Race", 14³/₄ x 11", stiff board. . . . . . .   **35.00**

### Catalog
- Madmar Quality Company, Utica, NY, Madmar Puzzles For All Ages, 6 x 9⅛", 16 pgs, undated, mid–1930s. . . . . . . .   **20.00**
- Parker Brothers Autumn List 1913 Famous Pastime Puzzles, double sided sheet, 9 x 15½", fold marks . . . . . . . . . . . . . .   **15.00**
  - Supplementary List for the Spring 1926 Famous Pastime Puzzles Manufactured exclusively by Parker Bros., Inc., Salem, Massachusetts, 8½ x 11½", 4 pgs, 22 illus . . . . . . .   **60.00**

### Comic Book
- Archie's Madhouse, Vol. 1, No. 1, September 1959, Archie Comic Publications, jigsaw puzzle theme cov. . . . . . . . . .   **15.00**
- Detective Comics, No. 367, September 1967, DC, National Periodical Publications,

*Man of a Thousand Parts*

Siren In the Night

Batman jigsaw puzzle theme
cov, 12¢ . . . . . . . . . . . . . . .   **20.00**
• Jigsaw: Man of a Thousand
  Parts, Funday Funnies, Inc.,
  Harvey Thriller, 12¢
  Vol. 1, No. 1, September
  1966 . . . . . . . . . . . . . .   **10.00**
  Vol. 1, No. 2, Dec 1966,
  *see illus* . . . . . . . . . . . .   **4.00**
• Ms Tree, "Jigsaw," No. 13,
  November 1984, Aardvark–
  Vanaheim, Inc., Max Collins
  and Terry Beatty artists, $1.70,
  jigsaw puzzle theme cover . . .   **10.00**
• The Man From U.N.C.L.E.,
  Golden Key, 10146607, July
  1966, "The Pizilated Puzzle
  Affair" story, opening page has
  jigsaw puzzle theme, story
  focuses on jigsaw puzzle . . . .   **5.00**
**Magazine**
• *Ellery Queen's Mystery
  Magazine,* Vol. 51, No. 6, June
  1968, jigsaw puzzle theme
  cover . . . . . . . . . . . . . . . .   **5.00**
• *Future,* No. 10, May 1979,
  space station jigsaw puzzle
  theme cover . . . . . . . . . . .   **8.00**
• *Jack and Jill,* July 1947, center-
  fold designed to be pasted to
  cardboard and cut as puzzle,

Statue of Liberty photo theme,
  13¼ x 9⅞" page spread . . . . .   **15.00**
• *Life,* Vol. 17, No. 2, July 10,
  1944, Nimitz of the Pacific,
  contains article on Par puzzles
• *People and Places,* Vol. 13,
  No. 1, February 1956, published by De Soto–Plymouth,
  back cover features jigsaw
  puzzle theme adv for DeSoto,
  "Easy way to solve your new
  car puzzle," distributed by
  Ludwick Motors, Inc.,
  Pottstown, PA. . . . . . . . . . . .   **5.00**
• *Playboy*
  Vol. 7, No. 9, 1960, jigsaw puz-
  zle theme cover . . . . . . . . . .   **20.00**
  Vol. 18, No. 9, Sept 1971, jig-
  saw puzzle theme cover . . . . .   **5.00**
• *Woman's Home Companion,*
  August 1993, illus of seated
  cat knocking apart puzzle of
  dog, Diana Thorne illus . . . . .   **25.00**
**Paperback Book,** Leslie Ford,
  *Siren in the Night,* Bantam
  Book, No. 303 *see illus* . . . . . .   **5.00**
**Sheet Music,** *"Juggling A
  Jig–Saw,"* pink, black, and white
  cover, Donaldson–Douglas &
  Gumble Music Publishers, 9⅛ x
  12", 1933 . . . . . . . . . . . . . . .   **15.00**

# DEXTERITY PUZZLES

**Army Wagon,** tin and plastic, Nabisco Shredded Wheat Juniors, 1¹/₄" d . . . . . . . . . . . .   **30.00**

**Black Man,** wearing red tie and hat, metal, glass, and cardboard, mirror on back, 2¹/₄" d . .   **90.00**

**Bowling Puzzle,** wood, paper, and glass, Joseph W. Drueke Co., 4¹/₄ x 5¹/₄", 1948 . . . . . . .   **45.00**

**Buy U.S. War Bonds and Stamps,** cardboard and plastic, 3¹/₂ x 3¹/₂". . . . . . . . . . . . . . .   **85.00**

**Carstairs White Seal Whiskey,** cardboard and plastic, 2³/₄" d . .   **12.00**

**Cat and Mouse Game,** plastic, Common Tatar Inc., 7³/₄" d, 1966 . . . . . . . . . . . . . . . . . .   **15.00**

**Circus Seals,** tin, glass, and cardboard, U.S.A., 5 x 3¹/₂" . . . . . . .   **35.00**

**Congo–Ringers,** plastic, bounce small ring inside large ring and slide onto Ubangi's lips, 5 x 3"   **35.00**

**Dive–Bomber, Sink The Enemy Fleet,** cardboard and glass, 5 x 3¹/₄" . . . . . . . . . . . . . . . .   **40.00**

**Duck,** wearing clown hat, cardboard and plastic, Japan, 1¹/₂" d, 1950 . . . . . . . . . . . . . . . . . .   **20.00**

**Gilbert Boxed Problem Puzzles,** cardboard and glass, A.C. Gilbert Co., 6 puzzles, Ball and Gear, Ring A Tail, Hungry Pup, Ring A Peg, Radio Tube Trick, and Topsy Turvy Rivets, 10³/₈ x 8⁷/₈" box, 1940 . . . . . . .   **275.00**

**Golf "Jiggle" Puzzle,** plastic and cardboard, Comon Tatar Inc., 2⁷/₁₆ x 3¹/₈", 1957 . . . . . . . . . .   **30.00**

**Goofy,** plastic, Walt Disney Productions, Hong Kong, 2¹/₄" d   **35.00**

**Holsum Bread,** tin and plastic, 2¹/₄" d . . . . . . . . . . . . . . . . .   **20.00**

**Keep 'Em Rolling For Victory,** tin, glass, and cardboard, U.S.A.. . .   **75.00**

**Nabisco Shredded Wheat Juniors,** Fighting Blue Devils 101st Cavalry, tin and plastic, 1¹/₄" d *see illus*. . . . . . . . . . . . . . . . .   **35.00**

*Fighting Blue Devils 101st Cavalry*

**Nancy,** holding ice cream cone, plastic, United Features Syndicate, 2¹/₄" d . . . . . . . . . .   **25.00**

**Natives and Alligators,** glass, aluminum, and cardboard, mirror on back, Occupied Japan, 2¹/₄" d   **50.00**

**Owl,** cardboard and plastic, Japan, 1¹/₂" d, 1950 . . . . . . . . .   **10.00**

**Popeye,** juggling balls, tin and glass, King Features Syndicate, Bar Zim Toy Mfg. Co., 3¹/₂ x 5"   **70.00**

**Red Goose Shoes,** cardboard and plastic, 2¹/₄" d . . . . . . . . . . . . .   **25.00**

**Road Runner,** plastic and cardboard, Cracker Jack Co., 1 x 1¹/₂"   **10.00**

**Spaceship to the Moon,** Baby World–NYC, 2¹/₂" d. . . . . . . . . .   **30.00**

**Striped Cat Puzzle,** wood and plastic, Germany, 2¹/₄" sq . . . . .   **15.00**

**TastyKake,** Kirchhof Advertising, 1¹/₄" d. . . . . . . . . . . . . . . . .   **15.00**

**The Jeep Board,** wood and glass with twine to strap to leg, George S. Carrington Co., 15 games and 10 puzzles, 1943, 3¹/₂ x 3³/₄" box. . . . . . . .   **60.00**

**The Lone Ranger Series No. 1 Target Practice,** tin, glass, and cardboard, T.L.R. Inc., 5 x 3¹/₂"   **60.00**

# SKILL PUZZLES

*Checkerboard Puzzle*

A–TREAT
GINGER ALE

A-TREAT
MYSTERY
PUZZLE

**DIRECTIONS**

The object is to arrange the nine pieces in a square - three rows of three each so that the upper and lower halves of twelve "A-TREAT" bottles are correctly matched and each of these bottles completely within the same color. For example, if yellow is the background of the upper half of a "A-TREAT" bottle, then yellow must be the background color of the lower half of that bottle.

IF YOU CAN'T SOLVE THIS PUZZLE - and want the answer - send an "A-TREAT" Ginger Ale neck label (the cocktail glass) with your name and address to:

A-TREAT BOTTLING CO.,
2001-09 Union Boulevard,
Allentown, Pennsylvania,
and the solution will be mailed to you.

*A–Treat Mystery Puzzle*

## KEY CHAIN

### Molded Plastic, figural
- Howdy Doody, blue, green, yellow, and red, orig selling price 10¢ . . . . . . . . . . . . . . . . . . .  **18.00**
- Mystic Jet Puzzle Plane, multicolored . . . . . . . . . . . . . . . .  **10.00**
- Telephone, white receiver and dial . . . . . . . . . . . . . . . . . .  **15.00**

## PUT TOGETHER

### Checkerboard Puzzle
- Checkerboard Puzzle Co., Detroit, MI, Wrobbell's Checkerboard Puzzle, mfg by The Western Paper Box Co., Detroit, 8 x 8", 14 pcs, orig selling price 15¢, orig 8¹/₄ x 8¹/₄ x ⁷/₈" cardboard box  **15.00**
- D. & S. Novelty Company, Harrisburg, PA, The Great Nut–House Puzzle, 3³/₈ x 3³/₈" puzzle, 14 pcs, double fold cardboard with punchout puzzle, 4⁷/₁₆ x 10¹/₈" open size, orig selling price 10¢ . . . . . . .  **5.00**

- J.W. Fose Printing Co., Niagara Falls, NY, Checker Board Puzzle, 6⁵/₈ x 5⁵/₈", 14 pcs, orig 5⁵/₈ x 4⁷/₈ x ³/₄" cardboard box, orig selling price 15¢ *see illus*  **20.00**

### Head and Tail Puzzle
- A–Treat Bottle Co., Allentown, PA, A–Treat Mystery Puzzle, A–Treat bottles on different colored grounds, 7⁹/₁₆ x 7⁹/₁₆", 9 pcs, different adv on back of each pc, 3¹/₈ x 5¹/₂" paper envelope *see illus.* . . . . . . . . .  **15.00**
- Calumet Baking Powder, match colors and 4 sides of baking powder cans . . . . . . . . . . . .  **25.00**
- Norton Company, Worcester, MA, Norton Abrasive Puzzle, portions of grinding wheel on different colored grounds, 6¹/₈ x 6¹/₈", adv letter on reverse

*Horse Blanket Puzzle*

makes puzzle easy to assemble, 3¹/₈ x 5¹/₂" paper envelope **18.00**

**Letter Dissection Puzzle**

• Royal Typewriter Company, New York, NY, The "R" Puzzle, 7 pcs, Royal logo on front, 4¹/₂ x 3" paper envelope . . . . . **20.00**

• B. Wise and C. Kipp, distributors, 6 pc "H" and 4 pc "T" in same package, plain black pcs, 6¹/₂ x 3⁵/₈" paper envelope, orig selling price 10¢ . . . . . . . **18.00**

**Sliced or Dissected Puzzle**

• William Ayres & Sons, Philadelphia, dealer imprint for Peerless Vehicle & Imp. Co., Stockton and Lodi, CA, 5A Horse Blanket Puzzle, 9 pcs, engraving of rider holding bridle of blanketed horse on larger pcs, 6¹/₄ x 6¹/₄", 3¹/₁₆" square cardboard box *see illus.* . . . . . . . . . . . . . . . . **25.00**

• Dickinson's Brands, 8 pcs, title pc and 7 product pcs including Globe Scratch Feed, Snowball Popcorn, Crescent Chick Feed, Evergreen Lawn Grass Seed, Santa Claus Popcorn, Dickinson's Lawn Seed, and Yankee Popcorn, colorful litho sketches, 9¹/₂ x 4³/₄", 6⁷/₁₆ x 3⁵/₈" paper envelope . . . . . . . . . . . . . . **30.00**

• Pratt Food Co., Philadelphia, PA, dealer rubber stamp for

W.D. Wilder, Laurenceville, NY, Pratt's Cut Up Puzzle, 2 Puzzles in One, 10 pcs, front shows animals laughing and making sarcastic remarks to gentleman attempting to feed them "Imitation Food," 9 x 6¹/₄", 6¹/₈ x 4⁵/₈" paper envelope . . . . . . . . . . . . . . . **65.00**

**Trick Mule Puzzle Type, The** Magic Shop, The Willard–Johnson Fight Puzzle, "four strips of cardboard, each 3 inches by 1¹/₂ inches, show Willard and Johnson in various absurd postures. The solution of the puzzle lies in arranging the strips that show, in the completed picture, Willard the heavy–weight champion," instruction sheet provides solution, copyright 1915, 4¹/₂ x 2⁵/₈" paper envelope, orig selling price was 10¢ . . . . . . . . . . . . . . . . . . **100.00**

## SEQUENTIAL MOVEMENT

**Hop–Over Puzzle,** J. Pressman & Co., New York, 4 black and 4 white balls, jump over opposite colored balls to reverse balls from black to white and white to black . . . . . . . . . . . . **18.00**

**Pike's Peak or Bust,** Parker Bros., Salem, MA, reach top of mountain with help of metal traveler, c1895 . . . . . . . . . . . . . . . . . . **100.00**

**Puzzle–Peg,** Lubbers & Bell Manufacturing Co., Clinton, IA, c1920s. . . . . . . . . . . . . . . . . **15.00**

**Sliding Block**

• Dad's Puzzler, The Standard Trailer Co., Cambridge Springs, PA, J. W. Hayward ©1926 . . . **15.00**

• Humdinger Puzzle for Puzzle Bugs, Wood Products Sales Co., York, PA, orig selling price 25¢ . . . . . . . . . . . . . . . . . . **20.00**

• Ma's Puzzle, divide 2 L–shaped pcs and empty space into 2 parts, 1927 . . . . . . . . . . . . **18.00**

• The Century of Progress, Chicago's 100th anniversary souvenir, 1933 . . . . . . . . . . . **35.00**

# SUBJECT INDEX – GAMES

More games are purchased by crossover collectors than by game collectors. While by no means encyclopedic, this subject index by title provides an initial checklist for what is available in each specialized category.

## WESTERN

# TITLE INDEX – JIGSAW PUZZLES